Twentieth Century

SPEECH AND VOICE CORRECTION

Twentieth Century
SPEECH *and* VOICE
CORRECTION

edited by

EMIL FROESCHELS, M.D.

President, International Society for Logopedics and Phoniatrics;
President, New York Society for Speech and Voice Therapy

PHILOSOPHICAL LIBRARY
NEW YORK

PRINTED IN THE UNITED STATES OF AMERICA

Contributors

EMIL FROESCHELS, M.D.
President, International Society for Speech and Voice Science.

ELLY SITTIG
Speech and Voice Therapist, Federation for the Handicapped, New York.

JEANETTE O. ANDERSON, PH.D.
Director, Speech Clinic, Rockford College, Rockford, Ill.

HELEN HULICK BEEBE
Speech Clinician, Easton Hospital, Penna.

MARTIN F. PALMER, SC.D.
Director, Institute of Logopedics, Wichita, Kansas.

SHULAMITH KASTEIN
Speech Correctionist, Speech Clinic, Brooklyn College, N. Y. C.

HELEN SCHICK LANE, PH.D.
Principal, Central Institute for the Deaf.

AUGUSTA JELLINEK, PH.D.
New York.

SAMUEL D. ROBBINS
Professor of Psychology, Emerson College Boston,
Managing Trustee, Institute for Speech Correction.

S. RICHARD SILVERMAN, PH.D.
Central Institute for the Deaf.

DOROTHY DOOB, ED.D.
Instructor, Dept. of Speech and Dramatics, Hunter College, New York.

EUGENE SCHORR, M.D., D.D.S.
New York.

ANNIE MOOLENAAR-BIJL
Speech Clinic, Laryngological Department, University Hospital
of Groningen, Holland.

MARY WOOD WHITEHURST
Formerly Supervisor of Auricular Training of Hoff General Hospital,
Santa Barbara, Cal.

WILLIAM G. PEACHER, M.D.
Philadelphia, Pa.

O. R. BONTRAGER
Director of the Reading Clinic, State Teachers College,
California, Pennsylvania.

CHARLES H. VOELKER, M.A.
Head, Department of Physics, Washington College, Chestertown, Md.

FREDERICA SCHMITZ-SVEVO
Voice and Speech Therapist of the Department of Oto-Rhino-Laryngology,
City Hospital, Welfare Island, New York, N. Y.

CHARLES R. STROTHER, PH.D.
Associate Professor of Speech and Psychology, University of Iowa.

FOREWORD

THIS VOLUME has been written at the request of the publisher. Its purpose is to offer to persons scientifically and/or practically interested in speech and voice correction the latest developments in this field. I have tried to include as many of the modern trends as possible so the reader will not be surprised if he finds divergent opinions expressed by the various writers on some subjects. I hope that this book will also serve to stimulate the interest of more and more people in the ways of improving and curing the impediments of voice and speech. There is no doubt that there is a great need for the contribution which this branch of science can make toward the social adjustment of mankind. The publisher's recognition of this fact is greatly appreciated.

E. FROESCHELS.

Contents

Twentieth Century

SPEECH AND VOICE CORRECTION

EMIL FROESCHELS, M.D.
President, International Society for Speech and Voice Science;
President, New York Society of Voice and Speech Therapy.

ELLY SITTIG
Speech and Voice Therapist, Federation for the Handicapped, New York.

Chapter I

ANATOMY AND PHYSIOLOGY

I. SPEECH DEVELOPMENT OF THE CHILD

1) Crying

The first cry is considered to be the reaction to the many stimuli which affect the new-born immediately after birth: Light enters the eyes, noise the ears, and above all, unaccustomed temperature touches the skin.

a) Breathing in Crying

These stimuli are supposed to cause the first deep breathing. Part of the air taken in with the first breath is used immediately afterwards for the first cry. We are probably right if we consider the first cry as a reflex to the above mentioned stimuli.

Pneumograms show that there is a great conformity between breathing for crying on the one hand and for speech and singing on the other. These forms of breathing differ mainly from breathing during rest insofar that inhaling is short and abundant, while exhaling is slow and thrifty. The pneumogram will show therefore a steep rising and a longer descending part of the curve returning to zero or near zero. It is obvious that the ability to lower the chest walls slowly from the height attained in inspiration is practiced during the crying period.

b) Phonetic Action of the Vocal Cords

Besides the vocal cords seem to be trained in the crying period. Although the sound-producing vibrations of the vocal cords seem to be passive, a result of the passing air, (D. Weiss[1]),

2

the degree of their approach is of great importance. If pressed closely together they produce not only an explosive onset, as will be explained later, but under certain circumstances also hoarse sounds; while vocal cords approximated to a slight touch, will produce a pleasing onset, free from any noise. When we learn that Gutzmann and Flatau had already found soft on-setting cries and cries with glottal coups in very young infants, again we must assume that this is the start of a pre-training for a fine gradation which in later life influences so much the meaning of an expression.

Kaiser[2] has found that the average pitch of the sounds of sucklings under the age of 8 months consists of about 460 double vibrations. The cries of older sucklings contain most frequently louder sounds in which 170 double vibrations are contained. She traces this phenomenon back to the fact that the lungs have about the same pitch in the percussion sounds (Martini). The same number of vibrations resonates in the lungs. Inspiratory crying sounds are frequent.

It is well known that differences in pitch are of great importance in singing as well as in speaking. The differences in the pitches of the sounds are due to the degree of extension of the vocal cords.* It is very possible that the action of the extending and tensing muscles of the vocal cords is also trained in the crying period, first independent of the will, as reflexes, later under the influence of the will. To understand this one must learn that the sounds of the cries gradually differ from each other, so that the attentive mother is able to recognize whether her child is hungry, or wet, or is crying for the crying's sake, or is in good humor. According to the examinations of Gutzman and Flatau the new-born child has a volume of about 3 half tones; only exceptionally they found larger volumes, comprising even 5 half tones. As a rule we could prove 9 half tones in children of 4 years of age.

---

*For other theories see Chapter XVIII.

The cries have a similarity to vowels, but it can be observed that very young sucklings often start their cries with a consonant, even with a nasal consonant. Han Piao Chen and Orvis C. Irwin[3] have found that for the first bi-monthly period the mean for vowels is 4.5 and for consonants 2.7.

2) *Babbling Period*

The babbling sounds and the babbling syllables have a great similarity to our articulated speech. They start with the fourth, sometimes with the fifth or sixth month of the suckling's age. The babbling syllables consist of a vowel and two adjacent consonants, more often of a consonant and a vowel, sometimes of two consonants. There is no doubt that these babbling products are originally pure reflexes. Even the congenitally deaf child passes through the babbling period. That fact is a physiological riddle, for the reflex causing sources are not known. Might it be a congenital occurrence, depending on the development of certain regions of the central nervous system?

It seems to be certain that the movements of articulation and the connection of sounds are trained in the babbling period. And it is very probable if we consider the great conformity which exists between chewing and speaking[4] that in this period a preparation for chewing also takes place. Furthermore, the babbling period is of great significance in the development of a central occurrence. It can be observed that babbling children repeat their babbling products for a while, and replace them later on with new babbling products. As the child becomes aware of his own babbling product which started as a reflex he receives its acoustic maybe even a kinaesthetic impression and is pleased to repeat it. As a result the most important relation between hearing and articulation is established. When the babbling child is imitating his own babbling sounds, he is rooting the neuron pathway which must exist between the center for speech reception and the center for speech performance. It has to be added that some babbling sounds and babbling syllables have no similarity to the sounds and syllables of highly developed languages, but conform to those of primitive languages. Kussmaul[5] has called these strange elements of that period "primitive sounds".

The normal start of speech is a clue for the normal hearing of the suckling. If speech fails to appear normally, it is the first warning for the mother to have her child's hearing tested. If the mother who has mistaken babbling for articulated speech informs the physician that the child has started to speak and has stopped later on, he could draw the wrong conclusion of an acquired instead of a congenital defect which might be present.

II. ANATOMY AND PHYSIOLOGY OF THE VOICE AND SPEECH ORGANS

1) *Breathing in Speaking and Singing*

a) *Chest and Diaphragmatic Breathing*

The inspiration movements of the chest walls consist in raising and enlarging them in depth as well as sideward. The three upper ribs move on a horizontal axis, because the processes of the respective vertebrae are horizontal, and the ribs articulate with these as well as with the vertebrae body. As a result of the raising movement the chest walls expand from behind forward, considering that the cartilages of these ribs are short. The processes of the lower vertebrae are directed obliquely backwards, and the cartilages are long. Therefore, the raising of these ribs expands the chest walls also sideward.

From a hygienic point of view a combined chest and diaphragmatic breathing should be recommended, especially as it is the physiologic form of breathing. (See Fig. 1).

In examining different people one can find that chest breathing predominates in some and diaphragmatic breathing in others. That is true especially for the two sexes. But always the other type of breathing is also more or less present, when no special exercises have been made.

b) *Breathing Types*

The examination of the breathing types of the two sexes

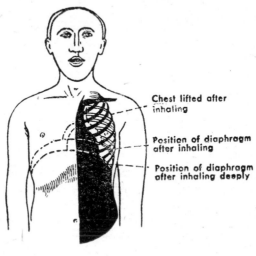

Chest lifted after inhaling

Position of diaphragm after inhaling

Position of diaphragm after inhaling deeply

Fig. 1

shows that men represent the diaphragmatic and women the chest type. Although it seems to be true that the majority of people of one sex could be classified as one type, however, there are many exceptions.

In children a difference according to the sex cannot be observed. After the tenth year of age, if at all, a shifting from the mixed to the type of the respective sex takes place. Schilling[6] refers to a costal (1), epigastric (2), and abdominal (3) type. The results of the examination in rest breathing and standing show in males even epigastric and abdominal types; in females a dominance of the epigastric type. In deep breathing the costal and epigastric types increase in males (man and child), however, the epigastric type is more frequent; in females the costal type is dominant. In singing of trained adults the types 2 and 3 occur. In children type 1 is dominant. The breathing excursions are smaller in singing than in deep breathing. In sitting and singing a shifting toward the abdominal type seems to take place, influenced mainly by the will. In rest breathing type 3 is dominant in males, while it is type 1 in females. The position of equilibrium of the chest was near the maximal position of expiration in deep breathing, in other words, was the position of relaxation, in all positions of the body (in rest, in counting, and in singing.)

In testing eight prominent singers we could establish the fact that each of them breathed differently. From this we concluded that singing teachers should not recommend one general type of breathing.

c) *Mouth and Nose Breathing*

These expressions mean that the air enters and exits through the mouth or through the nose respectively. The examinations by several physicians have proved that in rest breathing, that is to say, the breathing while not speaking or singing, the air passes physiologically through the nose. In speaking the air passes through the mouth. The necessary condition for nose breathing is that the passages of the nose are passable, for even a catarrh of the nose forces one to breathe through the mouth.

In accord with the physiological fact that speech breathing occurs through the mouth is the experience that singing and acting students breathe primarily through the mouth. Some physicians and most teachers oppose that habit energetically. The gliding of the air along the turbinates where the mucous membrane is flooded by blood, warms the air to a great extent. Measurements have proved that the increase in warmth is remarkable. Let us judge the conditions objectively. There is a certain relation between the swelling bodies of the turbinates, (the blood vessels beneath their cover) and the elastic tissue of the lungs and the breathing muscles. The better the swelling bodies are developed, the more strongly the breathing and the action of the breathing muscles must start to overcome the obstacle which the swelling bodies offer to the air. This powerful breathing strengthens the muscles. On the other hand the gliding air stimulates the blood circulation of the swelling bodies, so that they degenerate in constant mouth breathing. These are important reasons against mouth breathing; but to be exact, only against mouth breathing in rest. In the state of non-speaking a person inhales 17 times a minute. He speaks, or speaks and sings, disregarding people who talk very much, all in all two hours a day, inhaling less often, let us say, 8 times a minute. The result is 22,440 inspirations through the nose, and assuming that in speaking and singing he breathes through the mouth, 960 inspirations through the mouth. It is true that in speaking and singing often 2 to 3 times as much air is inspirated with one inhalation as in rest. However, the reasons given for nose breathing cannot be neglected. We have given these numbers to show only that one should not jump to conclusions by over-estimating the circumstances.

2) *Anatomy and Physiology of the Larynx*

a) *Anatomy*

a1) *Cartilages*

In human speech, also in the speech of a Demosthenes, and in human singing, as in the singing of a Caruso, the most important part is played by the wonderful little instruments the vocal cords, which are partly embedded in a cartilaginous box. That box is a protection and also serves for the attachment of the vocal cords. It is made of flexible material, of cartilages, so that stiff hard walls do not hinder mobility. Also cartilages are in some instances a better protection against injuries from outside. They can withstand a blow better than bones which have no flexibility.

On top of the windpipe is situated a ring-like shaped cartilage, with its lower part to the front, rising toward the back, and ending in a high plate, so completing the picture of a signet ring. Therefore it is called the Cricoid Cartilage (cartilage cricoidea). The upper part of the circumference of this plate is ground off on both sides of the middle line to cylindrical planes, descending in front and approaching each other. On top are situated the Arytenoid Cartilages (cartilagines arytaenoideae). They are 2 in number, pyramidal-shaped, with a triangular base that fits the plane of the cricoid cartilage to form a joint. This joint makes it possible for the anterior parts of the arytenoid cartilages to approach each other and to move apart. As mentioned, the cylindrical planes of the cricoid cartilages are inclined anteriorly, so that in approaching the arytenoid cartilages are lowered a trifle, while in moving apart they rise. The arytenoid cartilages as a whole can approximate too. All these movements are due to actions of muscles that are attached to the lateral muscle processes (processus musculares) of the arytenoid cartilages, the muscles going partly to the posterior surface, partly to the lateral angle of the base. The anterior processes of the arytenoid cartilages are called vocal processes (processus vocales), because the vocal cords are attached to them.

The Thyroid Cartilage, or shield-like cartilage (cartilago thyreoidea), envelopes the former mentioned cartilages nearly wholly, and serves not only for muscle attachment, but has also a protective purpose. It resembles a shield of which two wings (alae) are united in front at an acute angle, the protrusion of its front being called the Adam's apple (pomum Adami). The wings are inclined toward the front and their upper border in the middle line is curved irregularly, forming the thyroid notch (incisura thyreoidea superior). (The thyroid notch is of great diagnostic and therapeutic importance. With some experience in pressing the tip of a finger against it, one is able to feel very well a glottal stop (due to a firm closure of the glottis) and the rhythmical vibrations of the vocal cords). To the inner line, corresponding to the angle, are attached the vocal cords, ending, as mentioned at the vocal processes of the arytenoid cartilages. The two wings of the thyroid cartilage do not unite posteriorly, so that the plate of the cricoid cartilage can be seen. (See Fig. 2).

The posterior border of each wing ends above and below in

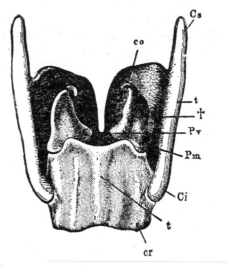

Fig. 2

Cartilage of the larynx from behind
Cs Superior Cornu (cornu superius) of the thyroid cartilage
Ci Inferior Cornu (cornu inferius) of the thyroid cartilage
cr Plate of Cricoid Cartilage
Pm Pv Muscle—and vocal—process of the arytenoid cartilages
† Arytenoid Cartilage
co-Cartilages of Santorini (cartilagines corniculatae)
(After Henle.)

stem-like cartilaginous processes, the horns (cornua thyreoidea).
The superior horn—of each side—affords attachment to the
thyro-hyoid ligament. The inferior horn—of each side—articulates laterally with the cricoid cartilage by a small oval facet.
The two cartilages move in that joint about a nearly horizontal
axis, thus producing either an approach or separation of especially the two anterior parts of these cartilages. Knowing that
the arytenoid cartilages and the thyroid cartilage afford attachment to the vocal cords, we will understand that they are
stretched by this movement. When the thyroid cartilage bends
toward the cricoid cartilage the anterior place of attachment
moves away from the posterior one, in the direction to the front

and downward. When the cricoid cartilage rises toward the angle of the thyroid cartilage, at the same time the plate of the cricoid cartilage moves down and backward, enlarging the distance between the vocal processes and the anterior place of attachment of the vocal cords.

The Epiglottis (cartilago epiglottica) shaped like a leaf or a spoon without a handle, is situated in front and above the vocal cords, but within the space bounded by the thyroid cartilage, standing like a sentry on top of a tower. It is a cartilaginous lid for the larynx. It protects the larynx by lowering itself over the vocal cords, offering a sloping plain over which food can glide into the esophagus.

a2) *Muscles*

The larynx as a whole can move, especially up and downwards. The upward motion is performed by the hyo-thyroid muscle (musculus hyothyreoideus), which is attached to the wings of the thyroid cartilage and the hyoid bone. The downward motion is performed by the sterno-thyroid muscle (musculus sternothyreoideus) which is attached to the thyroid cartilage and the sternum. The external crico-thyroid muscles (musculus cricothyreoideus externus), are situated externally in front right and left of the larynx. They connect the cricoid with the thyroid cartilage. Their contractions cause the approach of the two cartilages whose extending influence on the vocal cords we have mentioned before. These muscles also have horizontal fibres. Posteriorly, between the arytenoid cartilages, are situated crossed and horizontal muscles which approximate the two pyramids. They are the transverse and horizontal inter-arytenoid muscles (musculus interarytaenoideus transversus, obliquus). From the muscle processes of the arytenoid cartilages on each side extend the posterior crico-arytenoid muscle (musculus cricoarytaenoideus posticus) to the posterior surface of the cricoid cartilage, and the lateral crico-arytenoid muscle (musculus cricoarytaenoideus lateralis) extending to the lateral surface of the cricoid cartilage.

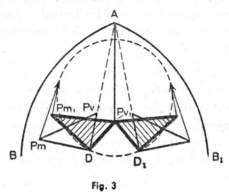

Fig. 3

a3) *Physiologic Forms of the Glottis*

The circle (see Fig. 3) signifies the cricoid cartilage, BAB[1] the thyroid cartilage, PmPvD the triangular base of the arytenoid cartilage, PvA are the vocal cords. The arrow, starting above Pm, signifies the lateral cricoarytenoid muscles. When these muscles move in the direction of the arrows Pm takes the place of Pm[1], and the anterior apexes of the arytenoid cartilages touch. As a result the vocal cords, which are attached at Pv, touch, leaving open only a triangle. That part of the glottis is called the cartilaginous glottis, the anterior, the larger part is called the ligamental glottis. This position is the whispering position of the glottis.

The stretching of the muscles which are in the vocal cords can only produce the position DAD[1], leaving open a long triangle between the vocal cords (exhaling position).

When the posterior crico-arytenoid muscles move from Pm (see Fig. 4) in the direction of the arrows, Pv takes the place of Pv[1], and a pentagon is the result. This position is the deep inhaling position of the glottis.

When the muscles between the arytenoid cartilages move in

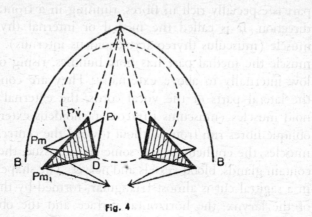

Fig. 4

the direction of the arrows (see Fig. 5) the medial surfaces of the arytenoid cartilages touch, producing a complete closure along the line AD. This position is the voice position of the glottis. (After H. Gutzmann).

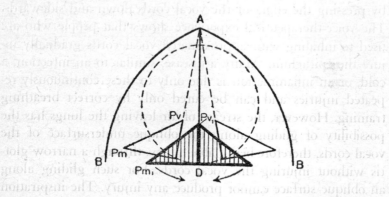

Fig. 5

a4) *Vocal Cords*

The vocal cords consist chiefly of muscles which protrude from the lateral walls of the larynx toward the middle. Their most medial part is shiny white on the surface. For that reason older scientists have called them "vocal bands." This medial part is especially rich in fibres, running in a frontal backward direction. It is called the medial or internal thyro-arytenoid muscle (musculus thyreo-arytaenoideus internus). Besides that muscle the medial part has fibre bundles, rising obliquely below internally to above externally. They are connected with the lateral parts of the vocal cords, the external thyro-arytenoid muscles (musculus thyreoarytaenoideus externus). Other oblique fibres run from without toward the center. Besides the muscles, the epithelium and some elastic tissue, the vocal cords contain glands, blood vessels and nerves. The shape of the cords in a sagittal cut is almost triangular, formed by the outer wall of the larynx, the horizontal surface and the oblique under surface of the vocal cord. When the vocal cords are approximated to a great degree the stream of air directed toward the lungs will hit the horizontal surface of the epithelium of the vocal cords, thus causing a noisy rather than an inaudible inhalation. The air will also try to produce a larger passage way, by pressing the edges of the vocal cords down and sidewards. The voice-therapeutical experience shows that people who are used to inhaling with approximated vocal cords gradually injure the epithelium. Many a disease, similar to an infection, a cold, or an inflammation is due only to these continuously repeated injuries and can be cured only by correct breathing training. However, the stream of air leaving the lungs has the possibility of gliding along the oblique undersurface of the vocal cords, therefore being able to pass through a narrow glottis without injuring the vocal cords. For such gliding along an oblique surface cannot produce any injury. The inspiration through a too narrow glottis is loud, the right inhaling is not audible. However, a loud expiration is considered physiological. The form of the vocal cords offers great difficulties to inspiratory speech. It is interesting to note that the vocal cords of some singing birds react with the same ease either to the inspiratory or the expiratory stream of air. For their vocal cords are sloping on the upper as well as the lower surface. We may therefore not wonder when a lark or a canary is warbling for minutes, apparently without inhaling, for both their inspiration and expiration can produce voice.

The role of all the muscles of the vocal cords is not yet clear. It is certain that the contraction of the sagittal fibres produces a shortening and, at the same time, a thickening of the vocal cords. They will react to a slackened condition as taut string reacts to a less taut one. In other words, the contraction will produce higher tones (Russell[7]). Here we will remember that we have learned of another mechanism, the mechanism of extending, which too is able to produce higher tones.

Above the vocal cords are two folds which consist mainly of mucous membrane, to a lesser degree of muscles; they are the false vocal cords or plicae ventriculares. Together with the true

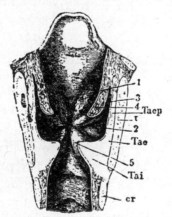

Fig. 6

t	Thyroid cartilage
1	Tubercle of the epiglottis
2	Sinus of Morgagni
3, 4	False vocal cord
5	True vocal cord
Taep	Thyro-epiglottideus muscle
Tae, Tai	Aryteno-epiglottideus superior and inferior muscles.

(After Henle.)

vocal cords they form the boundary for a sac, the sacculus or sinus of Morgagni. In many people this sinus has a lateral appendix that might be the remains of those mighty howling sacs which some monkeys have. The false vocal cords can approximate the vocal cords, so that the sinus of Morgagni will be greatly reduced. (See Fig. 6).

a5) *Nerves*

The larynx is supplied by two branches of the tenth brain nerve, the superior (nervus laryngeus superior), and the recurrent branch of the vagus (nervus recurrens). It has been believed that the superior nerve supplies motorically the crico-thyroid muscle only, the other part of the larynx sensorically, and that the recurrent nerve contains only motorical fibres for the other muscles of the larynx. It has been proved recently that both nerves have motoric and sensoric functions. The scientists could reach no agreement in regard to the localization of the brain centers for the larynx.

a6) *What Kind of an Instrument is the Larynx?*

If we ask what kind of an instrument the larynx is we will find the answer in describing it as a combination of a wind- and a string instrument. For the vibrating parts, the vocal cords, can change the degree of their tension as the tension of strings can be changed. What kind of wind-instrument it represents is not yet quite clear. But there is no doubt that it is a pipe. If it is a lip-pipe, a reed-pipe, or a cushion-pipe, as constructed by Ewald, is still a matter for debate. Ewald has constructed pipes in which 2 elastic cushions instead of tongues are used and found their sounds to be extraordinarily similar to the human voice. A great number of scientists believe that the larynx represents a cushion-pipe. If one imagines the effect of the stream of air on the vocal cords it will be understood that on the one hand the air wants to raise them, on the other, to push them apart. The resulting movement will be in the direction from inward below to outward above, and a backswinging movement from outward above to inward below.

a7) *Pitch and Volume*

According to a physical law the pitch of a sound depends on the number of vibrations of air in a time unit. The more rhythmical vibrations the vocal cords produce the higher is the tone. A sound moves on in the air in form of condensations and rarefactions, the so-called longitudinal waves. From the source of the sound the tone tries to expand in circles. The loudness of a sound depends on its amplitude*, that is to say, on the volume of the vibrations of the vocal cords. The amplitude is proportional to the breath used.

a8) *The most important Registers of the Human Voice*

The human voice has several different registers. A register is a sequence of tones of acoustically the same character, produced by the same mechanism. They differ from another sequence of acoustically related tones, produced by another mechanism. The most important registers are the head-, the chest-, and the middle register. The following physiological differences between the chest- and the head register are known: In the chest register a strong resonance of the chest is apparent. Laryngoscopy shows that the epiglottis covers the entrance to the larynx, (Negus denies the influence of that position of the epiglottis on the tone) and that the glottis closes almost completely after each opening. Stroboscopy shows that the entire body of the vocal cords is vibrating. In the head register the main resonance is in the head, the epiglottis is erect, and only the medial parts of the vocal cords are vibrating. The glottis remains open after the opening phase as a narrow oval, bottle-like, or like an hourglass. Physiologically the chest register comprehends the lower tones of the single voice, the head register the higher tones. Between these two registers is the middle register. It represents physiologically and acoustically a mixture of the two other registers. It is a challenge to artistic voice training to have the mid-

---

*See also Chapter XX.

dle register expand over the entire range of tones, and to have each single tone possess the qualities of both other registers. However, differences in degree cannot be avoided. A deep tone will always contain more chest resonance than a high tone, but should have as much head resonance as possible. A high tone should have as much as possible the qualities of the chest resonance. Bilancioni and Meldori found that the action of the diaphragm is not the same in both registers. We believe that individual differences must always be considered.

In describing the differences in the functions of the head- and the chest registers it is said that the same sound impression must not always derive from the same mechanism. If one sings e.g. the vowel "ah" in the chest register and goes over to "oo" without interrupting the voice, this "oo" generally has the character of the middle register, for head resonance has been added. In such personal experiments we did not have the impression of having changed the action of the larynx in shifting from "ah" to "oo." However, it cannot be denied that the function of the "Ansatzrohr" can influence the function of the larynx. Tonndorf has found that a sound of the vocal cords that resonates in the mouth cavity may influence the vibrations of the vocal cords in favor of the overtones that have the same number of vibrations as its own tone. We know that in pronouncing "oo" the position of the larynx is much lower than in pronouncing "ee." However, in this instance the influence of the "Ansatzrohr" on the larynx is not certain. It cannot be stated that the sound impression of a register is always produced by the same function of the larynx; acoustic impression and function must not necessarily be parallel. For the influence of the "Ansatzrohr" on vowels see O. Russell.[7]

a9) *Onsets*

The onset of each vowel can be performed in three ways; aspirated when an "h" precedes the vowel, and the glottis is opened entirely (triangular); hard when the glottis is tightly closed; and soft when the vocal cords approximate lightly. Artists are able to replace the hard onset, that is to say, the explosive beginning, by a push of air without a dangerous pressing together of the vocal cords.

b) *Physiological Range of the Voice*

The physiological range is the number of tones a person is able to sing without any strain. Under normal conditions it is still growing beyond the age of 20 years. The following table (see Fig. 7) shows the results of our examinations on children.

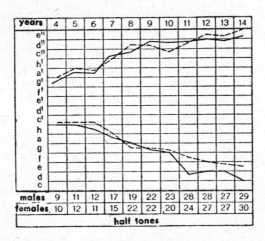

Fig. 7

Range of the voice in children

During voice change the voice of boys generally drops about one octave, the voice of girls about 2-3 tones. Changes in the larynx take place 2-3 years before actual puberty, as we could observe from a certain slackened condition of the muscles of the larynx. It can be concluded that maturing processes take place in the body before showing visible changes. The influence of other sexual processes on the voice has been described by different writers.

The different kinds of voices are: Bass, baritone, and tenor;

contralto, alto, mezzo soprano and soprano. In considering that the untrained singing voice comprehends about 2 octaves, the range for each kind of voice is the following: Bass: E to e¹, baritone: G to g¹, tenor: H to h¹; contralto: c to c², alto: e to e², mezzosoprano: g to g², soprano: h to h². Well trained voices often comprehend 3 octaves.

c) *The Swelling Tone*

First of all it has to be remembered that in wind-instruments the volume of a tone depends on the force of the stream of air. The more air that escapes from the glottis in a time unit, the louder the voice will be. However, this statements needs the restriction that air which passes through the vocal cords without influencing their movement, will not only not enlarge the volume of the voice, but will impair it by adding aspirated sounds. Furthermore, the beauty of the tone will suffer too. This symptom is called "wasting breath." The pitch of a tone depends also on the force of the stream of air, for a larger quantity of air passing through the glottis in a time unit will exert a greater pressure on the borders of the glottis, that is to say, the vocal cords, and produce a greater tension of the vocal cords. The pitch of a tone also depends on the degree of tension of the vocal cords. Thus each louder tone would be higher than a lower tone if we did not have the physiological ability to regulate the pitch of a tone according to our will regardless of its volume. Instinctively we bring into accord the degree of tension of the vocal cords, which is produced by the stretching muscles, with the force of the stream of air, so that the desired pitch is obtained. If we want to form the same tone with continually growing volume, we augment continually the force of the stream of air, and at the same time we slacken continually the stretching muscles. A tone which is produced with a continual change of volume is called swelling tone. D. Weiss could prove in vibrato which, according to Schoen consists of 6-12 pitch- and volume vacillations per second, that pitch and volume move reciprocally in each vibrato wave. (See also K. N. Westermann.[8])

III. ANATOMY AND PHYSIOLOGY OF THE CAVITIES ABOVE THE VOCAL CORDS PARTICIPATING IN VOICE AND SPEECH PRODUCTION (ANSATZROHR)

1) *Anatomy*

In analogy with an expression used with musical pipes, we speak in man too of the "Ansatzrohr." It includes all the cavities above the vocal cords with the exception of the brain cavity. It consists of the throat, the mouth cavity, and the nose with its sinuses. Special attention has to be called to the fact that the posterior wall, as well as the lateral walls of the throat, contain a great number of muscles that are able to change the form of the throat cavity. Of great importance is a group of muscles at about the level of the palate, which curves forward, particularly in pronouncing the non-nasal sounds. It is called the pad of Passavant. The palate is bony in its anterior, and mainly muscular in its posterior part. The latter part can rise until it touches the pharyngeal wall, that is to say, the pad of Passavant, and so produce a closing between the mouth and the nose. The speaking air cannot enter the nose in this position, and has to flow into the mouth, producing a so-called mouth sound. If the soft palate is lowered, the air passes partly through the nose and produces, if voiced, the curious phenomenon of physiologic nasality. It occurs in "m", "n", and "ng" and e.g. in French even in vowels preceding one of the three mentioned sounds. The examinations in the treatment of cleft palates seem to prove that the nasal sound of vowels occurs in the meatusses, and not in the middle nose. (See Fig. 8, 9).

2) *Reflexion and Resonance*

Of great importance for the timbre of the human voice are the conditions of reflexion and the connected conditions of resonance in the "Ansatzrohr." According to a physical law, when longitudinal waves reach a new medium, a reflexion takes place. The many arches and bays, as well as the angles of the "Ansatz-

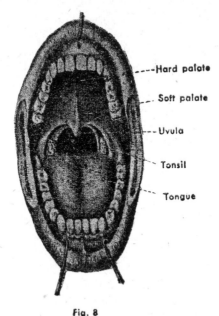

Fig. 8

rohr" produce of course countless reflexions. The impact of a longitudinal wave in a part of the "Ansatzrohr" will result in the resonance of that part. Even the sinus of Morgagni may be a resonator. Whether the sinuses of the nose are resonators seems to be an unanswered question. Russell[9] denies the influence "of any sinus functioning as a resonator "in reference to an observation of a case where all the sinuses and other open cavities above the palate had been removed and the voice was nevertheless very loud.

In the chest too there are resonances, probably particularly in the bronchial tree, hardly in the lung tissue itself. Above the apex resonate the higher, above the base the deeper tones.

As the vocal cords produce sounds not only by vibrations of their whole body as a unit, but also by simultaneous vibrations of single parts, a great number of tones will be produced at the

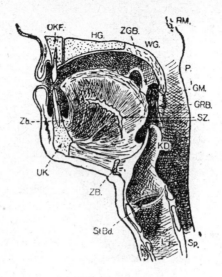

Fig. 9

OKF upper jaw
HG hard palate
WG soft palate
RM Pharyngeal tonsil
Zb Tongue frenulum
UK Lower jaw
ZB Hyoid bone
StBd Vocal cords

L Larynx
KD Epiglottis
SZ Raphé of the tongue
GRB Pharyngo-palatine arch
ZGB Glosso-palatine arch
GM Palatal tonsil
P Pad of Passavant

same time, of which one will resonate in one part of the "Ansathrohr," and another in another part. The voice of two people e.g. who sing the vowel "A" at the same pitch, will sound different if their "Ansathrohr" is built differently, or if they sing the sound "A" with a different mouth position. The pitch in which this vowel or another tone is sung or spoken will be the result of the vibrations of the vocal cords as a unit. This so-called basic tone will resonate differently in different "Ansatzrohren," as well as the numerous partial tones. The result of these differences is the different timbre of individual voices. In different musical instruments also timbre is produced by the resonance of different partial tones.

3) *The Different Kinds of Voices*

The kind of a voice depends first of all on the above mentioned facts.

4) *Vocal Theories*

The changing form of the "Ansatzrohr" is the reason that different sounds can be spoken or sung at the same pitch. The fact that e.g. one time the sound "oo", the other time the sound "ee" is heard is the result of the resonance, or rather, the different strong resonance of some parts of the sound material that has been produced by the vocal cords in the "oo"- and "ee"-position of the "Ansatzrohr." Now we will understand the vocal theory of Helmholtz which has been verified and completed by Stumpf.[10] That theory states that each vowel consists of a basic tone and several harmonic partial tones, the so-called overtones. Stump has stated that some of the over-tones are especially loud (formants) and that these have to be present in the tone mixture in order that the vowel in question will be recognized. In knowing only the above quoted theory of Helmholtz it would be incomprehensible why the same vowel is heard when sung at quite different pitches. For in such a case the basic tones are different. As all the over-tones have to be higher than the basic tone, it could happen that in a high pitch of the basic tone no more overtones would find the possibility to resonate, because the "Ansatzrohr" couldn't be shaped adequately. But such over-tones would still be present in another pitch of the basic tone. It could not be understood how tone mixtures so different from each other, should be able to produce in us the identical experiences which we write e.g. "oo". Now we know that the shifting of the basic tone without change of the mentioned identical acoustic experience, which is signified by the same letter, would be possible only as long as the loudest partial tones (formants) are still present in the tone mixture. If e.g. as we know the formants of the vowel "ah" have the pitch of g^2 and h^2, a singer would not be able to produce it if she wanted to sing it on the basic tone c^3; she would produce another vowel because the mentioned formants could no longer be contained in the tone mixture. We understand now why some singers do not pronounce certain words exactly when singing in a high pitch.

According to Eisenberg[11] the disturbance of the character of the vowels is particularly due to the omission of the over-tones with 800-1200 vibrations. That Fletcher's experiments have proved the contrary may be the result of the occurring differential and summation tones.

Fig. 10 shows the table in the book of Stumpf on page 179.

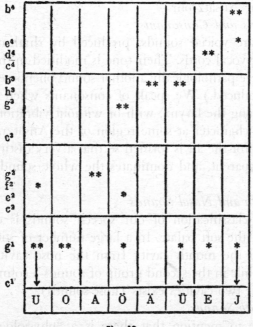

Fig. 10

Two stars ═ formant center
One star ═ secondary formant center
Stars with arrows signify the U-formant which can move downward;
at the same time it is the secondary formant for German "Ue" and "Ee"

The formant centers are marked by 2 stars, the secondary (less important) formants by 1 star.

The enormous literature cannot be discussed here. However, the opinion of Russell (1.c.) should be mentioned: The vocal cords produce sounds not by vibrations but by repeated puffs or explosions of air released from the trachea by the rapid opening and closing of the valve-like action of the vocal cords. They function just as do our lips playing the trumpet or cornet.

5. *Physiology of Articulation*

Articulation is the performance of speech movements which takes place in the cavities above the vocal cords ("Ansatzrohr").

Each sound has its specific articulation, that is to say, its own shape of the Ansatzrohr.

a) *Vowels and Consonants.*

Vowels are voiced sounds, produced by rhythmical vibrations of the vocal cords. Their tone is modified in the "Ansatzrohr" (where pathologically another sound phenomenon, noise, may be produced.) We speak of consonants when the stream of air escaping the larynx, with or without vibrations, changes its acoustic character at some region of the Ansatzrohr, where an obstacle for the air is formed so that a very distinctive noise becomes apparent, and dominates the whole sound phenomenon.

b) *Mouth and Nasal Sounds*

Another classification of our speech sounds is due to the function of the soft palate. In a large number of sounds it has to close off the mouth cavity from the nose cavity (mouth-sounds), while in the second group of sounds a communication between the two cavities exists (nose-sounds).

a1) *Mouth Sounds*

We have to mention that there is a "physiological limit" within which the articulation of the mouth sounds can take place, without becoming pathological.

The vowels should be classified according to the position of the tongue, or the shape of the lips, or the tension or shape of the tongue, or the duration. Here and also in describing some of the consonants we follow Nemoy and Davis.[12]

a2) *Zones of Articulation*

We distinguish three zones of articulation. The first zone is either between both lips or between the lower lip and the upper incisors. The second zone is between the tip of the tongue and the incisors, or between the tip of the tongue and the frontal part of the hard palate. The third zone is between the back of the tongue and the soft, or the posterior part of the hard palate.

The following examples will clarify the division.

When I close the lips and close my nostrils and then open my mouth suddenly, a "p" results, provided I had enough air in my mouth. The zone of articulation of "p" lies between the lips, or in other words, the lips offer to the air an obstacle which had to be overcome to produce the "p". Normally one does not have to close his nose to say "p". The purpose was to stop the air so that it could not escape through the nose. This task is performed by the soft palate. If the soft palate would not make the closure, as in many diseases, it would be impossible to collect the necessary air in the mouth, in order to produce the explosion of "p" by opening the closure.

As "p" requires a closure which is opened by an explosion of escaping air this sound is called a stop or plosive, as are called all sounds formed by a closure and an explosion.

In the first zone of articulation another plosive is formed, the sound "b". To produce this sound the lips close too and the air is stopped behind them for a short while, until the closure is opened suddenly and the air escapes the mouth explosively.

The differences between "p" and "b" are the following: The closure in "p" is tighter than in "b". In "p" only the edges of the lips touch each other, while in "b" also part of the lips behind the edges. The force of the escaping air is greater in "p", it aids to burst the closure. In "b" the muscles of the mouth help to open the lips. The "p" is voiceless, the "b" is voiced, that is to say, the vocal cords are vibrating. The sounds "p" and "b" are called lip, or labial, or bi-labial consonants.

If the lips are drawn together in a whistling position while the tip of the tongue rests against the lower teeth and the back of the tongue is raised toward the soft palate, so that the air passing out causes friction, the sound is called a lip, or labial, fricative. A fricative is formed when the air passes a narrow passage of the "Ansatzrohr."

There are two lip fricatives in English: "wh", voiceless or breathed, and "w", voiced. The sound of "w" is probably more often a glide-vowel or glide-consonant than a fricative; that is, the articulative organs are not approximated closely enough to cause audible friction, but they move quickly from their original position to that of the following vowel, producing a vowel-like sound, often called a glide-consonant or a glide-vowel.

If we approach our lower lip to the upper incisors, without pressing them against the teeth, and allow the air to pass through this narrow passage, we hear the sound "f". We did not perform a closure, therefore it cannot be a stop or plosive sound. The sound "f" is a fricative. Everybody can find out for himself that he can say "f" short or so long as he has breath in his lungs. This fact is another difference between the plosives and the fricatives. The plosives can last an instant only, the fricatives for quite a while.

The sound "v" is formed similarly to "f". The air passes between the upper incisors and the lower lip as long as desired, but voice is added. In "v" vibrations at the bottom of the mouth can be felt (as in all voiced sounds). The sounds "f" and "v" are called lip-teeth, or labio-dental, consonants.

To the second zone of articulation belong the teeth-ridge, or post-dental plosives "t" and "d", the tongue-teeth, or dental fricatives "th", the post-dental fricatives "r", "s", "z", "sh", and "zh", the palatal fricative "y", and the post-dental bilateral "l".

The plosives of that zone are formed when the outgoing air is checked by putting the tip of the tongue at the upper teeth and by raising the soft palate; then the air is quickly released by the withdrawal of the tongue. The tip of the tongue is more pointed in "t" than in "d" and is released with more air-pressure. The "t" is voiceless, the "d" is voiced. Disregarding the zone of articulation, "t" has the same qualities as "p", "d" the same as "b". "T" and "d" are called teeth-ridge, or post-dental plosives.

If the tip of the tongue is placed lightly against the upper teeth and the air forced out between, the sound produced is called a dental fricative. The voiceless form is the sound represented by the letters "th" in "thin"; the voiced form is represented by the letters "th" in "then". They are the only pure dentals in the English language, and even they are often pronounced as intra-dentals, the tongue being allowed to protrude between the teeth instead of being placed against the upper teeth. "Th" voiced and voiceless are called tongue-teeth, or dental fricatives.

If, without being grooved, the tip of the tongue is raised so near the teeth ridge that the voiced breath in passing through causes audible friction, the sound produced is called the voiced tip post-dental fricative "r". It is that of "r" in "rose". When "r" follows a voiceless consonant, as in "pray" or "pretty", the "r" is usually voiceless, in part at least.

This sound is often produced practically without noise and is then almost completely vowel-like in character. It is sometimes called a semi-vowel or glide consonant, its quality being due to the swift movement of the tongue from its original position to that of the following vowel.

Sometimes the "r" is rolled or trilled with the tip of the tongue, especially when it occurs medially or initially or after an initial consonant. This trilled form, because of its great carrying power, is sometimes used by actors and telephone operators.

To produce the sound "s" the tongue lies flat in the mouth, the tip of the tongue being directly behind the upper teeth, but without touching them. Some people press the tip of their tongue lightly against the lower teeth. In doing that, no new zone of articulation is entered, for the friction of the air takes place always between the tip of the tongue and the hard palate. Along the middle line of the tongue a slight groove is formed, and the breath is sent in a narrow stream through this groove and out between the teeth. In some people the lower jaw protrudes. The open lips are stretched sidewards, as in "e". The deeper the tongue is grooved, the sharper the "s" is pronounced. The sound "s" is called the tip post-dental fricative. There are two such fricatives: the one voiceless, or breathed, which is the sound in "so"; the other voiced, which is the initial sound in "zone". In English spelling the voiceless form is represented not only by "s", but also by "ss" as in "miss" and by "c" as in "mice"; it is also the second of the two sounds represented by "x" as in "axe". The voiced form is represented not only by "z", but by "s" as in "has" and by "zz" as in "puzzle"; it is also the second of the sounds represented by "x" as in "exist".

If the blade of the tongue is brought near the molar teeth while the tip which is farther back in the mouth than in "s" is raised toward the hard palate and the lips rounded, the sound produced is "sh". In case one would push back with a probe the tip of the tongue of a person while saying "s", the sound would become more and more similar to "sh". But a clear "sh" is obtained by moving the lips of the person forward and narrowing the mouth at the corners. In this so formed funnel the breath encounters another friction, the first having taken place between the tongue and the hard palate, thus producing the full "sh" sound. Also in "sh" the tongue is slightly grooved along its middle line. The sound "sh" is called a blade-front post-dental fricative. There are two such fricatives: the voiceless, which is represented by the letters "sh" as in "should"; and the voiced, which is represented by the "z" in "azure".

If the front of the tongue is raised nearly to the hard palate, the voiced breath in passing through the narrow opening produces the "y", the sound of "y" in "yes". It is called the voiced palatal fricative. "Y" is the consonantal form of the high front vowel "ee". Like "w", this sound is perhaps more often a glide-vowel or glide consonant than a fricative.

If the tip of the tongue is pressed against the anterior upper teeth as in "d" and the air allowed to pass out of the mouth over the sides of the tongue, the soft palate being raised to prevent the escape of air through the nose, and voice is produced, the sound "l" is formed. It is the voiced post-dental bilateral. A bilateral consonant is a sound made by the emission of the air over both sides of the tongue.

In English this consonant has two principal forms, called the clear "l" and the dark "l". The clear variety occurs initially or after an initial consonant, as in "look" and "glance". The dark variety is used finally or before a final consonant, as in "told". In both varieties of "l" the tip of the tongue should be pressed against the teeth; it is only the back of the tongue that changes position. In the clear "l" the back of the tongue curves downward; in the dark "l" it is raised toward the soft palate, which gives the sound a somewhat u-like character.

A third variety is the inverted, or retroflex, "l". This is formed with the tip of the tongue turned back toward the soft palate. The inversion gives a dull quality, not merely to the "l", but also to the vowels that precede and follow it.

The "l" as well as the "r" is a sound which is pronounced differently in different languages.

In the third zone of articulation are formed the plosives "k" and "g". If the back of the tongue articulates against the palate, and the outgoing air is checked by the pressure of the tongue against the raised soft palate, and the compressed air is then quickly released with a slight explosion by the withdrawal of the tongue, the sound is called a soft-palate, or velar, plosive. The voiceless or breathed sound of that zone is "k", the voiced sound is "g".

If the vocal cords are sufficiently approximated to cause friction or an "air blade" but not sufficient vibration to produce voice, the sound produced is the glottal fricative "h".

a3) *Nasal Sounds*

The nasal sounds are the bi-labial "m", the post-dental "n", and the velar "ng". They have in common that the soft palate does not rise in order to produce a closure; the position of articulation forms the closure. From there the air is thrown back and escapes through the nose where it produces a strong resonance. For this reason the nasal sounds are also called resonants. In "m" the stop occurs between the lips, in the first zone of articulation. The stop in "n" occurs between the tip of the tongue and the upper incisors or the hard palate, in the second zone of articulation. In the third zone of articulation the "ng" is formed, between the back of the tongue and the lowered soft palate. There are no voiceless nasal sounds in English, but in certain combinations, as in "warmth", nasals are often partly unvoiced.

The "ng" should be discussed more thoroughly. The position of articulation of "g" is taken, the tip of the tongue is at the bottom of the mouth, the back of the tongue pressed against the soft palate; however, the soft palate does not touch the posterior throat wall as in the usual g-position, but is lowered. In fact, we don't pronounce "n", we pronounce "g" with nasal resonance; except that for "g" the soft palate rises and the explosion occurs.

The sound "ng" in certain words, as "song", "singer", "singing", are pronounced "ng"; in certain other words, as "finger" and "English", they are pronounced "ng" + "g". In words such as "bank" the "n" is pronounced as "ng".

a4) *Mutual Influence of Sounds*

According to the principle of mutual accommodation during speech, in every language, the entire "Ansatzrohr" forms the position in which the positions of the sounds can be produced in the best way. This position is called the basis of articulation. We learn from these physiological facts, that in describing the formations of the sounds, we could establish only a fluctuative value. The constant gliding of the sounds within the physiological width is the reason that many teachers, especially the teachers for the deaf, have abandoned the forming of isolated sounds and advise primary syllable formation.

IV. CONTINUATION OF "SPEECH DEVELOPMENT OF THE CHILD"

We return now to the child who has started to speak. We have left him in the babbling state. Before the end of the first year he may enter the echolalic state, in repeating words he does not understand. We see in this event a direct link with the babbling period in which echolalic imitations of self produced sounds and syllables are present. We agree with Clara and William Stern who do not consider the echolalic state to be of great importance. At about the same time repeating with understanding starts and with it the spontaneous use of words. The first spontaneous speech utterances consist of single words only. These words have a wish character. When a child says "mama" in that stage of development, he does not want to express that this person is named mama, but he wants the mother to come, to give something, and the like. This stage of development is called the emotional-volitional period. When we learn that the next stage is the intellectual period, we will remember that in earlier stages the beginning towards this tendency has been made. It is characteristic for the start of the intellectual period that some words are used ambiguously. For a time a baby called every lady "Emma oh" who resembled a lady by the name of Emma who had thrown a spool to him exclaiming "Oh", and he also called every spool "Emma oh". In that period often only single words of a sentence are understood correctly, so that e.g. to the sentences "Give me the soldier" and "Do you want the soldier?" the reaction might be the same. Slowly and with some apparent effort the beginner in speech ascends to the stage of logic.

REFERENCES

1. *Weiss, D.:* Monatsschrift fuer Ohrenheilkunde. Vol. 64, 1930, 831-836.
2. *Kaiser:* Archive neerlandaise de phonetique experimentale. 1930.
3. *Han Piao Chen and Orvis C. Irwin:* Infant speech vowels and consonant types. The Journal of Speech Disorders, 1946, 11, 27-29.
4. *Froeschels, Emil, Jellinek Auguste:* Practice of Voice and Speech Therapy. Boston 1941.
5. *Kussmaul:* Die Stoerungen der Sprache. 2. Auflage, F. C. Vogel, Leipzig 1881.
6. *Schilling:* Untersuchungen ueber die Atembewegungen. Monatsschrift fuer Ohrenheilkunde. Vol. 59, 1925.
7. *Russell, O.:* Speech and Voice. The Macmillan Comp. New York 1931.
8. *Westermann, K. N.:* The Journal of Speech Disorders, 6, 4, Dec. 1941, 153-160.
9. *Russell, O.:* Physiologic cause of voice quality difference. Carnegie Inst. of Washington Year Book, Dec. 1938.
10. *Stumpf, Carl:* Die Sprachlaute, Berlin. J. Springer 1926.
11. *Eisenberg:* Ausloeschversuche an Vokalen. Pflüger's Archiv. Vol. 212.
12. *Nemoy and Davis:* Correction of defective consonant sounds. Expression Comp., Boston, Mass., 1937.

SOME EXAMPLES OF
ARTIFICIAL FORMATION OF SOUNDS

The question of artificial formation of sounds arises in cases of aphasia, congenital deafness, dysarthria and dyslalia. Since the shortest step to artificial formation of sounds can be made from the right understanding of the physiology of sounds, the methods are offered to the reader as a supplement to physiology.

In many cases persons with speech defects can imitate the correct formation of the mouth by themselves and without assistance after it has been explained and shown to them. Others can do it with the help of a mirror, while in many cases the therapist himself must shape the mouth. For this purpose it is advisable to adopt the following position of the hands:— With the two middle fingers the nose should be closed by side pressure on the alae nasi. The two index fingers are placed left and right, immediately above the ridge of the upper lip and the thumbs left and right below the ridge of the lower lip. In this way a ring has been formed around the lips and they can be moved in all directions.

If the lower jaw is drawn sufficiently downward the mouth will be opened widely for *ah*—(father). Sometimes it will be necessary to hold the tongue down, but in most cases it follows . the movement of the lower jaw. For *a* as in *have* a moderately

35

wide opening of the mouth should be formed. With this position of the mouth the patient will frequently make the mistake of sounding *a* so that a dull *a* sound is produced. In this event it is better to practice *i* as in *sister*. For this sound, if necessary, the angles of the mouth are drawn apart, and the thumb is used in order to exercise a slight pressure in an upward direction towards the floor of the mouth. In this way the tongue is lifted upwards. From *i* one can now go over to *e* (*met*) and to *a* (*have*), if this pressure is reduced and the lower jaw is drawn slightly downward. At the same time, the pull at the angles of the mouth should be relaxed.

For *o* the opening of the mouth should be rounded, whereby, starting from *ah,* a good *o* is obtained, as the narrow opening of the mouth dulls the sound of *ah.*

Of all vowels *oo* as in *pool* requires the smallest opening of the mouth. A slight pressure against the floor of the mouth produces the correct position of the tongue. By narrowing the opening of the mouth considerably, it can be produced directly from *ah* in a similar way as *o.*

The best way to teach the consonants is by proceeding according to the zones of articulation. The first zone of articulation can be surveyed completely by the eye, and can, therefore, be much more easily observed than the second. The third zone of articulation cannot be seen.

If you show a patient the position of the mouth in pronouncing *f* he will be able to repeat the sound quite easily while one blows on his hand. The second hand, placed against the floor of the mouth, will feel no vibration in the voiceless *f.* In *v* which otherwise resembles *f,* vibrations are noticeable.

The *s* is produced by having the patient pronounce *f.* While he does so, pull the lips away energetically from the upper and lower teeth, using your index fingers and thumbs. Later the patient learns to withdraw his lips from the teeth first with his own fingers and then with the muscles around his mouth.

If you allow the patient to add voice to this newly learned sound *z* is produced.

From the voiceless *s sh* can easily be developed, by slightly pushing the tip of the tongue backward and protruding the lips. The breath in *sh* should then be compared with that in *s*. The former is thin and sharp, the latter round and full

The *y* in *you* can be produced by joining *ee* (*feel*) to another vowel; *ee - ah, ee - a, ee - o, ee - oo* pronounced quickly results in *yah, ya, yo, you*.

To obtain the plosive sounds of the first zone of articulation the patient should be shown the closure of the lips, and he should be allowed to feel the escape of the breath in front of his mouth. For *p* a stronger closure and a more violent explosion of air is necessary than for *b*. The *b* contains voice, and this the patient ought to be made to feel on the larynx.

If one does not succeed in this way, lips and nose can be closed with your six fingers, as described above, until a sufficient amount of air has accumulated in the mouth. Then the closure of the lips should be released.

With *d* and *t* an optical demonstration of the right position of articulation is, in many cases, sufficient if the patient is allowed to feel the explosion at the same time. If this method produces a negative result the formation of the interdental *t* and *d* is recommended. For this purpose the tongue should be placed between the almost closed incisor teeth, and should then be moved downward, together with the lower jaw. In this way an interdental *t* or *d* is produced. The interdental position of the tongue can easily be corrected later on in teaching the patient to close the teeth first. The tongue then moves, on its own account, up to the upper incisor teeth. During the explosion the lower jaw should be pulled downward.

The *g* and *k* are often successfully produced by energetically pushing the tongue of the patient backward and releasing it with the explosion. The hands of the patient should be placed in front of the mouth and on the back part of the floor of the mouth of the therapist. There a kind of a thrusting, lowering movement can be distinctly felt corresponding to the quick descent of the back of the tongue which had been raised for the purpose of articulation with the hard palate. In many cases this procedure does not lead to a firm articulation between the palate and the back of the tongue and only a cough-like sound is produced. It should then be tried with the help of a nasal sound, namely *n*. If the patient says *n,* and if the tip of the tongue is pressed to the floor of the mouth, the patient will continue to pronounce *n,* while the back of the tongue is raised to the palate to form the closure. As a matter of fact, we have already achieved a nasal *g.* Now we need only close the nose firmly, and at the same time free the tip of the tongue, whereupon an explosive *g* is pronounced. Then one can gradually succeed in isolating *g* and lead the patient to conceive of it as a separate sound. Its voiceless partner is *k.*

In order to teach *l* the tip of the tongue is raised to the palate after which the voice need only be added.

JEANETTE O. ANDERSON, PH.D.
Director, Speech Clinic, Rockford College, Rockford, Ill.

Chapter II

APHASIA AND ITS TREATMENT

FROM the point of view of speech pathology, aphasia includes all linguistic disturbances, expressive or receptive, caused by a lesion of the brain but not attributable to faulty innervation of the musculature used in speech or writing, nor to pathology of the sense organs themselves, nor to general mental deficiency; these language disturbances are to be understood as failures in the symbolization, retention and production of mental concepts in association with conventional phonetic and chirographic symbols. The speech pathologist is interested in the specific language losses that make up or cause the usual mixed aphasia. He is concerned with a classification of these disturbances that will indicate the underlying anatomical, physiological and psychological bases of the dysfunction; this means, of course, that his knowledge of the interrelationships of these fields within the aphasic frame must be so familiar to him that he can, from the point of view of a single specialist, see the picture in three dimensions. From the point of view of one who must make use of the undamaged brain areas for restitution of function, he will add his own analysis of the dis-

39

order in terms of speech prognosis and therapy. Thus the speech pathologist's concept of aphasia should be not only as precise as that used in localization by the surgeon; it must be as general as that of the psychologist who insists that the linguistic mechanism is a *Gestalt* and functions wholly. The speech pathologist must, more than any other investigator in this field, see both the parts and the whole clearly and simultaneously in their mutual relationships. It is not enough for the speech pathologist to see clearly and in proper perspective aphasias and their various concomitants and combinations; he needs to evaluate linguistic failures in terms of agnosia and apraxia and to be able to recognize them as corollaries of apraxia and agnosia manifested in non-language activities. If he is to assume his responsibilities and discharge his duties, the speech pathologist needs a revised classification of aphasias.

He cannot agree with many psychologists that there is little or no localization of function; neither can he subscribe to exact anatomical localization. In general, he can follow the lead of the physiologist in admitting that certain areas subserve certain linguistic functions more than others and that the entire brain is needed for normal linguistic activity. In order to discover aphasic manifestations and to prescribe techniques of special reeducation in speech, the speech pathologist needs to consider not only the psychological, anatomical and physiological aspects of the problem, but also the possibility of retraining in terms of all three. He needs, first, a consistent classification of aphasic manifestations. This classification should be based upon manifestations actually observed, should be exhaustive, and should recognize aphasia as the basic linguistic disturbance of which some agnosias and some apraxias are parts. Aphasia as a gestalt is different from the sum of its parts. In order to minimize confusion and to serve maximally, this classification should be couched in simple terms capable of only one interpretation in any field of study.

The following classification of aphasic manifestations is suggested as a first step toward a practical solution of the problem confronting the speech pathologist:

I. Expressive manifestations
    A. Implicit (probably caused by a parietal lesion)
        1. Ideational aphasia
        2. Ideo-kinetic aphasia
    B. Overt (probably caused by a frontal lobe lesion)
        1. Spoken language
            a. Broca's aphasia (third left frontal convolution, cortex)
            b. Subcortical aphasia (subcortical Broca's region)
            c. Transcortical aphasia (questionable)
        2. Written language
            a. Agraphia (Exner's writing center, second left frontal convolution)

II. Receptive manifestations
    A. Auditory (superior temporal convolution)
        1. Agnosia (Heschl's convolution)
        2. Aphasia (posterior part of superior temporal convolution)
    B. Visual (temporo-parieto-occipital area)
        1. Agnosia
            a. For linguistic symbols
            b. For objects and colors
            c. Geometric-optic
        2. Aphasia
            a. Alexia
            b. Agraphia
            c. Anomia
    C. Other sensory media
        1. Tactile
        2. Cutaneous
        3. Kinesthetic

III. Associative manifestations
    A. Aphasia on lower levels
    B. Aphasia on higher levels
IV. Combinations of manifestations
    A. Wernicke's aphasia
    B. Total aphasia
    C. Other combinations of aphasic manifestations
 V. Manifestations indicating special abilities useful in planning speech therapy
    A. Expressive
        1. Oral facility for building new motor synergies
        2. Manual facility for building new motor synergies
        3. Kinesthetic imagery
    B. Receptive
        1. Visual imagery
        2. Auditory
            a. Imagery
            b. Memory span
        3. Other sensory imagery
    C. Associational
    D. Constitutional predisposition of patient

This suggested classification of manifestations includes the generally accepted aphasic duality: expressive and receptive disorders. Moreover, provision is made for positing general dysfunction and for the recognition of specific impairments within or superimposed upon the general one. Although its fundamental purpose is to guide the speech pathologist in diagnostic, prognostic and therapeutic procedures, this classification may prove of some use in the consideration of aphasic patients by other specialists.

There are certain aphasic manifestations that can be grouped under the several headings; a given patient may exhibit almost any combination of these signs. If he shows more manifestations from one group than from any other, he may be described as suffering from, for example, predominantly expressive aphasia. In most cases of aphasia, however, it seems more satisfactory to diagnose the case as an aphasia and then to list the specific linguistic findings. In no other way can an adequate picture of the patient's losses and residues, psychological, physiological and anatomical, be assayed. The very confusion within the field of study for over eighty years suggests that attempts to classify aphasic types is unsatisfactory. This may be because there are no clearly defined aphasic types.

The speech pathologist seems justified in postulating a synthesized concept of aphasia. He need not quarrel with existing definitions of aphasia. He must insist that classification of aphasic cases is arbitrary and not natural; confusion resulting from such attempts at classification may be minimized by classifying manifestations and not cases.

A basic concept of aphasia for the speech pathologist evolves: aphasia is a linguistic impairment; there tend not to be "pure" aphasias; each aphasic patient exhibits a disturbance made up of certain aphasic manifestations peculiar to the given case; any classification must be of aphasic manifestations and not of aphasias. Examination reveals the manifestations; they form the specific aphasic complex seen in each case. Once he has this concept of the inconstancy, unpredictability and irresolution of the aphasic problem, the speech pathologist is ready to examine and to attempt re-education of aphasic patients.

The problem confronting the speech correctionist is one of prognosis and education or re-education; he begins with the diagnosis, medical and linguistic.

When an aphasic comes or is brought to a speech clinic, the speech pathologist legitimately may encourage him. For, with the aid of a trained speech therapist, most aphasic patients can route or re-route impaired or undeveloped linguistic neurograms. Progress will be slow, but it will also be sure unless there is further pathological invasion of cortical tissue. The aphasic child will learn much less rapidly than the non-aphasic child. The aphasic adult must expect to spend years, not months, if he would regain a part of his former reading, speaking and writing ability. From one to six years of speech therapy may be expected to produce increasingly more efficient comprehension and production of written and oral speech symbols by adults rendered aphasic through injury or illness. After an initial period of training, varying in length from patient to patient, each individual tends to reach a plateau, somewhere short of his former level of excellence, beyond which he seems unable to go despite his will to learn or the extent of the training to which he is exposed. Many persons learn to speak, write and read enough to carry on uncomplicated lives at home or in simple employment.

Neither the aphasic child nor the aphasic adult profits from speech therapy until he wants so much to express his inner verbalizations that he spontaneously attempts some form of overt communication with other organisms, human or not, in his environment. This effort to speak may be made orally, manually, grimacingly, graphically or chirographically. It must be ontogenetic.

Once the aphasic tries to communicate, he will respond to speech training or retraining. During this period of relatively rapid progress, an aphasic child learns well when objects, toys, pictures, games and other situations are associated with speech sounds. The adult who has through physical or psychological trauma lost all or part of his once-learned ability to manipulate verbal symbols, incoming and outgoing, usually responds better to written or printed symbols than to the realities for which they stand. So completely is the average adult conditioned to living in a word-world that he readjusts to this world more easily and quickly than to the fact-world in which he had his postnatal orientation. Only when situations, objects, persons, colors or pictures are fraught with emotional significance do they provoke an attempt at speech as rapidly and successfully as do printed or written symbols. For example, unless an adult patient feels strongly about cats, the printed symbols, *c-a-t,* will probably cause him to respond orally twice as quickly and accurately as a pictured or actual cat. The same man, however, would be likely to respond more quickly, one way or another, to his wife in person than to the printed symbols, *w-i-f-e.* If an adult aphasic has been accustomed to using a specialized vocabulary, as one would, for example, in the field of medicine, he will usually respond best to oral, written or printed stimuli couched in the terms with which he is most familiar and which he has used most frequently.

Although it may be necessary at first to employ strongly emotional stimuli to secure overt response from an aphasic patient, this practice is to be avoided and discouraged because it leads in the aphasic, even more than in the so-called normal, to uncontrolled speech, to excesses of emotional response that eventually inhibit rather than stimulate volitional speech, to hysteria, to behavior on a thalamic level. Repetition of non-significant material; exclamations such as "Oh fudge!", "Dear me!", "Terrible, terrible!" and "Darn!"; and well phonated and articulated but non-propositional profanity are examples of speech responses to poorly controlled emotional stimuli. Properly and sparingly used, emotional stimuli may help the patient to recall proper names and may build self-confidence by demonstrating to him that he *can* produce meaningful phonetic combinations.

It is important to guard an aphasic from emotional excesses. He is no longer able to guard himself very effectively. His cortex is damaged, and since the cortex tends to function as a unit, injury to any part of it affects all of its workings. The aphasic's emotional behavior is often as uncontrolled as it was when he was a baby. He laughs and cries easily and without moderation. He has temper-tantrums. He experiences rapid changes in mood. He has to relearn cortical control not only of speech but of all his overt behavior. In this discussion, however, the primary concern is with the psychological and semantic aspects of linguistic impairment rather than with the spastically defective phonation and articulation that often accompany aphasia.

As the infant achieves more and more specialization of activity with the myelinization of cortical fibers, so the aphasic child or adult may be taught increasingly exact behavior patterns. The child, of course, learns speech in half a dozen indiscrete and overlapping stages: undifferentiated crying, differentiated crying, babbling, lallation, echolalia, true speech. The aphasic who is ready for speech training is usually babbling. Lallation and echolalia should be employed as useful steps leading toward true speech. Phonetics and the incorporation of speech sounds into nonsense syllables seem useful only as they are made an integral part of the normal speech learning process just described. In and of themselves, they seem non-valuable; used in a developmental learning sequence, they may be invaluable.

In helping an aphasic patient toward a volitional use of language, it is useful to know that there are more ways than one to approach the teaching or re-teaching of speech. When an individual learns new words, he more or less consciously employs one or more of these ways in stimulating himself to produce speech in audible or visible form. Those who are eye-minded depend mainly upon visual imagery; they count on being able to see the word in the mind's eye whenever they need to reproduce it in writing or oral speech. They learn by seeing and re-seeing. Others are ear-minded. These individuals are able to reproduce language orally and in writing, and they are usually better speakers than spellers, because of re-auditorization or hearing in the mind's ear. They depend chiefly upon auditory imagery. They learn by hearing and re-hearing. Still others are movement-minded. They learn by repetition of neuro-muscular patterns. They say or write a word over and over to learn it.

When they want to reproduce it at a later date, they depend upon kinesthetic imagery, upon a sense of re-moving. Visual, auditory and kinesthetic imagery account for most speech learning. For specific words there is dependence to a lesser degree upon tactile, olfactory and gustatory images as well. Most people use all of these images in combination as they learn, but one type of imagery usually predominates or leads.

Individuals learn, retain and reproduce symbols because they are able to summon and associate images at will. The aphasic can usually learn or relearn along the same pattern, but more slowly and less completely. At first, the speech therapist needs to present as many stimuli as possible with each word to be learned; later, the strongest or lead stimulus will become evident and can then be employed as an initial stimulus in further teaching and learning. It is always more effective, however, to use a combination of stimuli than to depend upon any one alone. The aphasic will speak and/or write a word more quickly if he hears *and* sees it while he tries to write it *and* say it than if only one stimulus were presented and only one response requested. There are at least two reasons for this: first, each stimulus and response tends to reinforce others made simultaneously; second, if one avenue of reception or expression is blocked, anatomically or psychologically, concomitant stimuli and responses provide alternate routes by which necessary neurological associations may be effected.

To effect these associations, neural impulses must be rerouted to their usual association areas through healthy tissue; remaining tissue of the dominant hemisphere must associate impulses previously synapsing elsewhere; or the intact, usually non-dominant, cerebral hemisphere may take over the function of damaged brain areas. This is the theory upon which neurologists and psychologists explain restitution of linguistic function. Such restitution occurs slowly, only partially spontaneously, never wholly and never *in vacuo*. It has been noted that the cerebral cortex functions as a unit. This is true of the entire central nervous system. This nervous system is capable of extreme selectivity and specificity, but it is also true that interference with the functioning of any part of the system is reflected throughout the system and its activities. This means that the speech therapist never works with aphasia but always with the aphasic individual. In teaching aphasic children, speech ought to be an outgrowth of daily experience. Speech should never be taught as an entity, an end in itself, but always as an integral part of the business of living, a means to an end. For the aphasic adult, retraining in speech cannot be separated from emotional, social and vocational retraining. Only as an aphasic patient achieves personal, social and economic stability will his speech stabilize. He cannot be taught speech while he waits to live. He has to go on living and his speech training will be useful to him only as it keeps pace with his needs. Speech therapy for aphasic children and adults must be planned to satisfy the special, biological, social and economic needs of each patient.

In summary, a working concept of aphasia for the speech pathologist defines aphasia as a basic disorder of symbolization that may exhibit any combination of many aphasic manifestations; many aphasics can be educated or re-educated in speech if a program of therapy is planned to utilize each patient's special abilities and to meet each patient's specific needs.

HELEN HULICK BEEBE
Speech Clinician, Easton Hospital, Penna.

Chapter III

PARAGRAMMATISM IN CHILDREN

THE term paragrammatism was introduced by Kleist[4] to apply to speech showing confusion in grammatical forms in contrast to agrammatism consisting of an abbreviated form of phrase formation, sometimes called telegram style. Froeschels[2] has pointed out that agrammatic speech means speech without grammar and that this is impossible because every meaningful junction of words, even the use of a single word to replace a phrase, involves a *kind* of grammar. For example, one may say "airplane ocean," and while the listener could ask for a more specific meaning, the two connected words convey a meaning different from that of the two words considered separately. This meaningful junction must contain a kind of grammar or syntax although it does not conform to the rules in accepted usage. If we see a house without a door or a train with the engine between the cars we don't conclude that the house or the train are missing, only that they are different respectively from the usual house or train. In cases whose speech shows a disturbance in grammatical and/or syntactical relationships we find at least a variety of grammar and this can best be described by the term paragrammatism as Froeschels[2] and Stein[7] have suggested.

49

The disturbance is often present in adult aphasia which is due to certain pathological conditions of the brain. In this case a skill already acquired has been damaged. When an expressive aphasic says to me, "Lesson five wife mad" I understand that his wife objects to the hour of his appointment. When a four-year-old child says, "Me bed no" I know he doesn't want to go to bed. In each case a meaningful junction—a kind of grammar—was present although neither was spoken in the usual form. The etiology of these two cases is, of course, different, but both can be correctly called paragrammatism. This chapter is concerned with paragrammatism as it appears in children in the course of speech development without any injury or intercurrent disease of the brain.

Paragrammatism is physiologic at a certain stage of development. This is in accordance with other phases of child development which follow a chronological order. The various skills are alloted a more or less limited time in which to develop. According to Stern[8] the speech skills are acquired in the following order:

1. Preliminary period to 1 year—Babble, mere imitation of sound forms.
2. To 1 year 6 months—Mastery of single word sounds, one word sentence.
3. To 2 years—Begins to combine words, learns that every thing has a name.
4. To 2 years 6 months—Complete mastery of uninflected speech, questions.
5. To 4 years—Rapid growth in use of subordinate clauses and finer differentiation in speech forms, questions of "Why" type.

It should be mentioned that babbling is not mere imitation of sound forms for it is well known that congenitally deaf babies babble. The babbling period for deaf babies is usually short because they lack the acoustic stimulation which prompts the hearing child to imitate his own babbling.

In order for the child to acquire speech a certain sensory-motor performance must take place and provided this can function properly he responds to his environment—finds that things have names, that talking gives him some control over his environment. But behind all this there seems to be an innate urge to talk, as Froeschels[3] puts it an *élan*.

The child's first so-called connected language does not fit into any formal pattern of syntax or grammar. It is well known that a child's speech vocabulary first consists mostly of nouns, verbs are added next and later other parts of speech. Some of this "ungrammatical" language calls for interpretation on the part of an adult, for example, when two-year-old Johnnie says, "Daddy car work?" the three words together express an idea. When my two and one-half-year-old nephew asked, "Aunt Helen wash dishes?" his mother explained that he expected me to stay after the meal to wash the dishes. An underlying feeling for grammar seems to develop gradually along with a growing vocabulary and only later does the child construct language by analogy with known forms.

If paragrammatic speech is present beyond the usual age the condition should be considered pathologic although not necessarily of a serious nature. For example, a three and one-half-year-old boy brought to me because he had started to stutter (clearly a case of imitation stuttering) besides having several consistent sound substitutions in his speech spoke in the following manner: "Why him fall?, Why elephant lift him feet up, Then him tan see." Statistics have shown that a great percentage of audimute children later develop speech which is paragrammatic. This may be due to a slight aphasic trouble or only to a delayed development, or to a kind of social resistance. Specific explanation can be ascertained during treatment. Paragrammatism also appears in children whose speech shows no other abnormalities although cases of this kind are in the minority of

all pargrammatics. It has been my experience that paragrammatism is frequently joined with a certain form of dyslalia
which is considered chiefly psychologic in nature. This form of
dyslalia, called asocial dyslalia, differs from the usual forms
(see Chapter X) in so far as not always the same sounds are
omitted neither are the same substituting sounds used. In other
words the omissions as well as the substitutions seem to be
caused not by a real inability to speak correctly but seem to be
subject to the will of the patient. These clinical observations
brought us to the conclusion that this form of dyslalia is one of
the ways in which the child shows an asocial tendency. In like
manner I believe that paragrammatism in such cases is due to
a resistance of the child to conform to the speech behavior appropriate for his age.

To reproduce single syllables and words, provided there is no
impairment of sound-hearing the child's acoustic memory and,
of course, the transmission to the expressive area must function. To produce series of words calls for an auditory memory
span of some length. Some studies have been made to determine the length of auditory memory span and different writers
have been interested in a variety of correlations.

S. D. Robbins[6] studied the relation between short memory
span and disorders of speech. He found that auditory memory
span for logical sentences is considerably longer than for digits,
consonants, and nonsense syllables. In testing cases of speech
disability for digit auditory memory span Robbins came to the
conclusion that while a short span seems to be an etiological
factor in dyslalia, this does not appear to hold for cases of stammering and cluttering.

R. W. Metraux[5] studied auditory memory span in relation to
age, sex, and intelligence. The results of her tests showed that
the span increased with age (5 to 12 years), the peak for vowels
reached at age 10 while the peak for consonants is reached at
age 12. The differences between memory span for boys and

girls and the relation between auditory memory span and mental age was not considered significant according to Metraux.

D. Weiss[9]* found in working with German speaking children that auditory memory span for a series of meaningless syllables is correlated with chronological age. Normally a child of three years repeated three syllables, one of four years four syllables and so on, progressing to about the ninth year. Both Weiss[9] and Froeschels found that in cases of paragrammatism auditory memory span fell below the normal level. Although for English speaking children not as specific a standard has been established, I have observed that paragrammatic children usually have comparatively short auditory memory spans. (The three- and one-half-year-old boy could not repeat more than two syllables).

The writer[1] studied English speaking children in order to compare their ability to repeat a series of meaningless syllables with that of German speaking children. The auditory memory spans were studied in relation to age, sex, and intelligence. According to this study auditory memory span for meaningless syllables increased with change in age level for English speaking children (4 to 8 years) but the average auditory memory span fell below that of German speaking children. The writer has suggested that the latter fact might be accounted for if we consider the importance of syllable arrangement in the construction of the German language. For example, *geben* = give, *gegeben* = have given. Thus, a German speaking child must give acoustic attention to the syllables in order to acquire skill in grammar and syntax.

No doubt further research on the subject of auditory memory span will be undertaken and may shed more light on the subject of paragrammatism. Meanwhile it seems safe to assume

---

*In a personal conversation D. Weiss stated recently that he found Spanish speaking children in Cuba could repeat a series of syllables correlated with chronological age, adding one syllable for each year of age.

that the child's ability to acquire the use of correct grammatical and syntactical forms depends at least partly upon the length of his auditory memory span. Clinical experience shows that auditory memory span can be extended in length by appropriate therapy. Most cases of paragrammatism in children can be corrected simply by having the child repeat after the therapist sentences commencing with the simplest forms and gradually increasing length and complexity. This is done most effectively in reference to pictures or well illustrated stories. If necessary the therapist will help with gestures or by having the child describe an actual performance. (I took the book from the shelf, Mrs. T. walked across the room). Gradually the child's feeling for grammatical and syntactical forms is aroused and is applied in his spontaneous speech.

REFERENCES

1. *Beebe, Helen:* Auditory Memory Span for Meaningless Syllables. J. Speech Disorders, Sept. 1944, 3, 273-76.
2. *Froeschels, Emil:* Zur Frage des kindlichen Paragrammatisms. Weiner med. Wchnschr., 1930, No. 35.
3. *Froeschels, Emil:* Psychological Elements in Speech, Expression Co., 1932.
4. *Kleist, K.: See* Weisenburg and McBride. Aphasia. New York, 1935. 32-33.
5. *Metraux, Ruth Watt:* Auditory memory span for speech sounds: norms for children. J. Speech Disorders, Mar. 1944, 9, 31-38.
6. *Robbins, S. D.:* The relations between short auditory memory span disability and disorders of speech. Laryngoscope, 1935, 45, 545-553.
7. *Stein, Leopold:* Speech and Voice. London, 1942.
8. *Stern, William:* Psychology of Early Childhood, 172ff.
9. *Weiss, D.:* Testuntersuchugen an normalen und sprachgestörten Kindern. Weiner med. Wchnschr., vol. 77, 5, 1930, No. 35.

MARTIN F. PALMER, Sc.D.
Director, Institute of Logopedics, Wichita, Kansas

Chapter IV

DYSARTHRIA

THE subject of dysarthria is extensive and complicated. Dysarthria generally occurs as the result of brain injury and is the central problem in cases of cerebral palsy. In this condition the speech is almost always affected where the involvement is at all severe. Occasionally dysarthria will occur in which very little motor involvement is found. Generally speaking, however, no cerebral palsy clinic can be successful without provision for adequate speech care. No person should work with a dysarthric who does not meet the full professional membership requirements of the American Speech Correction Association. However, these requirements are exceedingly minimal and do not guarantee successful preparation for this specialized field. In addition, the individual who attempts to work with dysarthrics should have had special training in a clinic which specializes in this type of work. There are very few training schools in this country at the present time which give this type of program.

The purpose in publishing this brief review of the problem is to call attention to its essential difficulties. Dysarthria cannot be classed as a separate problem since the remainder of the

55

motor involvements in cases of cerebral palsy require that a timing scheme be brought into play relative to the remaining condition. A child who has been trained from too many angles at once tends to go into a deadlock and makes progress in no direction. Even within the speech training process such deadlock can be encountered if the child is not prepared adequately for the experience which is being undertaken at the time. It is highly essential, therefore, that an individual working in this field be careful to affiliate properly with other specialists and that a coordinated plan of corrective work be developed.

Although the pathology of dysarthria is much confused today, there being a considerable divergency in the literature between clinical and basic research workers in dysarthria, at least it can be assumed that a definite lesion occurs which is irreparable and that any progress made occurs as the result of reintegration of the total organic function of the brain.

It is necessary to make a distinction in a particular case relative to the amount of other disorders that exist, since aphasia and stuttering are common in cases of dysarthria. It seems probable that the question of a cerebral dominant gradient need not be explored too carefully or routinely on any case, although in the aphasias the relationship is ambiguous, to say the least, and needs to have further attention.

It is possible to make recovery of the speech processes in almost all of the speech disorders without bothering in the slightest about whether the child is using the proper hand or not. Much more important than this are the other fundamental issues of neurological function which are met in these cases. It has been noted for many years by logopedists that it is possible for a case to make a gain in speech without any particular attention being paid to the speech process. For example, when a helpless child first begins to sit up, it will almost immediately, if it has normal intelligence, make its first efforts in speech, regardless of whether any change in the speech teaching has been made or not. Vice versa, it has been noted that when a child begins to talk it will also make a concomitant gain in gross body control. This is evidence that the corrective program is not a system of phonetic or articulatory exercise. The re-education process in dysarthria proceeds under two main headings, indirect and direct.

INDIRECT:

In all selective injuries to the central nervous system alterations in the environmental stimuli may transiently produce "near-normal" functions. The neural loops suddenly alter the fluxes to the cortical configurations, producing a distribution in which the damaged area need not serve for normal function. Sometimes very small changes in the amount of light, the arrangement, the temperature of a room, and even, it has been suggested, the barometric pressure, will mean progress in these cases. Thus a part of the re-educational procedure is based on a plan for the alteration of environment. This planning includes emotional, physiological and psychological patterns, etc. by parents, nurses and others caring for the child.

DIRECT:

Most of the direct techniques developed in logopedics have evolved from Pavlov and the studies by Kennard, Lashley, etc. on animals with controlled brain injuries. The methodologies used in aphasia have been developed to some extent through the contributions of German neurologists and psychologists after the first World War. The goal is the attainment of more or less inhibitory cortical motor discharges during the functions involved. Such permanent inhibitions are possible, although normal function is very rarely obtained. Although dysarthria is primarily an efferent problem, it is necessary to pay close attention to the afferent side of the problem. Actually, re-education is afferent, not efferent, and a review of the sensory abilities of each case must be made. In aphasia, effort is directed towards the development of integrated propositions, while in motor involvements the configurations desired are mostly inhibitory on the tracts.

Cases profit from speech instruction from the very first. Although volitional speech does not occur in the average normal before ten or eleven months, the receptive end of the process is active in the first few weeks. Since the retraining process is largely sensory, the earlier it is commenced, the better.

As in other brain injuries, the possibility of catastrophic situations in the training situation is ever present. Catastrophe occurs when a problem arises which may seem ridiculously simple to the observer, but which the case cannot solve. This event was first pointed out by Goldstein in his work in Germany after the first World War. Pressure to achieve produces changes in the whole vaso-motor system, and failure to progress may endure for many months. Careful control of the situation is imperative from the time that dysarthria is recognized.

Although early motor speech re-education sometimes brings about a gain in muscular control through the irradiation of inhibition, the effort to develop locomotion and motor speech at the same time usually results in deadlock. Normally, preliminary locomotor control is obtained before speech motor control. The usual sign of commencing motor speech work is control of the transversalis muscles of the neck. As soon as the child becomes able to hold its back and head fairly erect, drooling tends to diminish. The salivary flows so often found in these cases are, of course, due to lack of normal swallowing reflexes and very seldom due to irritation of the nerves supporting the salivary glands. All of the specific details of the speech continuity are developed from the chewing, sucking and swallowing reflexes. This was carefully pointed out by Dr. J. H. Muyskens of the University of Michigan shortly after the first World War, and its applications to these cases have been developed, primarily at the Institute of Logopedics during the past twelve years, and by Froeschels, particularly on the chewing process,

independently. These chewing, sucking and swallowing reflexes are merged synergistically with the respiratory and cardiac reflexes. When none of these are normal, or even when
one of them is not normal, the speech in each case will be characteristic of the type of general defect found.

Prior to any work in dysarthria of a motor nature, it is essential that the various types of mechanical difficulties be carefully
analysed. Actually, in dysarthria one is not dealing with a
separate single condition but a group of more or less loosely
organized conditions produced by different injuries to the brain
and reacting in different ways to produce the general dysarthria.
It is not possible to segregate these cases exactly at the present
time on the basis of the type of speech uttered, since this is an
anomaly in diagnosis. The difficulty must relate to the fact that
the symptomatology is impossibly presented at the present time.

In cerebral palsy it is generally recognized that the following
main types exist: spastic paralysis, athetosis, tremors, rigidity
and cerebellar involvement. These are not clear cut divisions,
and are primarily not clear cut because of the difficulty at the
present time in analysing the situation in athetosis. There are
at least eleven or twelve types of athetosis found now in cerebral palsy, according to Phelps, and naturally these athetotic
complexes must be reflected in the type of speech uttered by the
subject. The speech field has not yet developed to the point
where the type of athetosis can be detected on the basis of the
fundamental changes in the physical pattern of the speech process. With these exceptions a general description will be made
of the types of speech.

Spastic paralysis is distinguished generally by hyperactive antagonistic muscle reflexes. None of the other neurological signs
is adequate. In spastic paralysis, if an extremity is moved around
a joint, the muscle opposing this movement will, if stretched
quickly enough, undergo what is known as a stretch reflex.
What this means in speech is that the speech will be generally

labored, slow and draggy, accompanied by many grimaces, due to the fact that any movement made by the subject tends-to be opposed by a stretch reflex from the antagonist and it is only with tremendous effort that speech can be produced.

In athetosis there may be hyperkinesis of the vocal folds, involuntary respiratory movements and general incoordination. In true athetosis the voice is usually weak. Severe athetotic cases are sometimes speechless since motor neurograms cannot be developed because of constant shifting movements. Athetosis is the result of irregularly rhythmic synchronous muscular discharges to antagonistic muscles. There are many divergencies from these statements due to the varying types of athetosis which are found. Tension athetosis, for example, may very well produce a speech which resembles spastic speech.

A choreic type of explosive, hesitant speech is sometimes found, particularly in athetosis, standing in prolonged syllables which clearly cut into syllabic divisions.

In tremors the voice is slow, halting, interrupted, or delayed for many minutes, lacking in modulation and blurred.

Rigidity in the speech organs generally results in complete loss of speech, as much from the mechanical difficulty as from the rather predominant mental deficiency which tends to be found in this group. Rigidity is distinguished by the turgid consistency of the affected musculature.

In cerebellar lesions the speech may consist of an utterance which at the first part of the sentence may be fairly distinct, but with the movements becoming weaker and faster until unintelligible.

These differences in speech are probably due to the location of the lesions in the cerebellum, or along its paths. In general, logopedic procedures used must be modified to fit the type of defect observed.

Generally in procedure, attention is first given to the chewing, sucking and swallowing reflexes, the gag reflex being the most important. Control of the oronasal port is almost always defective when the gag reflex is absent. If lost on a central basis, this reflex may be developed medically by various means.

A few of the general difficulties found in the chewing reflexes may be mentioned as illustrative.

1. Contraction of the platysma for depressing the mandible. This is found both in spastic paralysis and tension athetosis.

2. Minimal use of the external pterygoid. This was first pointed out by the Institute of Logopedics. Here the external pterygoid may serve as a minimal motor depression of the mandible.

3. Occasional difficulties in elevating the mandible are encountered as a result of spasticity of the suprahyoids, and actual mandibular depressions may be seen when a case is attempting to elevate the mandible.

4. Failure of the elevation of the apex of the tongue is almost always present in spastic paralysis and tension athetosis, the tongue appearing small and often retracted.

5. Local two-point discrimination is sometimes defective, although speech may be improved, even on the basis of poor local discrimination.

6. Occasional cases protrude the tongue between the teeth, which is a vicarious function for elevation, and this function can be used for intelligible speech, but is non-aesthetic.

Similar difficulties are found in the sucking and swallowing reflexes.

The techniques used for the reduction of these abnormalities depend first on a careful diagnosis and analysis of the deformity, and secondly on various methods of reducing the deformity. These consist of techniques which are much too complicated to describe in this short paper, but which are very similar to the techniques used in general physiotherapy.

In general for dysarthria a very high sort of skill is needed in speech corrective or logopedic work, the goal being not normal function but usable function. It is possible to produce an intelligible speech by the use of proper techniques, and it is certainly true that the customary speech corrective techniques found in the literature are of little or no benefit in these cases. Unfortunately, some of the material alluded to here has become rather wide-spread by hearsay, and is used professionally with little understanding of the fundamentals involved. Chewing, sucking and swallowing materials are being put into play in many clinics without an adequate understanding of the complexities involved in producing these reflexes on a normal substratum. It is essential that an individual who attempts to work with this condition seek training in institutions which have developed these programs and applied them particularly to these cases.

The opportunities for the clinical worker in this particular problem are great. The distribution of intelligence is high enough so that the cases warrant proper attention, although mental deficiency is somewhat more frequent in cases of dysarthria than in the normal population.

Much more research is needed to clarify the points which are still not clear, but still it is safe to say that with present knowledge, many cases of dysarthria can be improved enough to become useful and intelligible citizens.

SHULAMITH KASTEIN
Speech Correctionist, Speech Clinic, Brooklyn College, N.Y.C.

Chapter V

ALALIA

THE place of alalia in the ontogenetic development is represented by the omission or delayed transition from the sign language to the spoken word. As Paget[1] so vividly describes the process: "as he gesticulated with his hands, his tongue, lips and jaw muscles followed suit in a ridiculous fashion, understudying the action of the hand. Later, movements of the jaw and mouth actually supplanted the manual gestures; then it was found that the expiration of air through the oral cavities produced a wide range of audible mouth gestures or voiced speech."

Following this concise outline of the development of speech we may say that any interference, at the point where gesticulation is transformed into audible speech, causes the development to halt and prevents the child from developing speech; after the physiological time of speech development, that is approximately after three years of age, and in children with normal or sufficiently normal hearing acuity, this constitutes a pathological condition which in this paper will be referred to as alalia. This term has been chosen because it determines the symptom without referring to the causes underlying it, the knowledge of which is as yet rather limited.

The term alalia was first used by Delius in 1757 in his work

63

De Alalia et Aphonia, to designate lack of speech, a-lalia meaning no-speech; this, in 1757, being as complete a description of causes and symptoms as could be given. With the gradually increasing knowledge of physiology and anatomy and with the localization of speech centers in the brain, a large terminology has been introduced and applied to describe symptoms traced to new neuro-pathological discoveries as well as to suit the preference and usage of the individual author. Thus, speechlessness in children has been referred to as Alalia, Kussmaul[2], Aphemia, Broca[3], Aphasia, Trousseau[3], etc., and in recent literature as Audi-Mutism, Coën[4], Hearing-Deafness or Idiopathic Dumbness, Froeschels[5], Dysphasia, West, Kennedy, Carr[6], Idiopathic Language Retardation, Nance[7], Delayed Speech, Werner[8], to name only a few in order to illustrate the semantic maze in which the speech therapist finds himself as soon as he embarks on his search for facts. The main source of confusion is the use of the term aphasia when applied to speechlessness in children. Aphasia, according to modern usage, means loss of speech and should, therefore, not be used to describe lack of development of speech as is the case in children. Since dyslalia is a generally accepted term denoting faulty development of speech, alalia, not having through usage acquired a meaning other than lack of speech, seems the best term.

The knowledge at the present time of the location and function of the speech centers is as controversial as it is hypothetical. After discussing the highly contradictory theories of Broca, Marie, Moutier and Head respectively, McDowall[9] reconciles these opposing views by considering the formation of speech as depending upon three distinct mechanisms:

"1. A receptor mechanism, which may involve any sensation, although normally hearing and seeing are utilized. In close relationship to the cortical center for these sensations are the association areas, in which memories of sensations appear to be stored. Thus in the second and third temporal convolutions are stored the names and objects and these are lost if this region becomes the seat of disease, e.g. abscess secondary to inflammation of the ear.

2. Association mechanism. Our knowledge of this mechanism is as yet quite crude, and we cannot relate its facts in any detail to anatomical areas. . . . There is a general agreement, however, that in right handed persons the area concerned is on the left side of the brain within a well defined cortical region extending from the lower posterior part of the frontal lobe, by the island of Reil to the temporal and lower parietal and occipital region, Kinner, Wilson. Of this region it is clear, that the anterior part is concerned with expression, and the posterior part . . . with reception. To each sensation is attached a certain significance according to the circumstances in which it is experienced. If an idea has to be communicated, or a reply made, the impulse passes to that part of the association mechanism concerned with expression where the proper means of expression is determined. Broca's area may be considered an association area in close relation to the vocal effector mechanism.

3. Effector mechanism. The message is then conveyed to the appropriate part of the motor cortex concerned with the vocal organs, but it may be, according to circumstances, the area for hand movements or any other part. A nod of the head, or placing the finger to the mouth, may even be more significant than a spoken word. It is, then fairly easy to understand why it is that certain parts of the general speech mechanism may become impaired, leaving other parts normal. . . . When we learn to speak we learn to think and to form ideas by a similar mechanism* and we know how impaired the general mentality of a . . . person may be simply because he has not the normal facility of communication with his fellows."

Any impairment in the complex structure upon which the formation of speech is based, will create an obstacle which the

---

*That probably refers to both overt and inner speech.

growing child must overcome in order to develop speech. Anatomical disturbances in any or each of the mechanisms of speech formation may lead to receptive, expressive or receptive-expressive alalia and represent one great etiological group.

In addition to these structural impairments there exists another, equally important factor, that is the psychological state which in many cases of alalia without apparent structural defect seems to account for the disorder, constituting the second great etiological group—psychogenic alalia.

To differentiate the two great etiological groups is not as difficult a task as it may appear, since a congenital anomaly is rarely found alone; rather, it appears in a set of developmental conditions. That means that in cases, in which we have to assume developmental causes of alalia in the associative or effector organs, we must look for and in most instances be sure to find other developmental conditions present in the body. It should not, however, be taken for the only sign or symptom and should not, of necessity, be expected to reveal the cause of the disturbance directly. There may be a great number of other signs and symptoms related to the maldevelopment of the personality which may offer a better clue to the origin and perhaps the treatment of the disorder. Thus we may consider alalia as a corollary either of maldevelopmental conditions (effector or associative or both) or of a psychopathic personality.

When we consider "language as elaboration of phonated bucco-labio-lingual gestures" and "articulate speech at times nothing but gestures rendered audible"[10] we shall the better understand the child who, be it through actual organic defect or lack of skill or lack of motivation, finds it easier to go as far as his gestures will take him—and in some instances this is surprisingly far, since the mother and the environment can interpret this "language" very easily—and give up the struggle against his own deficiency and the competition with his siblings or other children to whom language comes easily and naturally, and with whom he feels at so great a disadvantage.

Just as unskilled movements are often related to speech, lack of skill is not a chance occurrence but again the result of a faulty organic structure. By the same token we may define psychogenic mutism, that is alalia based on aversion, asocial behaviour, sibling rivalry, etc., not as a haphazardly developed symptom, but the symptom that offered itself, as it were, as the one best suited to express the underlying cause. Neurotic symptoms do not develop by chance; some defect, no matter how slight, some event involving the organic mechanism, suggests the pattern which in turn is spotted or remembered by the subconscious mind and fashioned into the symptom.

Other organic causes related to the first etiological group are lesions of the brain originating from birth injuries; cerebral palsy; encephalitis; meningitis; epilepsy or severe infectious diseases which have toxic effects on the brain; feeble mindedness; etc. Severe diseases, particularly rickets, often interfere with the normal development of speech, resulting in alalia. Moreover, malformations of the articulatory organs, such as cleft palate, adenoid growths, etc. often cause this disorder, while ankyloglossia, a symptom which, contrary to popular belief is exceedingly rare, is not responsible for it.[11]

Whatever the cause, the effect is in no way proportional to the causative organic defect since personality factors, environmental and psychological elements all determine the forces brought into play both in developing as well as inhibiting speech formation, and are of varying composition and strength in the child counteracting more or less successfully any given impairment. The same impairment, therefore, may offer an insurmountable obstacle to the development of speech in one child, while in another child it will be taken in its stride and compensated without a threat to normal progress.

Considering the wide range of varieties and combinations of causes and effects we may only sketch certain patterns according to the predominant impairment, realizing that very few cases run true to type. Thus we can say that the receptive alalic child shows little understanding of what is said, presenting at the same time a quiet, withdrawn personality; he will avoid contact with other children even though his longing for companionship may appear quite apparent. In some instances he may show compulsion to repeat words without understanding their meaning (echolalia).

Cases of expressive alalia, on the other hand, show considerable understanding of the spoken language, usually displaying agitation and restlessness, a symptom which distinguishes them from the deaf-mutes and which sometimes reaches a degree reminiscent of feeble mindedness.

Most frequent is the mixed, receptive-expressive type of alalia; these children often show defective acoustic memory in which case their behaviour offers resemblance to the genuinely deaf. In other words, in alalia we encounter the symptoms manifested in the various types of aphasia.

Children belonging in the second group might show short memory span for words or syllables; short attention span; asocial behaviour; lack of will; in other words the entire galaxy of psychopathic attitudes.

There is one profound difference between the two groups, however. While we are justified in assuming that the child in the first group has not learned to form words, due to structural impairment, the child in the second group usually has a passive speech function, that means he has at least a number of words and sentences ready in his mind and at his disposal which he might use were he willing to do so, or were he not prevented from using them through his inhibitions.

The diagnosis in the majority of cases depends on a thorough knowledge of the personality of the child and his response to treatment. The diagnostic techniques applied and the conclusions drawn from the study of the case are of paramount importance since success or failure to initiate and develop speech decides the fate of the child; when the therapist fails, the child is doomed to a life of mental darkness, hardly raised above the level of an animalistic existence; when we succeed, we help him develop into an intelligent human being, able to enjoy his share of happiness.

For, although we can think without words—the truth of which can be proved by the fact that we often "struggle for words," that a thought may be present in our mind and yet elude linguistic formulation—this verbal thinking is the thinking of homo loquens, the talking man, and is based on a system of concepts or at least categorical conception, which in turn is impossible without words[12]

The mute child is prevented from acquiring knowledge since he does not go through the physiological period during which the talking child, by asking questions, develops and accelerates his mental growth.

The foremost task of the diagnostician, therefore, is to determine the intellectual potentialities of the patient or the presence of feeble mindedness, mongolism, cretinism, idiocy, etc. so far as this can reliably be done. In case of doubt, however, any conclusion as to the mental capacity of a mute child should be deferred until at least an attempt at the initiation of speech has been made and proved futile, even though tests might support its possibility.

Next in importance and much easier to gain is the finding of the hearing acuity to exclude deaf-mutism. Hearing tests in infants and small children will be discussed in another chapter of this book. In testing the hearing, the noise should be made behind the child and attention should be paid that no tactile sense is involved, in order to obtain correct results, and to eliminate responses to movements of air or vibration of solid bodies.[11] The report of mothers as to the hearing of the child should not be accepted implicitly since the reported understanding may be due to interpretation of gestures.

In evaluating the history of the child particular attention should be paid to the development of motor skills and the manner in which those sounds that are present, are being produced. Motor activities of the child should be observed including the gait, use of arms and hands, since signs or traces of spasticity or disturbed equilibrium might be found revealing paralysis, myxoedema, etc. The mouth, tongue, palate, tonsils and larynx should be carefully examined. Determination of handedness and possible shifts might furnish valuable clues. The speech pattern of the parents and environment deserve investigation since they often account for the attitude of the child. The constant talk of a dominant mother might easily drive the child into refusal to talk.

As soon as we have collected all the data available and formed as complete and clear a picture as may be conceived after careful evaluation of the findings as well as of our personal impression of and experience with the child, we shall be able to plan the therapy.

Proceeding to the therapy the words of Kussmaul[2] might serve as a guiding motive: "Only practice establishes the connection between ganglionic cell and ganglionic cell, ganglionic center and ganglionic center . . . thus a central speech organ is gradually trained through language itself, or, if you will, is created." In order to achieve this aim we must appeal to those senses through which the speech mechanism receives its strongest stimuli. This in turn depends on the ideological make-up of the individual, on whether he is a visual, acoustic or motor-kinesthetic type. This fact, established by simple tests, is then utilized in the application of the specific method of therapy. In cases of receptive alalia it chiefly consists of training the understanding of words, through explanation and repetition of names of objects and pictures appealing to the child and used in play situations, eliciting interest and pleasure.

In expressive alalia a similar method is employed. This time, however, care should be taken in using one object or one picture at a time.

The child with a motor impairment in addition must be aided in the production of sounds and trained in the skill of sound formation through the sense best developed, that is visual, acoustic or motor-kinesthetic. In case the senses are equally poor, each one should be trained and used. In addition a great variety of sound stimuli should be offered the child; the radio and phonograph are of great help in this respect and should be used constantly. Simple stories repeatedly told, also serve the purpose of charging the hearing centers until the child "bursts" into speech.

The sound which can be produced most clearly and easily should always be the starting point of the actual speech training. No specific pattern or sequence of steps may be suggested for any one case; the complexity and psycho-somatic structure of the syndrome necessitates a treatment evolving from constant care and observation and should be subjected to change and adjustment according to the capacity of the child and his responsiveness and mood during the session. Each chance sound, each utterance should be utilized and through conscious effort and training made into what eventually may constitute parts of the spoken language.

Since the child has to overcome tremendous difficulties, we must be careful not to add to them by placing demands or pressure on him; rather should we try to attract his attention in the most pleasurable way and create an atmosphere of gaiety and complete relaxation. The desired response may take a long time in coming, and even though our patience may be taxed to the utmost, we must wait until the child is ready to start.

This becomes all the more important in cases of psychogenic alalia since here we are trying to break the patient's defence mechanism. We should therefore, first attempt to trace and remove the cause of resistance and give the child a feeling of security before we approach the speech problem as such.

Emotion and will are powerful forces and, when led into the proper channels, may be employed by the therapist to great advantage. If supplied with a forceful incentive, the child may overcome what seemed an insurmountable obstacle.

We may obtain a clearer understanding of the problems involved when we draw an analogy between the mute child and the adult who lives in an alien environment, and who is forced to learn the foreign language.

It is interesting to note in this connection that both in Hungarian and Russian there is only one word: neme, nemet and nemec respectively, to denote *mute* and *German*. One who cannot speak, and one being German. The Germans who lived in Hungary or Russia could not talk the language of the country —although they could talk their own—and consequently were considered, and called mute.

Another point of comparison is the role the ideological type plays in the teaching of languages to adults. We often hear remarks such as: I don't know the word, I have never *heard* it; or, I have never *seen* it; or, I have never *said* it. Thus the adult student unwittingly refers to his psychological make-up as the means of training. A fact which all too often is ignored or neglected in teaching foreign languages.

The analogy becomes more obvious when we realize that the foreigner, like the child, at first hears words without comprehending their meaning; then, although understanding many words, he finds himself unable to produce the sounds correctly in order to pronounce the words adequately. Gradually the names and objects and symbols fuse, and through constant training of the motor skill in producing the correct sounds, knowledge and use of the language are acquired.

Here too, emotion and volition are contributive or inhibitive factors. A familiar name which through education or experience has acquired emotional qualities, when differently pronounced, will be rejected and consequently not understood; indignation being the inhibiting factor. The same occurs where volition or motivation is involved. A man or woman in love, a man anxious to obtain a job will learn the foreign language much faster and more easily than someone lacking these incentives. Similarly, a person whose attitude is that of ridiculing and disparaging everything foreign, may not learn to speak or use foreign words correctly until he is made to realize that there is nothing 'funny' or 'silly' about the foreign language, that it is merely different and unfamiliar. In other words, here too the resistance must be removed in order to facilitate the process of learning a new language and of changing from a passive into an active speech function.

The alalic child, contrary to the normal child, does not develop speech naturally and unconsciously. Like the adult in an alien environment, he must *learn* the language. Both, however, the adult and the child,—no matter what the individual difficulties or impairments may be—may achieve this task. Man is endowed with the creative power of speech and language in all its phases, phylogenetically as well as ontogenetically, depends upon the spontaneity, activity and inventive genius of the individual.[12]

The prognosis therefore, is favorable in the great majority of cases. The process of training may take months or years and require great patience and understanding on the part of the therapist and the parents. Yet however difficult the task and however remote the end, if there is a pathological state in which unexpected turns for the better may occur, it is alalia, one of the very few conditions in which hope against hope appears medically justified.

REFERENCES

1. *Paget, R.:* The English, London, 1935.
2. *Kussmaul, A.:* Die Stoerungen der Sprache, F. C. W. Vogel, Leipzig 1881.
3. As quoted in *Kussmaul,* (2).
4. *Coen:* Die Hoerstummheit und ihre Behandlung, Wien 1888.
5. *Froeschels, E.:* Speech Therapy, Expression Company, Boston, 1933.
6. *West, Kennedy, Carr:* The Rehabilitation of Speech, Harper & Brothers, New York, 1937.
7. *Nance, L. S.:* Differential Diagnosis of Aphasia in Children, Journal of Speech Disorders, Vol. 11, No. 3, December 1946.
8. *Werner, L. S.:* Treatment of a Child with Delayed Speech, Journal of Speech Disorders, Vol. 10, No. 4, December 1945.
9. *McDowall, R. J. S.:* Handbook of Physiology and Biochemistry, The Blakestone Comp., Philadelphia, 1944. (Published in Great Britain).
10. *Critchley, M.:* Aphasia in a Partial Deaf-Mute, The Brain, Vol. 61, 1938.
11. *Froeschels, E., and Jellinek, A.:* Practice of Voice and Speech Therapy, Expression Company, Boston, 1941.
12. *Revesc, G.:* Ursprung und Vorgeschichte der Sprache, A. Francke, Bern, 1946.

HELEN HULICK BEEBE
Speech Clinician, Easton Hospital, Penna.

Chapter VI

PSYCHIC DEAFNESS IN CHILDREN

TESTING THE HEARING OF VERY YOUNG CHILDREN

AS the diagnosis of any kind of deafness depends upon an appropriate method of examining the hearing capacity a description of the methods for testing the hearing of children is given here. There is no doubt that audiometry is the most exact method of determining hearing losses. Unfortunately it is not the method of choice for testing young children and even not for older children if there is a pronounced hardness of hearing. The reason is that audiometry asks for active mental cooperation from the examinee which one cannot expect in children up to 6 or 8 years and in hard of hearing children who, because of the rare acoustic stimuli they receive in every day life, are not used to responding to acoustic stimuli.

To replace audiometry different kinds of instruments have been used, for instance, whistles, drums, horns. Testing by these methods does not give the examiners the exact answer about the entire hearing capacity but only for the few tones that have been tested. These methods are confined to using the tones only ad concham or at distance from the ear. The comparison of the

75

results obtained in this way with the results of the test by "direct tone introduction" has proved that the latter is far superior. Furthermore, *a series* of whistles comprising six octaves can be used. The whistles are taken from Urbantschitsch's organon and include tones from F^1 to f^4. For direct tone induction of a tone, a rubber tube to which an ear olive is attached is inserted into the external auditory meatus, while the other end of the tube touches the whistle through which the tone escapes. It is important to blow the whistles with a quick push of air rather than to produce a prolonged tone. The loudness should be gradually increased with single pushes if the softer tones do not bring a positive result. It is advisable to cover the ear olive with fine rubber in order to prevent the air stream from entering the ear. However, some subjects react positively only if the ear olive is uncovered. The objection that in the latter case a positive reaction may result from a sense of touch and therefore does not indicate the presence of hearing can be rejected by the fact that many patients react positively to one tone and not to another with the ear olive uncovered. It is inconceivable that the sense of touch would be stimulated only by air that enters the meatus from one whistle and not by the air of another one. Furthermore by simply blowing air through the rubber tube the examiner can check whether the patient reacts to the tactile stimulus. It has been proved in numerous cases that the tactile reaction if it occurs at all is different from reactions to the acoustic stimuli. The reactions achieved with direct tone introduction are reflexes consisting of blinking, grimacing, withdrawal and even jerking eye movements.[1] It is worth mentioning again that many children having been diagnosed as deaf by other methods proved to hear when tested by direct tone introduction.

The direct tone introduction should be used only if the whistle test from a distance and even ad concham is negative. If not one should increase the distance step by step as long as there is a positive reaction. However, the reflex reaction occurs at a very short distance even in people with normal hearing. Also newborns have been tested in this way.[2] Frequently hard of hearing children if taken by surprise turn toward the source but no complete test with all the whistles can be given in this way to infants. Children about three years old and upward can be trained to react to sounds heard from various distances in the following way. The examiner stands behind the child and blows a whistle. The mother or assistant facing the child lifts his arm (and lets it drop quickly) as soon as the tone sounds—thus training him to raise his arm spontaneously if he hears the tone. In this way a complete hearing profile as to the pitches and the distances can be achieved.

Study of the speech phenomenon to be discussed in this chapter reveals that speech pathology might well concern itself with two questions: namely, what is the underlying cause of psychic deafness in children, and are there many more cases that have escaped diagnosis?

The concept of "psychic deafness in children" was introduced by S. Heller[5] to apply to children who do not respond to acoustic stimuli although, in his opinion, the hearing organs—that is the external auditory meatus, the middle ear, the labyrinth, the acoustic nerve and acoustic center—are normal. According to Heller this pseudo-deafness could be due only to psychological, non-hysterical factors. To date there has been no approach other than a differential diagnosis. The relatively few writers who have studied the syndrome differ in their explanations of the basic trouble involved. Consequently, even the question of appropriate nomenclature has not been settled. The term "Psychic Deafness" is a direct translation of Heller's "Psychische Taubheit," but as Oppenheimer Fromm[6] and Froeschels[4] agree, it is too likely to be confused with hysterical deafness. The latter syndrome may appear in later life in contrast to psychic deafness, which has its inception in infancy.

Fromm is of the opinion that these pseudo-deaf mute cases can be explained on a purely psychological basis and therefore suggests using the term "Heller's Psychic Deafness" to distinguish it from hysterical deafness. Froeschels believes the basic trouble may consist of a slight defect in Heschl's convolution and so proposes the term "Central Deafness." Both writers mentioned above have presented case histories in support of these opinions. Because cases of this type are so rare*, (or have been so rarely diagnosed) it seems worthwhile to review the significant facts from each case in order to clarify the clinical picture for the reader. Anyone attempting further research on this subject should refer to the complete articles.

Fromm describes a case which she studied over a period of sixteen months at the Clinic of the University of Amsterdam, Holland.

"At the time the study was made the patient (Gerard) was ten years old. He was suffering from congenital osteogenesis imperfecta. At the age of two-and-a-half he had contracted an otitis media in both ears. Up to that time he had a command of language commensurate with that of children his age. After he contracted the otitis media, he neither spoke nor reacted to acoustic stimuli. He was pronounced entirely deaf by the Head of the Ear, Nose and Throat Clinic of the University of Amsterdam, and this diagnosis was confirmed on many subsequent examinations. The last of these was given at the request of the author shortly after she had started work with the boy."

G. had spent most of his life in a hospital because of his osteogenesis. At the time the study was made he was under psychiatric care. He was abnormally small and frail and could not walk. There were no neurological findings.

One day G. seemed to react acoustically when a pencil was dropped behind his chair. This incident prompted Fromm to

---

*Froeschels (1944) reports that among 60,000 cases of speech and hearing difficulties he has seen, he has found only 12 cases of psychic deafness.

make a psychological study of G.'s hearing. G. reacted inconsistently to acoustical experiments. His positive reactions did not depend upon pitch or intensity. The first positive reactions to mechanical toys, children's horns, whistles, sirens etc. came only if G. had first seen the instrument. Later there were both positive and negative reactions to these instruments although G. could have had no means of knowing the instrument was in his environment. There was proof that G. could hear and an indication that the failure to hear might be explained by psychological factors.

When a pistol which made a louder noise than the other instruments was used G. did not react as he had previously. No reaction to shots close to his ear while pistol was out of line of vision—not even reflex movements. When shown the pistol G. shuddered and motioned it away violently. Even after seeing it G. showed no acoustic reaction. Fromm states there were no reflex movements and since it is not possible to suppress such reflexes that G. did not perceive the shots at all. Later when G. saw the shot fired he started but experiments proved that he reacted only to optic and olfactory stimuli. After G. had handled the pistol and experienced some control over the frightening object by holding it under his blanket, he sometimes reacted to the sound when it was shot behind his back. Fromm thinks G.'s ambivalent attitude toward the pistol—sometimes a frightening and unpleasant object, sometimes a plaything—with the effect of libidinous kathexis—accounted for his inconsistent reactions.

Systematic tests with tuning forks, monochord and piano were given G. to determine whether there was sufficient range of hearing to learn to talk. Results were inconsistent, f. i., he had more positive reactions to the low than the higher notes of the piano, but heard the same high notes on the monochord or tuning forks. At one time or another he heard most of the tones presented. Of the sixth b' - g" (Bezold's speech text), which is said to be important for speech, he heard b', c", d", f". Whether he could hear e" and g" was not decided.

According to G.'s father, he had spoken up to the time of the middle ear infection—that is, words like daddy, mother and names of nurses etc. After this infection he did not talk, only repeated senseless syllables similar to a baby's babble. His voice had the tone of a person with normal hearing. The first attempt to teach G. to say words was successful. Articulation was approximate as in younger children learning to talk. The description of G.'s use of "sign language—gestures etc." shows not only that he was very proficient in this form of communication, but that he had a great deal of understanding, intelligence and a sense of humor. When intentionally he was placed in a situation where signs "wouldn't work," he said clearly the words, "Papa—Moeder" (Dutch for daddy—mother). Although the child had been considered a hopeless case of a deaf-mute invalid it was demonstrated that G. had quick comprehension, good learning ability and good practical intelligence.

Personality traits were of a positive nature. G. was extroverted, affectionate and friendly, excessively clean and orderly. He wanted to be master of the situation whenever possible. Fromm says the extreme orderliness was his means of controlling his own world.

In her discussion of the case Fromm makes a differential diagnosis on the following basis:

1. Organic deafness not indicated as it was proved the child had sufficient hearing to learn speech.
2. Idiopathic dumbness not applicable because chief causes are shyness and inability to ask questions in spite of normal hearing and speech organs.
3. Not hysterical for G. had no sign of other hysterical traits.
4. Motor aphasia ruled out because G. was a strong motor type with marked motor ability and no speech inhibition.

5. Sensory aphasias also ruled out in view of G.'s good general intelligence, well developed expressive sign language, ability to do abstract thinking and to transcend a given situation in order to plan and act.

6. Case diagnosed as "Psychic Deafness" (Heller's Psychische Taubheit). "Evidence in favor of this diagnosis is the affective conditioning of patient's hearing: G. does hear pleasant sounds, but does not react to unpleasant or neutral ones."

Fromm quotes Th. Heller's[7] description of psychic deafness. "Psychic deafness is extremely difficult to diagnose—a clear picture can be gained only after prolonged observation—cases of psychic deafness often are confused with or taken for censory aphasia, hysterial deafness or idiopathic dumbness—if when observing cases of deafness closely one finds any attempts at language which are more than immediate imitation of lip-reading and if some hearing capacity for musical impressions can be shown, there can be no doubt that this is not a case of deafness but that it is a case of psychic deafness—the cause of the disturbance must be sought in the unusual conduct of the children's attention." The reader should be reminded here that a hard of hearing child could also show the behavior described by Th. Heller.

Many factors in G.'s case history support Fromm's hypothesis that G. was unable to perceive sound until its source had become an object with libidinous kathexis. On this basis one questions the original acoustic reaction to the "dropped pencil" but even if there were no exceptions to the general rule stated above the fact that G. had spoken and had heard before the middle ear disease should be remembered when considering Froeschel's cases, where an initial deafness was the one thing his cases had in common.

Ewing[3] who has commented on the lack of consideration of

this subject in the literature has described a case* (without diagnosis) which shows this factor common to Froeschel's three cases. Froeschels does not state whether the 12 cases he has seen all shared this factor. The fact that G. had previously spoken also eliminates the diagnosis of idiopathic dumbness.

Fromm's decision to rule out hysterical deafness is no doubt well founded, but it must be acknowledged that a "monosymptomatic hysteria" is possible.

The following are the most significant facts from Froeschels' cases:

Case 1—4 year old boy suspected of being deaf—no reaction to acoustic stimuli of any kind tried over period of three weeks —suddenly turned around as bell rang 3 meters behind him— over period of three or four weeks gradually reacted to other stimuli—horns, tuning forks, human voice and at end of this time could be awakened by tones and noises, which had not happened before — after 4 months treatment he produced smacking sounds, and babbling started. Four weeks later imitated sounds and syllables—and in two more weeks all syllables and some monosyllabic words—parents satisfied and never reported relapse.

Case 2—6 year old girl referred because of deafness and poor speech—spoke a few words in a monotonous voice—not that of a deaf child but different from normal voice. Family and personal history negative—physical development normal— neurological and otological examinations negative. First attempt with direct tone induction reacted with strong tossing of the head—after that child responded by raising arm to tone

---

*Case 7—Total deafness of congenital origin. But one night when her name was called she sat up and called out, though unable to use words. At 16 years free conversation, fluid reading, writing. Her auditory acuity measured by a most thorough application of the audiometer test was normal. But a marked feature of the results was the improved response (10-20 percent) after 3-6 repetitions of any given frequency; f. i., two initial responses to 4.096 v. d. were at intensity step 20 but on returning to this frequency after the conclusion of the whole test a reaction took place at 5 and 10.

heard some distance from ear—test of 6 octaves revealed all tones heard at distance of 10 meters when whistles were blown softly—in a few days repeated sounds, syllables and words at a distance of 2 or 3 meters—because she did not react to any acoustic stimuli at home she was replaced in a home conducted by trained speech therapists. After 4 weeks she spoke spontaneously words and simple phrases in a normal voice—she continued to speak and react to all kinds of acoustic stimuli at home—training continued for several months until child was accepted in grammar school. A year later mother reported child had gradually relapsed into deafness. Examination showed she now reacted only to direct tone introduction and merely by blinking. No change in drum membrance or vestibular apparatus. Renewed attempts to restore hearing only moderately successful. After hearing exercises she repeated words at distance of 1 to 2 meters, but had to be placed in school for hard of hearing.

Case 3—Girl 2 years, 5 months, according to parents and physicians had never responded to acoustic stimuli. There were a few rare incidents, such as looking up at airplane, turning once or twice to her name, once to a bell, that might have been acoustic responses. Behavior abnormal, destructive, over-active, beat eyes with fists, no sense of cleanliness. Suspected of being feeble minded. Brother 2 years older and her parents normal. However, in mother's family there were several congenitally deaf cousins. S. presented great problems in being weaned, which started at 6 months (she stopped babbling which had started 2 months before). She almost starved to death when family had to leave fatherland.

Normal height and weight when brought to Dr. Froeschels March 7, 1941. Behavior and lack of ability to concentrate attention made examination difficult. Finally when Dr. F. succeeded in direct tone induction of one tone in left ear she reacted with strong withdrawal of her head. This raised the sus-

picion of "psychic deafness." Mar. 14 S. turned to whistles a
and c2 blown 1 meter behind her but not to g. By March 31
could introduce whistles and other tones through the ear olive
in the meatus. Continued introducing various singing, speaking tones (using funnel at end of rubber tube into which Dr.
spoke) and work with whistles as a treatment for 2 months.
S. became attentive and reacted with smiling during treatment
—at end of these 2 months S. listened attentively to knocking
at top of desk and to bells at 1.5 to 2 meters. She also produced
in a normal voice some almost exactly articulated sounds—all
this indicating that there was probably no serious organic lack
of hearing. S. gradually learned to imitate vowel and consonant sounds and by the end of May repeated Ah, O, E, W, B,
B. Two weeks later repeated for wood—woo; wheel; tree
(tee); piano (p). Skill in repeating grew during next 2 months.
Behavior improved and she stopped completely beating eyes—
more friendly to people—shows signs of intelligence in performing tests, answering commands etc.; during summer she
repeated 35-40 words more or less correctly every day usually
at 1.5 meters distance. Suddenly in Sept. she stopped repeating
and did not react to tones or noises. This lasted about 6 weeks
although by surprising her with a bell her acoustic reaction
could be induced. After this period of time she started again a
self-invented speech, with definite articulation and phrase mel-
odies. Toward the end of 1941 she willingly repeated words
(names of colored pictures) and in the next five months this
skill grew. In July 1942 she repeated 40 words in the presence
of speech teacher. In the fall of 1942 there was another relapse
in willingness to repeat and lack of interest in acoustic stimuli
—although she still reacted positively when taken by surprise
acoustic stimuli. After 5 weeks intermission she began to repeat words again—understanding was still poor. Her willingness and ability to repeat words grew (with short relapses) until she could repeat words whispered to her. She spent 2 months

at summer camp in 1943 where her mother said she made some friendly contacts and was willing to repeat but did not speak unless asked to. By the fall of 1943 S.'s spontaneous repetition was much better, also her word understanding.

Froeschels says in Case 3, "One must assume the presence of a gradually decreasing defect in the acoustic center. Not before this trouble has been reduced to one of moderate degree could any regular charging of Wernicke's center be expected." Until she received sufficient stimulation of that center she would not be expected to have much spontaneous speech or understanding of words.

In Froeschels' discussion of the three cases he points out that in each case there was an initial deafness and that in spite of some different responses all three gained ability to hear by psychological treatment and hearing exercises. He reports similar experience in other cases. Because there has been no anatomical description of the underlying causes in the literature, Froeschels states that his explanation of the cause or causes of the clinical picture must be hypothetic. In case 2 he rules out what might be taken for an hysterical deafness because the suddenly invoked normal hearing turned into permanent hardness of hearing. There were no changes in the middle ear or the vestibular apparatus, no infectious disease at the critical time which lead to the conclusion of a degenerative process in the acoustic centers. Froeschels concludes that the initial deafness was due to a slight disturbance of these centers which kept them in a state of inactivity. He further assumes a psychic component in the initial deafness. In case 3, proof of the psychic component is indicated by the sudden changes from good hearing acuity into inactivity and back again. But the assumption of a pure psychic component does not account for the fact that the second patient never relapsed into deafness during the first series of treatments while the third frequently did so.

Froeschels believes that a slight defect in Heschl's convolution can easily create an aversion to auditory impressions and that both these components may by a vicious circle aggravate the clinical picture. To support this hypothesis he explains that in normally developed centers of children there is a passive charging preparatory to an active "discharge when he first answers to the demands of his environment. One might speak of an over-abundance of former impressions which demand of themselves an active discharge."

In a case where the center is not normally adjusted the extra effort required for the child to fulfill the demands of his environment could lead to a feeling of uneasiness on the part of the child. Froeschels says this feeling might appear as resistance, opposition and still greater isolation than that caused by the missing function of the center in question.

That the first reactions to acoustic stimuli are of an involuntary nature was demonstrated in testing the hearing of the newborn.[2] Babies a few days, even less than a day old, turned toward the source of the tone (Urbantschitsch whistles). Before the motor speech centers function in early infancy they passively receive an amount of stimulation derived from the acoustic centers until a kind of saturation point is reached at which time there occurs an active discharge in the form of speech utterance. So in considering Fromm's hypothesis the question arises: Could a psychic component influence this involuntary type of reaction? It seems improbable that an infant with no organic impairment of the hearing centers or the hearing organs would be capable of showing resistance to acoustic stimulation. In the one case Fromm uses to demonstrate her hypothesis, the boy apparently heard and spoke up to the time of the middle ear infection at 2.5 years, so the psychic component appeared after infancy.

It is possible that there was no organic basis for the boy's deafness at the time he was examined by Fromm; but could not the bilateral middle ear infection have produced a temporary severe hearing trouble which was fixed by C. as a neurotic symptom?

Fromm considers Froeschels' cases similar to the one she describes but there is no evidence that it can be brought in line with the cases of Froeschels because of the time in which the deafness first showed. But as Fromm and Froeschels both state, since there are no neurological nor anatomical findings any theory about the cause of "psychic deafness in children" must be hypothetical.

REFERENCES

1. *Froeschels, Emil:* "Testing of the Hearing of very Young Children." Archives of Otolaryngology. Feb. 1946.

2. *Froeschels, Emil, and Beebe, Helen:* "Testing the Hearing of New-born Infants." Archives of Otolaryngology. Dec. 1946. 44 pp. 710-714.

3. *Ewing, A. V. G.:* "Aphasia in Children." London, Oxford Press, 1930.

4. *Froeschels, Emil:* "Psychic Deafness in Children," Arch. Neurol. & Psychiat. 51, 1944, pp. 544-549.

5. *Heller, S.:* "On Psychic Deafness in Childhood," Convention of German Biologists and Physicians, Vienna, 1894.

6. *Oppenheimer Fromm, Erika:* "Study of a Case of Pseudo Deaf-Muteness. Journal Nervous and Mental Disease. Vol. 103, No. 1, Jan. 1946, pp. 37-59.

7. *Heller, Theodor:* "Grundrus der Heilpaedagogik. (Fundamentals of Child Guidance). 2nd Ed. Leipzig, 1912.

HELEN SCHICK LANE, PH.D.
Principal, Central Institute for the Deaf

Chapter VII

THE EDUCATION OF THE DEAF CHILD

RECOGNITION of a hearing loss in a young child rarely occurs before the age at which speech normally develops. Parents usually seek the help of the family physician or the pediatrician when the baby has reached the age of 18 months or two years. Sometimes they are sent to an otologist (ear specialist) who may brutally tell them the child is deaf without any advice about his future or who may furnish the parents with information about schools.

Attempts have been made to develop tests of hearing of infants. New born babies have been conditioned to respond to sound by several investigators but there is no certainty that the child was not conditioned to the situation including the sound stimulus or to the vibration. Meyer and Schick measured responses to sound through sudorific reflexes. Although this technique seemed promising, there were no deaf infants available for study. Dr. and Mrs. A. W. G. Ewing of Manchester, England, have developed a series of responses to sounds of varying intensity and quality. After several test appointments they were able with some degree of accuracy to indicate the frequency and intensity level of residual hearing in a child. Further re-

88

search on the testing procedures of the Ewings is now in progress.

The majority of parents accept the advice of the physician and make plans for the education of the child. Unfortunately, a few wait for a miracle to happen and some exhaust their finances seeking a "cure" or hoping to find a doctor who will tell them the child will "outgrow" his deafness.

Since the parents seek help first from the physician, medical schools should incorporate in the curriculum lectures on the educational possibilities for handicapped children and should be informed concerning the resources for such education.

Perhaps the first source of consolation to the parent of a deaf child is the knowledge that the child can learn to speak. The majority of people think of the congenitally deaf as deaf-mutes or as deaf and dumb, not realizing that the speech mechanism in such an individual is normal. We learned to speak through imitation of what we heard. For the deaf child, to learn to speak, vision and the sense of touch must be substituted for the defective sense of hearing. The teaching of speech, however, requires a trained teacher.

The parents of a deaf child soon realize that they need help in meeting the behavior problems. The deaf child may be so frustrated in his attempts to make known his needs that a series of temper tantrums result; he may develop a habit of complete indifference to his environment; or he may become so skillful in satisfying his own needs that the parent is in a constant state of anxiety concerning his safety. At this time the Volta Bureau, 1537 35th Street, N. W., Washington, D. C., begins to serve as an information center to the bewildered parent. Correspondence courses, such as the one available through the John Tracy Clinic, 924 W. 37th Street, Los Angeles, California, are of great value to parents and child. Visits to schools for the deaf to observe classes, contacts with other parents who have had a similar experience are all helpful.

Attendance at nursery school for all children is now recommended—as here they learn how to share with others, how to participate together in play, and how to follow routine procedures. To the normal program of nursery school, the school for the deaf adds beginning speech and lip reading. A hearing child of nursery school age is talking in sentences, asking questions, expressing ideas, and sharing them with others. A deaf child is dependent upon educational procedures for the acquisition of speech and is limited to gestures in expressing his ideas.

Contrast the speech and language of a hearing child entering the first grade of school with that of a deaf child without training and you can readily understand the grading system of some schools for the deaf into three preparatory grades before the first grade. This means that at the average age of nine the deaf child is ready for first grade. How much better if these preparatory years could be at ages 3, 4, and 5, so that first grade work could begin at 6. If the early education is postponed until he reaches school age, a retardation that is seldom surmounted is present before the learning of speech and of language begins.

If the frustration is prolonged by a delay in education, the behavior problems of the deaf child are magnified and he may behave as an untamed animal in some extreme cases or as a cowering introvert in others. With nursery school education including speech and lip reading, the behavior problems disappear in proportion as learning progresses.

An additional argument favoring the early development of speech points to the fact that the muscles of articulation and the intrinsic muscles of the larynx are at their most pliable and plastic state during these early years. Speech is one of the finest of muscular coordinations and in order that any muscles function to their maximum efficiency, both practice and correct use are essential. The deaf child, therefore, needs to learn to use his speech muscles correctly and at an early age.

If the deaf child lives in a large community where there is a school for the deaf that accepts nursery school age children, he is fortunate. If he lives in a community where such education is not possible, the parents must decide whether it is preferable to help him at home until school age or whether he should be placed in a residential school. In spite of all of the advantages of the nursery school, the parents are worried about the feeling of insecurity of the child when separated from his home.

Fortunately, children adjust easily to new situations, find happiness in association with other children and thrive in the school environment. The home-sick child is the exception and not the rule if the school adequately provides for the child. The momentary insecurity of the child at preschool age is insignificant compared to the lasting insecurity of an overage deaf child in a high school for the hearing.

The health problems of nursery school children in a residential school often discourage the school administrator in admitting these children. It is true that they are frequently absent and that childhood diseases spread rapidly—but again the advantages far outweigh this inconvenience.

The selection of a school continues to be a problem for the parent. In a residential school homogeneous grading is possible because of the large number of pupils. The child is in the care of "experts" all day long—people who understand his needs and urge him to use speech and lip reading. Educational and recreational programs are planned to spare him the loneliness he might encounter in the hearing world.

In a day school the child maintains the same school program as a hearing child. Contacts with the parents and siblings remain unchanged,—association with hearing friends is stimulating, and he acquires all the experience of a home environment.

Only by visits to both types of schools can the parents weigh the advantages and disadvantages of the schools and make the selection. Such factors as size of classes, size of dormitory groups, quality of supervision, training of teachers, method of instruction, number of grades in the class, and physical equipment of the school, should all enter into the decision.

Methods of instruction are still a controversial issue among the educators of the deaf and should be seriously considered in the selection of a school. Thus far, we have mentioned only the oral method, by means of which the deaf child learns to talk and read lips and can communicate with anyone. Following this method the deaf develop speech that is not the same as the normal because the deaf lack the hearing to control it—but the speech is intelligible to all—and education with the hearing is eventually possible for the deaf child of normal intelligence.

The manual method consists of instruction in the manual alphabet, signs and writing. In finger spelling, the normal word order of a sentence is retained—in signs this is sacrificed for speed. Communication by this method is limited to those who know the manual alphabet or signs. Those favoring the method indicate that the principal educational objects are mental development and facility in the comprehension and use of written language.

Many schools favor a combined method — all pupils are started orally, but the manual method is used in dormitories and on the playground. If a child is slow in learning speech, his educational program is made manual also. This combination does not give both methods equal weight as oralism is limited to classroom use and children are only in the classroom 25 hours each week. A portion of this time must be devoted to reading, lip reading, writing and other subject matter that does not involve the practice and use of the speech muscles.

The writer's experience has been with oral methods—and therefore she cannot discuss the merits of these methods without prejudice. Parents should observe schools and methods without bias, keeping in mind as an ultimate guide the greatest future happiness of the child socially, educationally and in a chosen vocation and remembering always the competition of the hearing world.

Almost all deaf children have some residuum of hearing—and utilization of this hearing will lead to better speech. In teaching children too young for accurate hearing tests, it should be assumed that some hearing is present until subsequent tests disprove the assumption. For instruction of these children the Acoustic Method was developed by Dr. Max A. Goldstein. The acoustic method is defined as the stimulation or education of the hearing mechanism and its associated sense organs by sound vibration as applied either by voice or any sonorous instrument. Other educators use the term Auricular Method for techniques of stimulating residual hearing.

Until 1930, psychologists who were pioneering in measuring the intelligence of the deaf reported a mental retardation of the deaf of from two to three years. The assumption was made that deafness and mental retardation were due to the same cause. Observations of the behavior of the deaf did not support this conclusion as a valid one. Careful examination of the tests indicated that the tests used were not non-verbal in instructions; that experiences not possible for the deaf were included as test items; and that in many schools children were enrolled whose greatest affliction was mental retardation and not deafness. With better selection of tests and some elimination of the extremely low mental cases, the trend of recent test results has been toward a normal distribution of test scores. The following table summarizes the results of mental tests in recent years.

In addition to speech and lip reading the deaf child must also learn all the subject matter of the school curriculum. Few persons in addition to those trained to teach the deaf and the deaf themselves appreciate the difficulties involved. The layman can understand the techniques of teaching speech—but then expects normal development in reading. Again, those of us who

INTELLIGENCE TESTS OF DEAF
1930 - 1947

Examiner	Date	N	Test Used	Results
Drever & Collins	1930	200	Drever-Collins	Less than 1-year retardation
Peterson & Williams	1930	466	Goodenough	Med. I.Q. = 80.0
Illinois Institute of Juvenile Research	1931	169	Pintner Non-Language / Pintner Performance	Med. I.Q. = 84.0 / Med. I.Q. = 91.0
Meyer & Schick	1932	Hearing = 1251 / Deaf = 132	Lectometer	No difference between Hearing & Deaf
Goodenough & Shirley	1932	406	Goodenough Test / Pintner Non-Language	Med. I.Q. = 87.7 / Med. I.Q. = 98.4
Schick (Lane)	1933	Pre-school Age 59	Randall's Island Test	Med. I.Q. = 97.0
MacKane	1933	Deaf = 130 / Hearing = 130	Grace Arthur / Pintner-Paterson / Drever-Collins / Non-Language	M Score in Points Deaf / Hearing 119.6 / 126.6 121.1 / 126.8 } Less than 1 year difference 140.0 / 146.9 } 244.5 / 320.6 — 2 years retardation
Peterson	1936	100	Kohs Block	Med. I.Q. = 95.0
Bishop	1936	90	Grace Arthur	Mean I.Q. = 97.16
Amoss	1936	288	Ontario School Ability	Range, 49-192 / Med. I.Q. = 94.0
Bowers (W. Va.)	1937	201	Pintner-Paterson / Kohs Block / Goodenough / Porteus Maze	Range, 27-148 / Med. I.Q. = 87.7 / Mean I.Q. = 89.2
S. Dakota School	1938	108	Grace Arthur	Range, 61-157 / Med. I.Q. = 95.2

INTELLIGENCE TESTS OF DEAF
1930 - 1947

Examiner	Date	N	Test Used	Results
Kirk	1938	89	Grace Arthur	Mean I.Q. = 99.4
Streng & Kirk	1938	97	Grace Arthur Performance Scale Chicago Non-Verbal Test	Mean I.Q. = 100.9 Mean I.Q. = 95.5
Springer	1938	Deaf = 330 Hearing = 330	Goodenough	M.I.Q. 　　Boys　Girls　Total Deaf　96.26　96.01　96.24 Hearing　97.06　107.06　102.21
Bridgman, Olga	1939	Deaf = 90	Grace Arthur Ontario Binet Healy Information Randall's Island	Med. I.Q. = 70.0 (83 educational or behavior failures, 7 superior)
Lane & White	1939	Deaf = 133 Hearing = 106	Advanced Performance Series	M.I.Q. Deaf = 103.57 Hearing = 101.96
Zeckel, A. and Van der Kolk	1939	Deaf = 100 Hearing = 100	Porteus Maze	M.I.Q. Deaf = 86.09 Hearing = 99.36
Morrison, W. J.	1940	Deaf = 30 Hearing = 50	Ontario School Ability	Percentage of deaf in normal and superior groups lower
Burchard & Myklebust	1942	Congenital Deaf 121 Adventitious Deaf 68	Grace Arthur	M.I.Q. = 102.5 M.I.Q. = 101.3
MacPherson, Jane	1945	Deaf = 61 Hearing = 66	Hiskey Test of Learning	M.I.Q. = 113.87 M.I.Q. = 101.67
Lane, Helen S.	1947	Deaf = 242	Randall's Island Performance Series	M.I.Q. = 102.7
		Deaf = 453	Advanced Performance Series	M.I.Q. = 113.4

hear are fortunate in our ability to hear and repeat new words, to change tenses, to use irregular verbs, to substitute the correct pronouns for nouns, to speak in complex sentences without being aware of this learning. Until the time we study a foreign language or take a course in formal grammar—we are not conscious of the language principles we use.

A young deaf child builds his vocabulary word by word as his teacher presents them to him and subsequently through his reading and the use of the dictionary extends his limited vocabulary further. He must be taught sentence structure and how to ask a question. He must be aware of the past, present and future tenses. Although a deaf child, whose education is started at nursery school age, is advanced over hearing children by school age—he does not keep this lead. Parents get very discouraged at the slow progress at third and fourth grade level when the child must spend more time fixing through repetition the new language principles, the vocabulary of new subjects, and the mastery of complex language structures.

Think of the complexity of our language and the multiplicity of meaning of many words in our vocabulary. A mathematics teacher made a study of vocabulary used in arithmetic texts and showed the many meanings that confuse a child. For example in the arithmetic textbooks, the word "figure" was used in seven ways, namely; (1) as a numeral, (2) as a geometric design, (3) as a doll (a figure of Santa Claus), (4) as a drawing (figure A shows . . .), (5) as an adjective (a 2 figured number), (6) as a print in "figured material" and (7) as a verb (figure the cost).

Reading becomes a most important subject in the life of the deaf child. The teacher has a two-fold task:—that of teaching the mechanics of reading—and also that of stimulating in the child the desire to read for pleasure. A hearing child or adult can acquire enough current information by listening to the radio and to group discussions to keep in touch with world affairs and local news. A deaf child is dependent upon reading current news and literature to be well informed. A deaf child, who does not enter school until he is six, is hampered in developing the love of reading. He is usually nine years old before he is ready for first grade and a boy or girl of nine with normal intelligence cannot be greatly stimulated by the stories in a primer. This gap between his interest and ability continues and reading is frequently limited to the classroom assignments.

Fortunately, some energetic teachers will add to their programs a club designed to stimulate in the child the desire to read. These clubs may simply be an added reading hour with books available to be read for fun and include stories told by the teacher. Perhaps the teacher will encourage the children to dramatize the stories. The club may function at a higher level and include book reviews and dramatizations planned by the children to entertain each other.

Achievement tests should be a portion of the psychological program of every school for the deaf. In the selection of these tests, the deaf child must be subjected to the same procedures as the hearing because by means of such tests, the educators wish to determine how retarded the deaf child is according to normal school standards.

All psychologists and teachers recognize this retardation although the amount varies from an average of five years to an average of two or three years. In testing a large group of hearing children, individual differences in school subjects would cancel each other and at a single grade level all subjects would be equivalent in difficulty. This is not true of the deaf as the language handicap is more severe in some subjects than in others.

Greatest retardation occurs in tests requiring reading for meaning or comprehension, knowledge of vocabulary, literature and arithmetic reasoning. A deaf child will omit or fail a simple arithmetic problem if the vocabulary is new or if he cannot understand the directions. For example, using equivalent forms of a test—a group of deaf children all worked a problem requiring the addition of "marbles" but failed the equivalent problem of adding refrigerator cars and flat cars on a freight train.

The least retardation is found in tests of arithmetic computation, language usage and geography. We would expect arithmetic computation to be an easy test because no language handicap occurs here. If the deaf child knows a language form, he knows only the correct one—and so should be able to score better on a test requiring visual recognition of these forms. The reason for better scores in geography can only be a guess. It is possible that geography has visual appeal and that the interest of the children is aroused by the travels of many residential children to the school.

The task of lessening the gap between intelligence and school achievement is one for teachers and parents. Some recommended techniques are:

1. Start the deaf child's education at nursery school age. There is conclusive evidence that the educational retardation of these children is greatly reduced and that they can be prepared for admission to high school at approximately the normal age.

2. Stimulate in the deaf child the desire to read for pleasure. Teachers can give outside emphasis to reading; parents and teachers can give guidance in the use of libraries; parents can set a good example by personal interest in reading for fun.

3. Encourage the use of reasoning. There is a great temptation for both teachers and parents to give too much guidance in problem solving. Because the deaf child has so much to learn, we try to save him any loss of time by following a false assumption that he should be spared wrong approaches to problems but we rob him of valu-

able experiences. He needs trial and error approaches to a problem even more than the hearing. Give the deaf child multiplicity of experiences and he can then apply reasoning to select the procedure to follow.

4. Use residual hearing to the maximum. A child with usable residual hearing can progress more rapidly than a totally deaf child. By use of the acoustic method this hearing can be trained. Group and individual hearing aids when they can be used should be made available and worn for all school instruction.

The deaf child must also have a well rounded social life—and a well balanced personality. This also is the joint responsibility of school and home. The congenitally deaf child does not portray the same characteristics of introversion, suspicion, feelings of inferiority and neurotic tendencies attributed to the deafened adult. Personality tests show individual differences within the deaf group that are as divergent as test results of a comparable hearing group. As a source of information to be used in guidance, the results are of value in a school for the deaf.

To assist the deaf child in his adjustment socially, the school curriculum must again be expanded to include lip reading, speech and vocabulary of games. How simple it is for the hearing child to learn "take your turn," "shuffle the cards," "choose your partner," and many similar commands. Parties should be planned for deaf children to learn to play games in order that they may skillfully participate in these when in a hearing group. It then becomes the responsibility of parents to provide opportunities for the use of this information in the home.

The Scouting program for boys and girls should be sponsored by the school. Again such a program gives the deaf boy or girl opportunities for contacts and competition with the hearing in Council-wide activities, at camp or with "buddy troops."

The program of the high school adolescent is filled with club activities. If the deaf child is to take his place with the hearing at high school level, he must be prepared for this activity also. Who will teach him parliamentary procedure if his teachers at the school for the deaf have not prepared him? How will he learn how to make a motion, how to serve on a committee, how to preside as an officer? With this information taught at a school for the deaf, he will win social approval with the hearing.

Dancing and sports prepare the deaf child for social acceptance. The rhythm program at schools for the deaf begins at nursery school and extends through the eighth grade. Rhythm has several values in the education of the deaf, namely:—

1. It improves bodily coordination through conscious control of bodily movements. This assumes added significance if the sense of equilibrium has been destroyed as well as the sense of hearing. In these cases kinaesthesis must be substituted.

2. It helps in academic work by developing attention and concentration.

3. It aids in speech development by producing better voice placement, by improving accent and phrasing of speech, and by augmenting the vocabulary through learning the words of songs.

4. It supplies social and aesthetic benefits by bringing the deaf child sensory pleasure and by making him at ease with hearing groups. In rhythm classes he has learned rhythmic games, familiar songs and dancing—all social tools that help him fit into a hearing environment.

The future of the deaf child depends upon his educational background, his mental ability and his talents. A deaf child of normal intelligence should complete the requirements of the elementary grades in ten to twelve years. If his education began at nursery school age, he is ready for high school at the normal age. If his starting age was delayed, he will be older than the average high school freshman. Orally trained deaf children can continue to high schools or vocational schools for the hearing. Manually trained deaf pupils must continue their education in schools for the deaf.

To watch a deaf child develop physically, mentally and socially is a gratifying experience to all who have contributed to this development. For no other group is the responsibility of the school as great. Only through a well-rounded teaching program, cooperation of home and school and the efforts of the deaf child can the fullest measure of security, happiness and success in the hearing world be achieved.

BIBLIOGRAPHY

Bishop, Helen: Performance Scale Tests Applied to Deaf and Hard-of-Hearing Children. Volta Review 1936, *38*, 447.

Bridgman, Olga: The Estimation of Mental Ability in Deaf Children. American Annals of Deaf 1939, *84*, 337-349.

Burchard, E. and *Myklebust, H.:* A Comparison of Congenital and Adventitious Deafness with Respect to Its Effect on Intelligence. American Annals of Deaf 1942, *87*, 140-154.

Drever, James and *Collins, Mary:* Performance Tests of Intelligence. Edinburgh 1938.

Goodenough, Florence and *Shirley, Mary:* A Survey of Intelligence of Deaf Children in the Minnesota Schools. American Annals of Deaf 1932, *77*, 238-247.

Kirk, Samuel: Behavior Problem Tendencies in Deaf and Hard-of-Hearing Children. American Annals of Deaf, 1938, *83*, 131-137.

Lane, Helen S.: The Relation between Mental Test Scores and Future Achievement. Proceedings of National Forum on Deafness and Speech Pathology, St. Louis, 1947.

Lane, Helen and *Schneider, Jennylouise:* A Performance Test for School Age Deaf Children. American Annals of Deaf 1941, *86*, 441-447.

Lyon, V. and *Associates:* Survey of the Illinois Schools for the Deaf. American Annals of Deaf 1933, *78*, 157-175.

MacKane, Keith: A Comparison of the Intelligence of Deaf and Hearing Children. T. C. Contribution to Educ. No. 585, 1933. Columbia Univ. Press.

MacPherson, Jane: A Comparison of Scores of Deaf and Hearing Children on the Hiskey Test of Learning Ability and on Performance Scales. Unpublished Master's Thesis, Washington University (St. Louis) 1945.

Morrison, W. J.: Ontario School Ability Examination. American Annals of Deaf 1940, *85*, 184-189.

Peterson, Edwin: Testing Deaf Children with Kohs Block Designs. American Annals of Deaf 1936, *81*, 242-254.

Peterson, E. and *Williams, J.:* Intelligence of Deaf Children as Measured by Drawings. American Annals of Deaf 1930, *75*, 242-254.

Roth, Stanley: Survey of the Psychological Examination Given by Dr. Stella Bowers,—May 1937. West Virginia Tablet 1938, *61*, No. 7.

Schick, Helen (Lane): The Use of a Standardized Performance Test for Preschool Age Children with a Language Handicap. Proc. of International Congress on the Education of the Deaf, Trenton, N. J. 1933, p. 526-533.

Schick, Helen and *Meyer, Max:* The Use of the Lectometer in the Testing of the Hearing and the Deaf. American Annals of Deaf 1932, *77*, 292-303.

Springer, N. Norton: A Comparative Study of the Intelligence of a Group of Deaf and Hearing Children. American Annals of Deaf 1938, *83*, 138-152.

Streng, Alice and *Kirk, S.:* The Social Competence of Deaf and Hard-of-Hearing Children in a Public Day School. American Annals of Deaf 1938, *83*, 244-254.

Zeckel, A. and *Von der Kolk, J. J.:* A Comparative Intelligence Test of Groups of Children Born Deaf and of Good Hearing by Means of the Porteus Test. American Annals of Deaf 1939, *84*, 114.

AUGUSTA JELLINEK, PH.D.

Supervisor, Veterans' Speech Clinic, affiliated with Hard of Hearing Clinic of Polyclinic Hospital, New York City.

Chapter VIII

ACOUSTIC EDUCATION IN CHILDREN

NORMALLY we are born with a capacity to hear, and it has been shown that most newborn babies react to sounds either by reflex movements or by turning the eyes or the head towards the sound (Froeschels and Beebe[1]). Even reactions of the embryo to sounds have been described. These congenital reactions, however, are not actions, inasmuch as consciousness plays a negligible role in them. A newborn child has no experience and no identification of sounds or relation of them to some processes or objects has been established. A process of learning takes place before hearing becomes a means of communication and of contact in our lives. Sounds become signals for objects or processes and they are identified with their source after they have been experienced a number of times. We actually learn to hear intelligently. To the reactive functions of the peripheral organ and of the deep cerebral pathways higher cerebral processes are added. According to recent theories the acoustic centers of the cortex quasi are "loaded" with stimuli until they are sufficiently "charged" to produce acoustic identifications, concepts and spontaneity of acoustic patterns and conscious vocal production.[2]

The formation of intelligent acoustic behavior takes time. Learning one's native language by ear belongs to it. It takes an

103

enormous amount of acoustic stimuli until acoustic functions are actually fixed to such an extent that they remain active even if the continuous afflux of acoustic material is cut off. Proof of this is the fact that up to about six years of age a child may lose the use of articulated language if he or she loses his hearing.

A normal child under normal conditions acquires acoustic experience without difficulty. If this is not the case, there is always some pathological reason. This may be either of a psychological nature or situated in the central or peripheral hearing organs.

We cannot entirely exclude from our discussion the use of physical means to increase the hearing capacities, but we shall consider here chiefly the educational means of increasing the use of hearing. The complex of educational methods used for the development of hearing has been called *acoustic* or *auditory* training.

The first question to solve is whether a child's hearing capacity is normal or not. In case of an unquestionable hearing disorder it has to be decided whether there is any residual hearing or whether the child is completely deaf. *Complete deafness is very rare*. The methods of testing differ according to the age of the child and especially according to the fact whether the child uses language or not.

In order to test a young child who does not speak yet and who does not react definitely to acoustic stimulations, the methods of audiometry[3] and testing with tuning forks are inadequate. We test these children by observing their motor reflexes to sounds and, if possible, by training them to react to sounds with spontaneous responses.

Acoustic reflexes to sounds appear normally under the following conditions:

1) Minimal reflexes always occur in different organs but they can be put in evidence only by special apparatus.

2) Intense stimuli produce palpebral, pupillar and general muscular reflexes which may involve the whole body.

3) In special states of tonicity, acoustic reflexes are evident which otherwise are suppressed (for instance during sleep).

4) Under increased irritability, they also become more apparent.

5) Pathological conditions in the inner ear, especially in the labyrinth, often cause the appearance of acoustic reflexes.[4, 5]

Under direct conduction of intense sounds into the meatus, movements of the eyes, of the head and of the extremities may be produced which are usually found only under pathological conditions.[6, 7] Characteristics of an injury to the inner ear are the nystagmiform acoustic reflexes of the eyes described by Froeschels.[7] They appear only under pathological conditions and are provoked only by tones which are actually perceived by the subject. A normal person tested with these strong tones responds with intense irrepressible shrinking away from the sound.

Repeated acoustic stimuli lead to fatigue of the reflexes, which finally stop because they are inhibited. This may be the reason why normal people do not react to the continuous afflux of sounds with motor reactions. The hard of hearing person, however, is stimulated in direct tone conduction by a rare impressive stimulus and reacts promptly to it; even there the reflexes cannot be provoked ad infinitum because a person gets accustomed to them. However, they can be produced again after a period of recovery.

These reflex reactions are independent of the subject's cooperation. In order to produce them we use intense whistle sounds, which are led into the meatus by a rubber tube terminated by a perforated, tightly fitting earpiece. The sounds must be brief and intense. The forms of the reflexes differ according to the pitch used and also depend on the state and on the position of the subject.[6, 7]

In examining the eye reflexes, the head of the subject is to be fixed and light is to be projected on his eyes. He should look straight at the examiner. If the reflex is positive, one or several nystagmiform movements of the bulbus may be observed; these may be directed towards the sound or away from it or up or down or they may consist in rotatory movement towards right or left. Pupillar reflexes often are seen under these conditions. In some cases no eye movements occur but rather movements of the head and swaying of the body, which is always connected with head reflexes and which is especially evident when the subject stands upright. Often one can observe motor reflexes of the arms if extended forward, upward or horizontally to both sides up to the level of the shoulders. These reflexes consist in lifting or lowering of one or both arms, of swaying or vacillating and less frequently in movements of the fingers. Frequently the reflexes of the arms are more intense if the eyes are closed.[6]

It is necessary to test each ear separately with different tones which should not be used in musical sequence. In rare cases reflexes can also be produced by short, intense sounds from a certain distance.

The testing of spontaneous action to sound consists in a kind of training of the children. (See Chapter VI.)

In these tests we do not use pure sounds, only complex sounds, but pure sounds practically never occur in nature and have no biological importance. The most important stimuli for the human ear, namely voice and speech, never contain pure sounds, but only complex ones. Audiometric examinations, made for control purposes, which in small children are not reliable anyhow, sometimes give much poorer results than those obtained by testing the acoustic reflexes.*

If the results of these tests are positive, they give us a rough

---

*H. Bloomer has published a method of audiometry for young children in which the child is trained to touch certain pictures when certain tones are perceived.

picture of what and how much the child hears at the time of the test, but if they are negative, this does not mean that the child is deaf. There may be psychological or central factors which inhibit the child's reaction and even his perception (psychical deafness, see Chapter VI). In addition to these methods, every child is to be tested with speech; if he does not respond to natural speech even of great loudness, he should be tested with the help of a hearing tube and of electric amplification, either using the microphone of an audiometer or a hearing aid.

By the training method we also test a child's willingness to react to sound and to answer it with motor reactions. If we are unable to induce a child with sufficient hearing to react in this way, the reeducation will be more difficult, because such a patient probably has withdrawn and isolated himself from the acoustic part of the world.

According to the imaginal type, the importance of acoustic stimulation varies. A child of a prevalently acoustic type may be more disturbed by a comparatively slight hearing deficiency than a child of another type. In some cases deficiencies in the hearing of high tones, which make speech sound appear less distinct, are sufficient to suppress the formation of speech.

In every case of abnormal hearing behavior, from apparently severe deafness to minor disorders of identification and memory, an attempt to improve hearing through training must be made.[8] Patients who do not react at all at first may perceive sounds after an initial period of training. If acoustic responses have been established at all, these perceptions can be increased and made conscious through auditory education. When working with an apparently severely hard of hearing child, we begin by stimulating the ear by strong sounds which as far as we can see are perceived by the patient. If the hearing is very poor, we use direct sound induction into the auditory meatus with a hearing tube or with an electro-acoustic[9] hearing aid (amplifying apparatus). Often loud sounds of the voice produced near the ear may be more readily perceived than sounds transmitted electrically, because these latter may have a peculiar quality. We also use musical sounds of different instruments in various pitches, decreasing their intensity as far as possible in order to educate attention to sounds of medium intensity. The child must learn that the sounds which he perceives have a definite connection with certain objects (trumpet, bell, etc.) or that they mean definite speech sounds, related to visible positions of the mouth. We try to achieve this by letting the child see the position of the mouth while he hears a sound and later have him produce the sound as he hears it. In this way we connect acoustic with visual and kinaesthetic perceptions. In order to emphasize these connections, we can also use life-sized schematic pictures of the face, which show the positions of the mouth in articulation, such as we use in the therapy of aphasia.

As soon as perception for more than single sounds is achieved, we expose a few objects or pictures to small children and name them, so that the child begins to associate an object with its name. The visual aspects of articulation are presented simultaneously with the acoustical ones, at first, but later the child tries to hear the word while the instructor's mouth is hidden. The use of pictures is especially desirable for those children who must learn to speak. The words we choose in describing the pictures contain those consonants and vowels which we want especially to be heard and distinguished. From there on, we teach speech nearly in the same way as we would teach a normal child, emphasizing however the acoustic aspect inasmuch as we ask the child to repeat without being able to read the lips.

If we deal with children who already speak, the approach is somewhat different. They already have definite speech concepts. If they are so-called deaf-mutes (in the great number of cases children with severe hearing impairments and more or less important residual hearing), these speech concepts are merely visual, kinaesthetic and tactile ones.

The use of a hearing aid is favorable in all cases with severe hearing impairments. It should be worn as much as possible from an early age on. With training, hearing may increase to such an extent that the hearing aid finally becomes unnecessary.[9]

It is important that the child listens to himself and compares his own voice and articulation to that of other people he hears. This will not only improve his perception and understanding but also his speech capacity.

If a child loses his hearing, acoustic training with its demand of increased attention and the training of memory may compensate sometimes for the physical defect and conserve socially usable hearing. It will also eliminate the habit of turning away from sound to visual stimulation alone.

Where speech and intelligence are well developed we can use more elaborate exercises for the discrimination of words and sounds, which we shall describe in detail in the following method for the acoustic training of adults.

Augusta Jellinek, Ph.D.
Supervisor, Veterans' Speech Clinic, affiliated with Hard of Hearing Clinic
of Polyclinic Hospital, New York City.

Chapter IX

ACOUSTIC TRAINING FOR ADULTS

IN adults just as in children acoustic perceptions can be developed by training towards a higher efficiency and a hard of hearing person can be taught to understand what he hears.

"Deaf mutes" who have reached the adult age without conscious use of their hearing and are firmly convinced that they are actually deaf, nevertheless often can be taught to hear. Most frequently they have some residual hearing. Education in many deaf-schools orientates these subjects chiefly towards the visual and kinaesthetic aspects of speech. Their attention is directed toward lipreading. Thus acoustic stimulation and the sound of words are not connected with meaning, they have no significance. For some of these adults, who have grown up as deaf mutes, sounds in the beginning of acoustic training are disagreeable and disturb them. Obviously if their hearing defect is so important that it hindered them from developing speech spontaneously, we have to use loud sounds, intense acoustic stimuli, in order to attract their attention and to provide them with acoustic patterns that they can identify and remember.

Amplification either by electrical means or simply by using

110

hearing tubes or by speaking in the near vicinity of the ear, will provide many severely hard of hearing patients with acoustic material, which they can utilize.

The personal structure of a subject is a decisive factor in the different types of acoustic behavior.[10] His willingness or unwillingness to accept normal contacts with the world enters into his acoustic function. Aside from the emotional complication, the question of the imaginal type is important. As said before, a person who is an acoustic type, which means that he gets his most vivid impressions and memories in the acoustic sphere, might be more disturbed by changes in the acoustic patterns than another person who is prevalently a visual or motor-kinaesthetic type.

During acoustic training it is interesting to observe the attitude of the subject towards his increasing share in the acoustic world. Many severely hard of hearing persons, who have never listened before, are deeply shocked by sound and complain that they do not want to hear, that it disturbs them. Especially when amplifying devices are used and sounds of uncommon intensity act upon the person, acoustic motor reflexes may be produced in the subject, which upset him and disturb him. On the other hand, it is also interesting to note in intelligent subjects how they build up their acoustic world. A very clever 27 year old girl, who had been brought up as a deaf-mute and who learned to hear first with a hearing aid and later without it, complained one day that she did not know where the sounds came from. After having been shown with visual control of the sound source whether the sound came from the back, from the left, right, etc., she located sounds fairly well. Since she acquired this capacity so quickly, she probably had it before, and the demonstration brought it finally to her conscious awareness.

Psychogenic and hysterical disorders may also produce an inhibitory mechanism which will cut off the person's consciousness from his own acoustic perception. The patients may behave as if they were deaf or severely hard of hearing, but the reflex mechanism in such cases functions well and the record-ings of these reflexes show clearly motor responses to sounds, though the subject may not have been aware of having heard anything.[11]

Response of the person to the sound world is a complex phe-nomenon. It consists not only of a passive reception, but also of an active acceptance and integration. Hearing, to a wide ex-tent, is an act; deafness, to some extent, may consist in an active increase of the hearing difficulty by a person affected with a hearing disorder. This offers a possibility for a therapeutic ap-proach beyond the purely medical approach, inasmuch as the integration of the hearing experience can be increased by a voluntary acceptance of sound and by a greater amount of at-tention directed to the source of sound. We teach the patient again the meaning of the changed symbols, so that his under-standing of these symbols may be restored. But often it is suffi-cient to prove to him in a short demonstration that he is able to understand what he hears and in this way induce him to change his morbid attitude actively and directly. An example is a young woman who came to see me wearing a hearing aid, who said that she had great difficulty in understanding the words when she was spoken to, even in a small room. A short demonstration proved to her that she was able to repeat num-bers without a hearing aid at a distance of 20 feet. She was told to take off her hearing aid and to listen without it. In this case, the experiment was successful and she came back next day telling me that she had been able to carry on a conversation without the help of amplification. This person had been able by her own will and determination to direct her attention toward sounds to such an extent that they became meaningful to her. On the other hand, there is the case of a teacher, who had formerly been a musician and with gradually increasing hear-

ing impairment had to give up her musical career. She wore a
hearing aid very conspicuously with which she heard so well
that I was at once convinced that she could also hear without
it. I began with her acoustic training which very soon disclosed
the presence of a usable amount of hearing even when no hearing aid was applied. As soon as this person acknowledged the
very noticeable progress she made, she stopped the treatment,
took up her hearing aid again and behaved as she did before.
Apparently, her personal neurotic situation which had led to
the sacrifice of her career demanded again that she should not
give up the motivation of an incorrigible hearing defect.

Hearing is a sense of vital biological importance and to a
great extent a warning sense, and therefore even the strong
inhibitions of hysteric deafness and also those in psychic deafness, often are broken down by means of repetitions extended
over long period of time. Few persons can resist the impact in
their bodies of the acoustic and motor-kinaesthetic reactions
based on reflexes. It is the same mechanism that wakes us up
from our sleep, when sounds produce motor reactions in us
which end the state maintained during sleep and cause our
awakening.

As we do not know at the beginning how great a part in a
hearing impairment is played by psychic factors, i.e. how great
is the marginal area over which hearing may be extended
though the physical state of the organ remains unchanged,
there is a good chance of increasing the understanding of
speech and the hearing of sounds by expert psycho-therapeutic
means.

Adults or adolescents who become hard of hearing not only
suffer a change in the intensity of their perceptions but also
their hearing disorders usually include acoustic distortions. The
hearing of some tones suffers more than that of others, and
the natural relation of perceptions for different pitch has been
destroyed. Every noise, speech sound or musical tone is based

on a definite relation between the intensities of its composing tones. These changed conditions influence especially the understanding of speech.[12]

The hard of hearing person does not any longer hear speech the way he knew it as long as his hearing was normal. It becomes increasingly difficult for him to identify sounds and words and to understand them. Therefore, he withdraws his attention more and more from the acoustic world and directs it towards vision. He stops listening.

We can teach the patient to understand whatever he hears, even if his new perceptions do not any longer correspond to his former speech memories. He can learn to identify his new perceptions again as the names of objects, concepts, etc.

We begin again by providing stimulations which are intense enough to be clearly perceived; if necessary we use for this purpose a speaking tube or a hearing aid. In very severe cases we begin by presenting a few pictures and by naming them. The patient is encouraged to use guessing in order to recognize the names from the few sounds he may perceive in the beginning. The distance is gradually increased. Later, simple sentences describing the pictures are used. From this we proceed to conversation and loud reading, allowing the patient to use lip reading only if he cannot understand without it. After the lip reading the same word or sentence is presented to him in sound alone.

For finer discrimination of sounds we add to these exercises word lists in increasing difficulty. For best results, the patient should be trained by several people so that he learns to understand different voices.

Self-exercise using his own voice with a hearing tube or a hearing aid is very helpful.

Acoustic training is often necessary in order to get full benefit of a hearing aid, as the central factor of adaptation is involved. The same is true when hearing capacity is increased by medical means: though the audiogram may show significant improvement this improvement need not come to the patient's consciousness continually and he may need additional training.

Central disorders of hearing (receptive aphasia, acoustic agnosia, disorders of the musical functions) may be greatly improved by acoustic training. In aphasic patients we try to re-establish the original relationship and coordination of sound and meaning, of name and object.

Objects and pictures are presented and named aloud. The patient repeats these names, if he is able to, while he looks at the objects and eventually touches them. Later he is asked to repeat words without seeing the objects. He is not allowed to read the words from the therapist's mouth, but must try to recognize and remember the sound patterns. Only before he reaches that state we often have to show him the speech movements which belong to the sounds.

In many cases of receptive aphasia where not only the understanding but even the perception of acoustic elements is more or less severely disturbed, we resort to acoustic drills. We present to the patient first simple, then more complicated auditory patterns. In slight cases repetition of nonsense syllables (Froeschels[2]) (up to 6) is a good means of training attention and memory. Increase of conscious attention may greatly improve the understanding of speech of such patients. Later, words and sentences are repeated, always without having the patient look at the therapist.

In some cases of central hearing disorders the reaction time is increased and the hearing range is not constant but may fluctuate between the extremes of normal hearing and complete deafness. They also have to be trained acoustically.

REFERENCES

1. *Froeschels, E. and Beebe, H. L.:* Testing the Hearing of the New Born. Archives of Otolaryngology. December 1946, pp. 710-714.

2. *Froeschels, E. and Jellinek, A.:* Practice of Voice and Speech Therapy. Boston, 1941.

3. *Bloomer:* A simple Method for Testing the Hearing of Small Children. The Quarterly Journal of Speech. XXVIII. 3, October, 1942.

4. *Tullio, P.:* L'Orecchio. Bologna, 1928.

5. *Tullio, P. and Jellinek, A.:* Methodik der Untersuchung der Orientierungs-schallreflexe. Abderhalden's Handb. der biolog. Arbeitsmethoden, Abt. V.

6. *Jellinek, A.:* Motorische Schallreflexe bei Schwerhoerigen und Taubstummen. Monatschr. f. Ohrenhlk, 1933.

7. *Froeschels, E.:* Über einen durch Schallreiz ausgeloesten Reflex bei hochgradig Schwerhoerigen. Ztschr. f. Hals-Nasen-und-Ohrenheilkde, 1930. Monatschr. f. Ohrenlk, 1923, 1926. H. 9.

8. *Urbantschitsch:* Ueber Hoeruebungen. Wien, 1895.

9. *Jellinek, A.:* L'emploi des appareils elektroactoustiques dans les exercises d'education et de reeducation auditive. Rev. Franç. de Phoniatr, 1938.

10. *Jellinek, A.:* Psychosomatic Factors in Hearing. Journal of Clinical Psychopathology. New York, 1946.
Jellinek, A.: Ueber Hoeruebungen und ihre Anwendungen. Wiener Med. Wochenschr., 1931.

11. *Loewenstein, O.:* Experimentelle Hysterielehre; Bonn, 1923.

12. *Froeschels, E.:* Ueber eine wenig beachtete Komponente des mangelhaften Sprachgehoers bei Schwerhoerigen und ihre Bedeutung fuer die Hoeruebungen. Monatschr, f. Ohrenhlk, 1932. H. 4, pp. 454-461.

ADDITIONAL SELECTED BIBLIOGRAPHY

Barcsi: Sordomutitas Corticalis. Bericht ueber den VI. Kongress d. int Ges. f. Logopaedie und Phoniatrie, Wien, 1935.

Berry: The Use and Effectiveness of Hearing-Aids. Laryngoscope, 1939.

Bourgeois: Audition et Hysterie. Otolog, internat., 1934.

Doniselli: Udito e Sensi Generali. Milano, 1923.

Escat: Des Acouphemes Subconscients, etc. Rev. de Laryng. 58, 1938.

Ewing: The Problems of the Partially Deaf Child. Report on the Conference of Educational Societies, London, 1933.

Ewing and Ewing: The Use of Hearing-Aids in the Treatment of Defects of Hearing in Children. Journ. of Laryngold., etc., 1936.

Goldstein, M. A.: Problems of the Deaf. St. Louis, 1933.

Goldstein, M. A.: The Acoustic Method. St. Louis, 1939.

Hallpike: Hearing Aids and Hearing Tests. Journ. of Laryngol. a. Otol., 1934.

Kaiser: Das Hoeren der eigenen Sprache. Arch. neérland. de Phonet. exper. 1936.

McFarlan: Testing the Hearing of the Pre-school Child. Arch of Oto-laryngol., 1934.

Malherbe, Vilenski, Herman: Exposé concernant les reliquats auditis décele chez les sourds-muets, etc. Instit. des Sourds-Muets, etc., Paris, 1935.

Nemai: Gehoerpruefungen an Taubstummen. Ber. ueber den VI. Kongr. der intern Ges. fuer Logopaedie, etc., Wien, 1935.

Newhardt: Report of the American Otological Society Representatives of the Committee on Hearing Aids, etc. Laryngoscope, 1939.

Novik: Methoden der Entwicklung der Gehoersaufmerksamkeit bei taubstummen Kindern. Acta-Oto-laryng. XXII, 1935.

Parrel: Les Sourds-Muets. Paris, 1928.

Ranjard: Symposium before the American Otological Society, Toronto, May, 1935. Annals of Otolog.

Volta Review: Many papers on hearing tests, acoustic training, and re-education of residual hearing. On hearing aids in this periodical see the annual reports of J. Timberlake.

SAMUEL D. ROBBINS
Professor of Psychology, Emerson College, Boston,
Managing Trustee, Institute for Speech Correction

Chapter X

DYSLALIA

DYSLALIA includes all functional defects of articulation.
Dyslalia may be sensory or motor in origin. Some children perceive speech inaccurately and articulate speech just as they perceive it. Others perceive speech accurately, but articulate incorrectly.

The most common receptive causes of dyslalia are deafness*, late maturation of the ability to discriminate between speech sounds in children whose hearing is normal, short auditory memory span disability, and imitation.

The most common expressive causes of dyslalia are inactivity of the muscles concerned with articulation, weakness of these muscles at the time speech was being acquired, mental deficiency, hyperemotionality, lack of unilateral cerebral dominance, structural anomalies** of injuries to the lips, teeth, tongue,

---

*The revised edition of "A Students' Dictionary of Terms Dealing with Disorders of Speech" (4), published by the American Speech Correction Association, places all disorders of articulation due to deafness in a new class, *dyseneia*.

**The publication (4) described in the above footnote places all disorders of articulation due to structural anomalies of the organs concerned with articulation in a new class, *dysglossia*.

118

jaw, and soft palate, and habit resulting from any of the above sensory or motor causes of dyslalia.

The following tests should be given to dyslalic patients before therapy is begun:

1. Intelligence tests. If the speech defect is so severe that the examiner cannot understand the patient, a non-verbal or performance test should be administered.

2. Articulation tests. The patient should read aloud or repeat after the examiner a series of sentences, each containing a certain speech sound in initial, medial, and final positions. The examiner should confine the recording of errors in pronunciation to the single speech sound being tested in each sentence. If the consonants are tested first, and no incorrect enunciation of vowels is noted, it is often unnecessary to test the enunciation of the vowels.

3. Auditory Memory Span test. How many of the following digits, speech sounds, and syllables can the patient repeat correctly after the examiner without reading his lips? 146, 852, 937: 4983, 6271, 7395: 24158, 31864, 57269

   dog, cat, bite: bread, train, milk: drink, street, asks
   gingerbread, butterfly, grandmother: Kindergarten,
   automobile, everybody: multiplication, university,
   uncharitable

4. Speech Sound Discrimination tests. These tests are described under therapy for sensory speech defects. The only test of this kind which is suitable for young children is the picture speech sound discrimination test in Robbins[2].

5. Mental Imagery Type tests. Children who have passed the primary grades may be given a series of words found in primers which appeal to several senses (such as ball, bath, car, clock, dog, fire, gun, radio, ring, typewriter, water, whistle, and write), and asked what they first think of when the examiner says the word. The eye-minded person will see a gun in his imagination, the ear-minded person will hear in his imagina-

tion the bang of a gun, and the motor-minded person will feel himself pulling the trigger of the gun or feel the kick of the gun as it is fired. About the only way to test the imagery type of a younger child is by studying his vocabulary as he speaks spontaneously.

6. Audiogram. If the speech sound discrimination tests indicate that the patient's hearing is impaired, he should be tested on an audiometer and the speech therapist should be given a copy of the resulting audiogram.

7. Personality tests. If the speech defect appears to be of psychogenic origin, a personality test should be administered, and the patient referred to a psychiatrist if this test indicates that he needs psychiatric advice.

8. Motor Co-ordination tests such as the following should be given to rule out the possibility of dysarthria or apraxia. Patients who manifest dysarthria should be referred to a neurologist.

(a) Can the patient protrude and retract his tongue rapidly?

(b) Can the patient lap the roof of his mouth with the tip of his tongue?

(c) Can the patient touch the last tooth on each side of each jaw with the tip of his tongue?

(d) Can the patient alternately open and close his jaw rapidly?

(e) Can the patient alternately purse and spread his lips?

(f) Can the patient blow out a candle without pinching his nose?

(g) Can the patient stand on tiptoes for five seconds and then walk a straight line?

(h) Sitting in a chair with a hand resting on each knee, can the patient alternately touch his nose with the forefinger of each hand?

TYPES OF DYSLALIA

The following types of dsylalia are recognized by the

Nomenclature Committee of the American Speech Correction Association[4]:

Asapholalia, mumbled speech, in which the patient can usually produce each vowel and consonant correctly by itself or a consonant with a vowel, but speaks so rapidly or moves his lips, tongue or jaw so little, that he sounds as though he were talking with his mouth full.

Atelolalia, delayed development of speech.

Barbaralalia, foreign dialect.

Bradylalia, abnormal slowness of speech.

Dialectolalia, provincial dialect.

Embololalia, interpolation of speech sounds or syllables which do not belong to the word.

Idiolalia, invented language, in which the patient uses a language all his own which bears no resemblance whatsoever to conventional speech.

Leipolalia, elision, omission of speech sounds or syllables which belong in the word.

Metalalia, transposition of speech sounds, such as "er" for "re".

Paralalia, mispronunciation or substitution of one speech sound for another.

Pedolalia, baby-talk, a syndrome composed of elisions, sound substitutions, and the omission of articles, prepositions, conjunctions, and many pronouns.

Rhinolalia, aperta (hyperrhinolalia) functional cleft-palate type of speech, with nasality, nasal fricatives, and the substitution of the glottal click or nasals for plosives. Rhinolalia clausa (hyporhinolalia) sounding like speech with a plugged nose (see Chapter XII).

Tachylalia, abnormal rapidity of speech without mumbling.

THERAPY FOR DYSLALIAS OF SENSORY ORIGIN

In correcting dyslalias in young children, it is often helpful to give to each consonant a catchy name which resembles some non-speech sound with which the child is familiar as well as the sound represented by the consonant itself. The following catchy names are suggested:

B, bouncing ball sound, rug beating sound.

CH, train sound, sneeze sound, chopping sound.

D, drip sound, drum sound.

F, fizzing sound, spitting cat sound.

G, bull frog sound, hungry pig sound, bottle sound.

H, panting sound, sigh sound.

J, jumpy motor sound.

K, coughing sound, clucking sound.

L, wave lapping sound, wire singing sound.

M, humming sound, yum-yum sound.

N, whining dog sound, power-dive sound.

NG, bell ringing sound, auto-horn sound.

P, motor boat sound, pipe puffing sound.

R, self-starter sound, gear shift sound.

S, teakettle sound, hissing sound.

SH, hush sound.

T, tick-tock sound, clock sound, tapping sound.

th, (unvoiced), pinwheel sound, radiator sound.

TH (voiced), airplane sound, vacuum cleaner sound.

V, shiver sound, electric razor sound.

W, whistle sound, delight sound.

WH, wind sound, whip snapping sound.

Y, yipping sound, smiling sound.

Z, buzzing sound, bumble bee sound.

ZH, scraping sound, filing sound, buzz saw sound.

The speech therapist might read aloud to a class of dyslalics and ask them to raise their hands at each word which begins with the hissing sound or any other sound upon which the class happens to be working.

It requires an auditory memory span for five speech sounds

to pronounce correctly even such monosyllabic words as "asks," "spry," and "street". If it is necessary for a person having an auditory memory span for but three speech sounds to learn one of these longer words, it is necessary to break up such words into larger units within the person's memory span. If the patient lives on Indianapolis Street, and it is necessary to teach him to say his address so that he may be taken home if he gets lost, it will be necessary to break up the long word "Indianapolis" into the three shorter words "Indian", "apple", and "iss", and gradually reduce the pauses between these three words until they blend into the single word "Indianapolis". To learn the word "street" the patient should begin with the word "eat", then say "tr-eat", pausing between the "tr" and the "eat" at first and then gradually blending these two components into "treat"; he should then prefix an "s" and say "s-treat", and gradually blend these two elements into the desired word "street".

Persons who are handicapped with short auditory memory spans are likely to omit speech sounds of low phonetic power, and to retain only vowels, semi-vowels (including *l, m, n, ng, r, w,* and *y*), and a few of the louder consonants such as *ch, j,* and *sh.* Some patients omit all consonants. Others omit final consonants and the fainter consonants in blends. These patients understand what is said to them because they get the meaning of each word from the part which they reproduce: they do not realize that there are other sounds in these words which they do not notice.

In testing the degree of maturation of a patient's ability to discriminate between speech sounds, it is well to ascertain just what types of sounds he has difficulty in discriminating between, and to confine treatment to improving his ability to discriminate between those types of sounds most often failed. It is well to test separately the patient's ability to discriminate between vowels, between semi-vowels, between nasals, between cognates (voiced and unvoiced consonants made from the same mouth mold), between plosives and fricatives (including sibilants) made from approximately the same mouth mold, between unvoiced plosives, between voiced plosives, between unvoiced fricatives and sibilants, and between voiced fricatives and sibilants.

Various types of speech sound discrimination tests will be found in the writer's "Better Speech Sound Discrimination"[2]. Six pairs of pictures are printed at random on a single page and the patient, after he has memorized the names of these pictures, is asked to point to each picture in turn. If he keeps pointing to the *cat* instead of to the *cap* or vice versa, he is evidently having trouble in discriminating between the high-frequency unvoiced plosives. Or the word *cat* is read once and the word *cap* is read twice and the patient is asked whether the first, second, or third word was different from the other words, or whether all three words were alike. Or each word is read once and the patient is asked whether he heard one word spoken twice or two different words. More instruction and practice of this kind on the types of speech sound which the patient confuses will help him to listen more attentively to those speech sounds of low phonetic power which he has overlooked or confused as he hears these spoken by others.

When using speech sound discrimination as therapy, the patient should observe closely the speech therapist's mouth and notice just how he makes the sound or the word which the patient confuses. He should then reproduce this with the aid of a mirror, feel the different movements of muscles concerned with articulation required to make this correctly, together with any tactual impressions that may be present, and concentrate on the difference between the sound which he produces and that which the speech therapist makes.

Other devices for improving the patient's ability to discriminate between speech sounds are to be found in Van Riper[7], pages 235-238.

Speech defects due to impaired hearing are discussed in chapters 7-9.

THERAPY FOR DYSLALIAS OF MOTOR ORIGIN

Paralalia. As sound substitutions are present in several types of dyslalia, and constitute more than half of all dyslalia cases, it is logical to consider paralalia first, and then to take up the other types of dyslalia in alphabetic order.

A different technique is indicated for patients who are ear-minded, eye-minded, and motor-minded, respectively.

Therapy for Audiles. Stimulation methods usually work well with audiles. The speech therapist first produces very distinctly the correct speech sound at least five times at intervals of approximately a second; then, three seconds later, he asks the child to reproduce that sound. If the child fails, more ear training work is done with this sound before the patient tries it again. After the patient learns this sound in isolation, the speech therapist repeats at least five times a familiar word which contains this sound, pauses three seconds, and then gives the patient one chance to pronounce this word correctly. Or the therapist pronounces five different words, all containing the given sound, and, after a pause of three seconds, asks the patient to repeat that word of the series which he names. Stimulation methods are most useful in teaching vowels and semi-vowels. Other ear training exercises are to be found in Van Riper[7], pages 223-238.

The word-pair technique described in Robbins[3] often proves helpful if the patient is taught to listen attentively to the contrast at the beginning or end of each of a pair of words which are identical save for the change of a single speech sound, and then to repeat each word after the speech therapist, being sure that he makes each word sound just as the therapist's word sounded.

Therapy for Visiles. Eye-minded persons should be shown diagrams of the comparative mouth molds of those speech sounds which they are unable to make correctly. Excellent diagrams are given in Borden and Busse[1] and in Scripture[5]. The patient should watch the speech therapist's lips, tongue, and jaw movements and try to duplicate these exactly while looking in a mirror. Care must be taken to have both the therapist's and the patient's articulatory organs adequately illuminated, and to have the patient so seated that he can observe the therapist's mouth simultaneously with his own mouth in a mirror. After learning these mouth molds with the help of a mirror, the patient should try to recognize them by ear and by feeling so that as soon as possible he may dispense with the mirror outside of formal practice periods.

The word-pair technique described in Robbins[3] is often useful in comparing the difference in appearance between the correct and incorrect mouth molds.

Therapy for Motiles. The patient should first be taught the feelings experienced in forming and in holding those mouth molds which are made incorrectly. It is often necessary to place his lips, tongue, jaw, and soft palate in the correct position with the help of the fingers outside his mouth and with a sterile flat throat stick or sound probe within his mouth, as described in Stinchfield[6].

The word-pair technique described in Robbins[3] is often successful if the patient is taught the contrast in feeling between the correct and incorrect mouth molds. The patient may, at the same time, observe these mouth molds in a mirror, and compare the right and wrong sounds.

Therapy for Mixed Imagery Types. It is usually desirable to correct mispronounced vowels and semi-vowels first, using the stimulation methods described under therapy for audiles.

All consonants and those semi-vowels which do not improve promptly by the stimulation method often respond to the word-pair technique described in Robbins[3]. The patient should be taught to discriminate between the speech sounds of specified parts of each word-pair; to compare the mouth molds used by the speech therapist when making these word-pairs with his own as seen in a mirror; and to study the contrast in feeling between the parts of these word-pairs which are changed, the therapist pointing out what differences in feeling the patient should study at each point where muscular movement or touch sensations are evident.

Any speech sounds which do not clear up by the preceding methods should be corrected by the moto-kinesthetic method described in Stinchfield[6] with this difference—the patient should study the sound made by the speech therapist and compare it carefully with the sound which he himself produces, and should check with a mirror to make sure he is forming each mouth mold correctly as it is made by the therapist.

Errors in the articulation of consonants are apt to fall within one of the following three types. (1) Cognate errors are those in which the patient fails to voice or to unvoice one of those consonants which are made exactly alike except for being voiced or unvoiced. (2) Pressure pattern errors are those in which the patient explodes fricatives (including sibilants) instead of blowing them, or vice versa. (3) Height of tongue tip errors are those in which the patient holds the tip of his tongue low in his mouth instead of raising it against the alveolar ridge on such speech sounds as T, D, N: L, R: S, and Z. (4) Using the dental-labial instead of bilabial articulation. (5) Lateral emission of some sounds.

If the patient substitutes F for V, he is likely also to substitute unvoiced TH for voiced TH, SH for ZH, CH for J, S for Z, P for B, T for D, and K for hard G. Although the patient may be able to distinguish whispering from speaking, he may not realize that parts of a word may be whispered although most of that word is voiced. When using such word-pairs as "fine"-"vine" it is helpful to have the patient whisper the entire word containing the unvoiced cognate and speak loudly the entire word containing its voiced cognate. If it is difficult for the patient to voice the sonant cognate at the ends of words, he should interpolate a neutral vowel at the end of the word, since he will tend to keep voicing between two voiced sounds. The patient should palpate his Adam's apple to feel vibrations on the voiced fricative or sibilant which are lacking on its unvoiced cognate, or place his little fingers in his ears and hear the roar manifest on the voiced cognate which is lacking on its unvoiced cognate.

If a patient substitutes CH for SH and J for ZH, he is likely also to substitute T for S, D for Z, T for unvoiced TH, D for voiced TH, P for F, and B for V. Merely speaking a fricative or sibilant too quickly without exploding it will make it sound like a plosive made from the same mouth mold. To correct such faults, the patient should be drilled on word-pairs in Robbins[3] which begin or end with the correct and incorrect sound, but are otherwise alike: while producing such word-pairs the patient should study the difference in feeling between pressing a speech organ firmly against another and retracting it quickly as pent up air escapes explosively, and of a gentle contact in the same position while slowly blowing out a candle.

If a patient neglects to raise the tip of his tongue on L and R, he is likely also to fail to raise it for T, D, N, S, and Z. As T, D, N, and L may be articulated correctly with the tip of the tongue at any point between the normal positions for TH and for R, they are often pronounced correctly from incorrect mouth molds unless they occur in blends which are difficult to articulate with the tongue placed in this lower position. With the use of a mirror, the patient must become familiar with the feeling at the base of his tongue as its tip is raised for these speech sounds, and with the touch sensation of the tongue tip against the alveolar ridge or hard palate, before attempting to produce these sounds. The patient must also be taught not to purse his lips unduly while producing L and R. Suitable word-pairs will be found in Robbins[3] for bringing out the contrasts just described.

Having considered a few very general types of paralalia, it is now in order to take up a few of the more common and more difficult specific types of paralalia.

Lambdacism. Defective pronunciation of the semi-vowel, *l*, is known as *lambdacism*.

If the tip of the tongue is held against the lower incisors and the blade of the tongue is kept well away from the alveolar ridge, *y* is likely to be substituted for *l* if the lips are spread, and *w* is apt to be substituted if the lips are protruded.

The therapy consists in pressing the tip of the tongue firmly against the backs of the upper incisors while voicing, allowing the breath stream to escape at the corners of the mouth. With the use of a mirror the patient can learn not to purse his lips unduly. When saying words beginning with *bl, cl, fl, gl,* and *pl* it is helpful to make the mouth mold for *l* before pronouncing the letter which immediately precedes it; this letter will then blend perfectly with the *l*.

Rhotacism. Defective pronunciation of the semi-vowel, *r*, is known as *rhotacism*.

If the tip of the tongue is not sufficiently raised and retracted for *r*, *y* or *w* is apt to be substituted for *r* as described for *l* under *lambdacism*.

The therapy consists in gently lapping the hard palate with the under side of the tip of the tongue from the alveolar ridge to a point just forward of the center of the hard palate, thinking of the speech sounds *t* or *d* while the tongue is against the alveolar ridge and of the sound of initial *r* when it reaches the center of the hard palate. The patient is then asked to vocalize while thus lapping the roof of his mouth as he pronounces such words as "dry" and "draw", being careful to have the sides of his tongue in close contact with the hard palate and the center of the tongue lowered just enough to permit the breath stream to pass out through the space between the midline of the tongue and the hard palate. The patient is then told to think the initial *t* or *d* as he speaks the corresponding word beginning with *r*, "rye", "raw". If he tends to purse his lips too much on *r* have him hold back the corners of his mouth with his thumb and index finger or hold down his lower lip as indicated. The patient must be careful to drop the tip of his tongue promptly for the vowel which follows, once *r* is completed. When saying words beginning with *br, cr, fr, gr,* and *pr* it is helpful to make the mouth mold for *r* before pronouncing the speech sound which immediately precedes it. The initial sound of the word will then blend perfectly with the *r*.

Asapholalia. The patient should first develop the muscles concerned with articulation by performing the muscle training exercises described under motor coordination tests, and in West[8], pages 203-205 and 243-248.

He should observe himself speaking in a mirror and make sure that his lips, tongue, and jaw are moving adequately, and that no set of muscles is performing exaggerated movements.

He should correct any sound substitutions or elisions as indicated under *paralalia* and *leipolalia*.

He should also slow down the tempo of his thinking and speaking by lengthening the vowels of all accented syllables, making their lengths proportional to the relative importance of these words in the context.

Atelolalia. Therapy will be found in chapter 5 on Audimutism.

Barbaralalia. Certain English speech sounds are missing in several foreign languages. These must be taught the patient as described under *paralalia.* Patients must be taught that many English words are not spelled phonetically, and be given a few of the simpler rules of English spelling. Patients should record in their notebook lists of English words which resemble foreign words in appearance but which are pronounced differently. Patients must be shown that, although voiced consonants may never come at the ends of words in their native language, they frequently come at the ends of English words, so that final *s* is voiced when it follows a voiced speech sound in all English plurals, possessives, and third person singulars of verbs. The patient should first pronounce very slowly one of the words in his native language which contains the voiced consonant in question, isolate this consonant, tack it on the end of nonsense syllables beginning with vowels, and then place it at the ends of conventional English words.

A person whose native language is not English should be shown that English is the only major language which maintains a uniform outflow of breath throughout the syllable, word, and breath group of words. In order to accomplish this, the speaker needs to begin to form the next speech sound before the preceding sound is completed. The mouth molds for L and R are formed in English before the speaker utters the B, P, F, G, or K which precedes them, whereas the L and R are not commenced in most foreign languages until the preceding sound is completed. Although each of two consecutive plosives (i.e. that boy) is exploded in most foreign languages, with the interpolation of a voiced or unvoiced neutral vowel after each explosion, the first plosive is merely occluded in English, and just the second plosive is exploded into the sound immediately following it without the interpolation of any neutral vowel. Two adjacent plosives thus take the time of a single plosive in English, but of two separate speech sounds in most foreign languages.

Elisions should be corrected as described under *leipolalia*.

Foreigners should be taught a basic English vocabulary of a few hundred of the most concrete and useful words at first. They must be taught the differences in sentence structure in

English and in their native language. They must be taught to think in English and to use English idioms correctly.

Errors in stress placement and inflection should be corrected, and the patient should be taught to reduce gestures and inflection to the extent he observes these in persons who were born in this country. Whereas the patient may have accented many words of his native language on their last syllables, the stress is more apt to come on the first or second syllable in English. Because of the tendency to weaken the vowel in unstressed words and syllables, and to use secondary accents in words of many syllables, there is a tendency to alternate stressed and unstressed syllables in English which is not present in most of the other languages.

Bradylalia. The patient must be taught to think in short sentences and to formulate a sentence in his thoughts before he attempts to express it orally. He must be taught to relax his articulatory mechanism while speaking, and to touch unaccented words and syllables very lightly and quickly. He should read aloud in unison with another who speaks at a normal rate.

Dialectolalia. Sound substitutions, elisions, interpolations, and transpositions should be corrected as indicated under *paralalia, leipolalia, embololalia, and metalalia,* respectively. The patient should be taught the dialect of the locality where he expects to spend the rest of his life.

Embololalia. The patient should be taught to break up mispronounced words and syllables into their component parts as indicated under *leipolalia* and shown which speech sounds or syllables are superfluous.

Idiolalia. The therapy is much the same as for *atelolalia.* The speech therapist should speak to the child in his own invented language and show the child that it is impossible to understand any language but the conventional language which all persons speak; that his wants will be fulfilled more quickly if he expresses them in a language which other people speak and understand. Those who spend much time with the child should be advised not to understand his invented language.

Leipolalia. If the patient has a short auditory memory span, he should be taught to build up necessary words which contain more speech sounds than he can integrate as described under therapy for dysalalias of sensory origin.

If a patient omits an entire syllable, the mispronounced word should be broken up into syllables, and the omitted syllables added in the proper place. If the patient omits one or more speech sounds within a syllable, all speech sounds which constitute that syllable should be separated with slight pauses by both speech therapist and patient, and the patient shown where to add the missing sounds. The pauses between speech sounds should then be shortened gradually until the speech sounds which constitute the syllable blend together normally.

Metalalia. The therapy is much like that for *leipolalia.* The patient should be taught to break up the mispronounced word or syllable into its elements and shown which of these elements are transposed. If this error occurs more often in oral reading than in oral speech, the patient must be taught always to move his eyes from left to right across the printed pages while reading.

Pedolalia. Baby-talk is a syndrome made up of sound substitutions, elisions, and the omission of subordinate words in sentences. Sound substitutions should be corrected as outlined under *paralalia,* elisions as outlined under *leipolalia,* and the omission of subordinate words should be allowed to take care of itself as the child matures.

Rhinolalia. The therapy for rhinolalia is indicated in chapters 12 and 13.

Tachylalia. The patient must be taught to slow down his eye movements in reading and his thoughts in speaking. His eye should pause at each punctuation mark in reading aloud until his voice catches up, and his thoughts must stop at the end of each phrase until his voiced speech comes up to them. Choral speaking is excellent. The patient should prolong the vowels of all accented syllables of all prominent words in sentences as these are prolonged by the best radio announcers and public speakers.

Sigmatism. Defective pronunciation of the sibilants (*s, z, sh,* and *zh*) is known as *sigmatism.*

The smaller the physiological latitude used in the articulation of a speech sound, and the less visible the mouth mold required for the production of that sound, the greater is the incidence of mispronunciation of that sound. Although the letters *t* and *d* may be exploded from any mouth mold between that for *th* and that for *r,* the correct enunciation of the sibilants *s* and *z* is determined by quite definite rules. The tip of the tongue must be pressed lightly against the lower incisors or lie close to the upper incisors, the breath stream must be concentrated in a narrow groove formed along the midline of the front of the tongue and must rub against the biting edges of the incisors as it leaves the very center of the mouth in a thin stream under exactly the right pressure from below. The lips must be slightly spread, the jaw slightly opened, and the soft palate raised sufficiently to prevent air from escaping through the nose. If any of these rules for the production of *s* and *z* are violated, a special speech defect will result. The following types of sigmatism are recognized.

STRIDENT SIGMATISM

If too deep or too wide a groove is formed along the midline of the tongue, a sharp, piercing, whistling sibilant results. If this sound is produced with too much breath pressure, this fault is further accentuated.

The therapy consists in reducing the size of the groove along the midline of the tongue, and in reducing the breath pressure until a correct *s* is produced.

ADDENTAL SIGMATISM

If the tongue is pressed against the edges of the upper incisors in the conventional mouth mold for *th* without forming a small groove down its midline, or if the tongue is pressed against the lower incisors without forming this groove, so that the breath stream spreads over the front part of the tongue in a fanshape, the fricative, *th,* will be produced instead of the intended *s.*

Addental sigmatism is usually caused by defective functioning of certain normal tongue muscles. Pressure of the tongue against the teeth makes the formation of the necessary tongue groove difficult.

The therapy consists in raising the front of the tongue to the alveolar ridge as in the conventional mouth mold for *t,* reducing the pressure of the tip of the tongue at the very center, and blowing out an imaginary candle with varying degrees of breath pressure until a correct *s* is produced. The writer has had excellent results with the use of such word pairs as "tar-star", "tick-stick". The patient is told to feel where he places his tongue when he starts to say the first word which begins with *t,* to feel his tongue in the same position before he starts to speak the second word which begins with *st,* but to reduce the pressure of the tip of his tongue at the very center of the alveolar ridge and blow out an imaginary candle before he says this first word a second time. Before using this method the therapist should make sure that the patient lifts his tongue adequately, because many lispers make *t* with the tongue held too low in the mouth. It sometimes helps to tip the head well back to reduce the pressure of the tip of the tongue against the teeth.

INTERDENTAL SIGMATISM

If the tip of the tongue is suspended between the upper and lower incisors in the attempt to produce *s* or *z* the fricative, *th,* results.

The therapy is the same as that for *addental sigmatism,* but it may be necessary at first to tell the patient to close his jaw so that he cannot protrude his tongue.

A patient who produces *s* and *z* interdentally is likely to make several other dental sounds interdentally, a fault known as *multiple interdentalism.* This fault has not been generally recognized because the addental and interdental productions of such speech sounds as *d, t, n,* and *l* are not noticeable acoustically, and observation of these lowered positions of the tongue is obstructed by the upper lip.

The therapy for multiple interdentalism consists in teaching the patient to raise the tip of his tongue to the alveolar ridge when producing *d, t, n,* or *l,* and in teaching him to purse his lips slightly and to press the tip of his tongue against his lower incisors, varying both this pressure of the tongue against the lower incisors and the breath pressure until a correct *sh* is produced.

Interdental sigmatism is usually caused by defective functioning of certain normal tongue muscles. It must be remembered, also, that the sibilants *s* and *z* are usually the last speech sounds acquired by young children, and that hence some children are learning these sibilants during the interval between losing the central deciduous teeth and the full growth of the permanent incisors, when it is all too easy for the tip of the tongue to protrude.

Lateral Sigmatism

If the front or tip of the tongue is pressed against the lower or the upper incisors and one side of the tongue is raised more vigorously than the other and one side drops away from contact with the molars while the breath stream is forcibly expelled through the resulting opening, *lateral sigmatism* results. This strong fricative resembles a laterally exploded *k* or *t* followed by an embarrassed snicker. If there happen to be wide spaces between the upper teeth where the sides of the tongue drop away from contact with the upper molars, this fault is likely to be accentuated. Lateral sigmatism is usually due to improper functioning of certain normal tongue muscles rather than to anomalies of the teeth or to spaces between them. Any fricative or sibilant may be emitted laterally.

It is possible to determine on which side of the mouth air leaves the row of teeth by rapidly and repeatedly tapping the cheeks while *s* is unduly prolonged. The sound is interrupted or toned down when the side is tapped through which it is omitted.

The therapy for *multiple lateralism* consists in teaching the patient to seal with his tongue all spaces through which breath can be emitted laterally and to leave an adequate aperture at the center of his mouth through which a jet of air may be forcibly emitted. Lateral *f* and *v* are corrected by pressing the sides of the lower lip firmly against the upper teeth. Lateral *th* is corrected by broadening the tip of the tongue until it touches both corners of the mouth. Lateral sibilants are corrected by raising the sides of the tongue sufficiently to seal all spaces through which the breath stream might be emitted laterally.

The writer has had good success in correcting lateral *s* by using the *t-st* word pairs described under *addental sigmatism*. If the tongue is pressed firmly against the entire length of the alveolar ridge before *t* is exploded, the tongue will automatically close all apertures through which the breath stream was previously emitted laterally. If the patient is careful to keep the sides of his tongue in this *t-contact* with the alveolar ridge while he relaxes the center of his tongue he should produce a correct *s* or *z* as soon as he has learned by trial and error just how much breath pressure is needed.

The Stents Plate described on pages 170-173 of Froeschels' "Speech Therapy"[9] often corrects lateral sigmatism in a surprisingly short time. Kerr's Modeling Compound, obtainable at any dental supply house, is probably the nearest substitute for stents wax which is available in the United States.

If more direct methods fail, the patient may be taught temporarily to make an interdental *s* until the lateral *s* has been corrected, and then taught to make a conventional *s*.

BILATERAL SIGMATISM

Sometimes the breath stream is forcibly emitted at both sides of the mouth instead of on a single side as in *lateral sigmatism.* This fault sounds exactly like *lateral sigmatism* and the therapy is identical. Bilateral sigmatism is sometimes a degeneracy of *addental sigmatism,* in which the breath stream escapes at both sides of the mouth instead of being forced between the tongue and the incisors.

PALATAL SIGMATISM

This form results if the tongue is too distant from the incisors. The sound resembles an *sh.* The therapy consists of transforming *f* into *s* by holding the patient's lips away from each other and from the upper incisors while he unduly prolongs *f*.

OCCLUSIVE SIGMATISM

Sometimes *s* is produced with excessive tongue pressure, resulting in a sound which closely resembles *t.* This is rather a common fault in neurotic lisping.

The therapy consists in inserting a sterile probe just over the midline of the tongue and pressing down the tongue as the patient produces *s,* or in asking the patient to make a sharp hiss. The use of the *t-st* word pairs described under *addental sigmatism* is also indicated.

LABIO-DENTAL SIGMATISM

If the lower lip is placed against the upper incisors, as in articulating *f,* while the tongue is held in the correct mouth mold for *s,* a sharp, whistling fricative is heard.

The therapy consists simply in holding down the lower lip

while emitting *s* until the lip no longer tends to approach the upper teeth while making *s*.

NASAL SIGMATISM

If the soft palate fails to close the nasal passages while *s* is being produced, there results a softened *s* accompanied by a weak, sometimes a loud fricative snort produced by forcibly emitting a strong breath stream through the nasal passages. Some lispers permit all or the greater part of the breath stream to escape through their noses when emitting *s*. If a mirror is held in front of the patient's nose while *s* is produced, the amount of clouding of the mirror will indicate how much of the breath stream is escaping through his nose.

The therapy for both *nasal sigmatism* and for *stertorous sigmatism* is quite different from that for those forms of sigmatism which result from incorrect positions of the tongue. It is necessary to bring about correct action of the soft palate, and to direct the outgoing breath stream through the mouth. A simple therapy consists in having the patient blow into a small glass tube placed against his lower incisors while the therapist removes the patient's upper lip from the tube and pinches the patient's nose so tightly that no air can escape through it. Another simple therapy is to transform *f* into *s* as described above.

Sh and its cognate equivalent, *zh,* are sometimes produced nasally. The therapy consists in pinching the patient's nose as he protrudes his lips and puffs, while exerting a slight pressure with the tip of his tongue against his lower incisors.

STERTOROUS SIGMATISM

Some patients who fail to close their nasal passages while emitting *s* produce, in addition to the symptoms described under *nasal sigmatism,* a kind of snoring sound in place of *s*. The therapy is the same as that for *nasal sigmatism*.

CONFUSION OF S AND SH

The speech sounds *s* and *sh* are sometimes confused, especially when the patient's hearing is impaired in the high frequency range, or when a patient who hears normally has not learned to discriminate between the fainter high-frequency speech sounds. The contrasts between the mouth molds of these two sibilants must be pointed out to such patients. They must be taught that the lips are slightly spread for *s* and *z*, whereas they are protruded somewhat for *sh* and *zh;* that *sh* is a much louder and more penetrating sound than *s;* and that *s* is made with the tip of the tongue raised against the alveolar ridge as for *t,* but with the center of the tongue relaxed, whereas *sh* is produced by pressing the tip of the tongue against the lower incisors until the blade of the tongue is forced forward and upward sufficiently for a correct *sh.*

CH AND J

Although many phoneticians consider the speech sound denoted by the letters *ch* to be composed of *t* followed by *sh,* and its cognate, *j,* as composed of *d* followed by *zh,* the palatograms and mouth recorder kymograms of Scripture[5] and others show that these sounds more closely resemble single plosives in nature, although not exploded so suddenly as are true plosives such as *t* and *d.* The writer has found that children soon learn *ch* as an exploded *sh* and *j* as an exploded *zh.*

REFERENCES

1. *Borden, Richard C.* and *Busse, Alvin C.:* Speech Correction. F. S. Crofts & Co., New York, 1929.
2. *Robbins, Samuel D.* and *Rosa Seymour:* Better Speech Sound Discrimination. Expression Co., Magnolia, 1947.
3. *Robbins, Samuel D.* and *Rosa Seymour:* Correction of Speech Defects of Early Childhood. Expression Co., Magnolia, 1937.

4. *Robbins, Samuel D., Hawk, Sara Stinchfield,* and *Russell, G. Oscar:* A Students' Dictionary of Terms Dealing with Disorders of Speech. American Speech Correction Association, Columbus, 1947.

5. *Scripture, E. W.:* Stuttering and Lisping. Macmillan Co., New York, 1912.

6. *Stinchfield, Sara M.* and *Young, Edna Hill:* Children with Delayed and Defective Speech. Stanford Univ. Press, 1938.

7. *Van Riper, C.* Speech Correction Principles and Methods. Prentice-Hall, New York, 1939.

8. *West, Robert, Kennedy, Lou,* and *Carr, Anna.* The Rehabilitation of Speech. Harper & Bros., New York, 1937.

9. *Froeschels, Emil.* Speech Therapy. Expression Co., Boston, 1933.

ADDITIONAL MATERIAL FOR PRACTICE

Schoolfield, Lucille D.: Better Speech and Better Reading. Expression Co., Magnolia, 1937. This book contains many drill words, sentences and verses for each speech sound.

Stoddard, Clara B.: Sounds for Little Folks. Expression Co., Magnolia, 1940. This book contains for every English speech sound 36 pictures to illustrate familiar words which have that sound distributed equally in initial, medial, and final positions. Jingles for each speech sound are also included.

McCausland, Margaret, Miller, Marie, and *Okie, Isabel:* Speech Through Pictures. Expression Co., Boston, 1947.

S. Richard Silverman, Ph.D.
Central Institute for the Deaf

Chapter XI

EDUCATIONAL THERAPY FOR THE HARD OF HEARING: SPEECH READING

Definition

SPEECH reading is the process through which an individual, regardless of the status of his hearing, understands speech by carefully watching the speaker. Historically this process has been called "lip reading," but we have adopted the more inclusive term, "speech reading," because, as we shall see in our discussion, the latter term connotes more than observing only the lips of the speaker in order to understand speech.

Historical Development

The development of speech reading as an art and science closely parallels the history of the education of the deaf. The notion of the Greeks that the hearing of speech constituted the chief means of adding to one's "intelligence and knowledge" gave rise to the idea, which unfortunately prevailed for more than twenty centuries thereafter, that the deaf were wholly lacking in intelligence and consequently were unteachable. Furthermore, since the congenitally deaf could not express themselves through speech, deafness and dumbness (muteness)

142

came to be associated. And, if we pursue this course of poorly conceived association one step further, it is easy to understand how the word "dumb" came to imply inferior intellectual capacities. It is obvious, therefore, that speech reading as a method of communicating with the deaf could hardly flourish in such an atmosphere.

It was not until the middle of the seventeenth century that John Bulwer, an English physician, published his *Philocopus* or *The Deafe and Dumbe Man's Friend* in which he stressed the potentialities of speech reading as an eminently desirable and feasible way of expressing spoken language to the deaf. Although immediately prior to Bulwer's time sporadic attempts were made to show that the Greeks were wrong and that the deaf were educable, speech reading came in for relatively little attention. The rise of manualism and the language of signs in the latter part of the eighteenth century and in the early part of the nineteenth century, given impetus by the widespread influence of De l'Epeé and his disciples, postponed the general development of speech reading despite efforts of German educators of the deaf to popularize it.

The principles of De l'Epeé's system of manualism and the language of signs spread to America via Thomas Hopkins Gallaudet who exerted a powerful influence in their establishment in schools for the deaf. Nevertheless, shortly after the middle of the nineteenth century, with the encouragement of Samuel Gridley Howe who in a tour of the continent had been impressed by the German system of oralism and by the efforts of Mr. Hubbard, the father of Mabel Hubbard, a little deaf girl, the Clarke School for the Deaf was established at Northampton, Massachusetts, aided principally by a grant from philanthropist John Clarke. The school was committed to a program of oralism (which included speech reading) and was headed by Miss Harriet Rogers who had previously had some experience in teaching speech and speech reading to the deaf. The value of oralism was soon recognized by many educators of the deaf who previously had adopted a resolution advocating at least an opportunity for all deaf children to learn speech and speech reading. The method immediately spread to other schools aided by the prestige and encouragement of Alexander Graham Bell.

Since speech reading appeared to have value for deaf children, it was inevitable that it should be taught to the deafened adult whose hearing was so impaired that communication by auditory means was impossible or severely limited. Teachers in schools for the deaf began to instruct adults and in 1902 Martha Bruhn established in Boston a school of speech reading for adults based on the system of Julius Muller-Walle, formerly a teacher in the School for the Deaf in Hamburg, Germany. Miss Bruhn emphasized the importance of differentiating the movements of speech through syllable drills as they appeared to the speech reader. Immediately after Edward B. Nitchie founded his school of speech reading in which he stressed the importance of the psychological factors in speech reading, primarily the ability to synthesize meaning from contextual clues. In addition, Mr. Nitchie, aided by his devoted and able wife, Elizabeth Helm Nitchie, pioneered in social welfare for the hard of hearing adult. Dr. Emil Froeschels in Vienna also stressed the need for the ability to get meaning out of speech movements which were either hidden or ambiguous, teaching first only those with the help of a special phonetic alphabet. In 1917 the Kinzie sisters, Cora, Elsie and Rose, founded a school in which they attempted to combine the best features of the Muller-Walle and Nitchie systems and they also introduced the idea of speech reading material graded to various levels of difficulty. Later Professor Jacob Reighard of the University of Michigan translated the principles of Brauckmann's Jena Method into English and advocated their adoption in America. The Jena Method seeks to associate movements of speech with the process of speech reading and it has met with good success.

More recently the audio-visual-kinaesthetic method which is based on the association of hearing-vision-and feeling of movement and which stresses situational speech reading through the use of situational motion pictures has been introduced by Professor Boris Morkovin and Miss Lucelia Moore at the University of Southern California.

Speech reading has come a long way since the days of Bulwer, and it is now part of the curriculum of all schools for the deaf and it is universally recommended to hard-of-hearing adults.

The Speech Reading Process

Speech reading is essentially a psycho-physical process since it involves seeing plus the cortical integration of what is seen.

Among the more important physical factors related to the speech reading process are the following:

1. Visual factors
   a. Light—There must be sufficient light to permit visibility of the face of the speaker. Speech reading obviously cannot be practiced in the dark.
   b. Vision—The speech reader must have sufficient visual acuity.
   c. Distance—The speech reader must be close enough to the speaker to see his face, particularly his lips.
   d. Angle of vision—The angle of vision must be such that movement of the speaker's lips are not obscured.
2. Speech factors
   a. Slovenly speech—Speech which is articulated without a reasonable measure of precision is difficult to read.
   b. Sectionalisms—Unfamiliarity with sectional pronunciations rends speech reading difficult.
   c. Rate—Speech which is either too rapid or too slow is difficult to read.

d. Accent, phrasing, intonation—These factors which contribute materially to the intelligibility of speech for the hearing person are extremely difficult for the speech reader to comprehend.

e. Hidden movements—Movements such as "h" and "k" are difficult or in some instances impossible to see and they, therefore, challenge the ability of the speech reader to take advantage of contextual clues.

f. Homophenous words—These are words which look alike on the lips, such as "man" and "ban", "smell" and "spell", "baggage" and "package". Again the speech reader must rely upon contextual clues for differentiation of homophenous words or movements.

Among the more important psychological factors related to the speech reading process are the following:

1. Orientation to the situation—It is advantageous for the speech reader to be familiar with the specific situation in which he is called upon to read speech and to avail himself of situational clues.

2. Concentration—The speech reader must develop powers of concentration for long periods without fatigue in order not to be distracted from his speech reading.

3. Alertness to change—The speech reader must be alert to changes in the subject of conversation.

4. Interest and motivation—Speech reading is facilitated when the speech reader is interested in what is being said.

5. Vocabulary and language structure—Familiarity with a large vocabulary and various complex language structures is an asset to the speech reader.

6. Background of information—It is advantageous for the speech reader to have as wide a background of information as possible.

7. Emotions and sociability—The speech reader who has been guided to a wholesome and realistic understanding

of his handicap and who associates freely and voluntarily with others gives himself greater opportunity for practice in speech reading which should lead to greater proficiency.

8. Kinaesthetic and motor associations—It is helpful to the speech reader to "feel" and "move with" the speech presented to him visually.

At the present time it is not known which of the above factors or combinations of factors are of greatest relative importance in the speech reading process. It is obvious, however, that speech reading is an extremely complex and integrated process which, at the moment, is difficult to analyze. Certainly, as we said in our introduction, it involves more than merely watching movements of the lips.

METHODS OF INSTRUCTION

Methods of instruction in speech reading can generally be placed on a continuum ranging from analysis of basic movements of speech to complete dependence on synthesis of meaning derived from contextual clues. The former approach begins with the reading of simple syllables, moving progressively to words, phrases, sentences, and ultimately connected discourse. The synthetic approach emphasizes practice in the reading of connected discourse with relatively little attention focused upon individual movements or combinations of movements. The analytical approach assumes that constant repetition of syllable drills will fix recognition of individual movements in the mind of the speech reader, whenever he encounters them. The synthesist, on the other hand, recognizes the dynamics of phonetic movements and the impossibility of distinguishing some of them in certain combinations and words. He, therefore, feels that the context must in the long run reveal the speaker's meaning, and hence he emphasizes practice in the comprehension of connected discourse.

Along the continuum between the extremes of analysis and synthesis we find methods which stress the relationship among the various senses as it applies to the process of speech reading. Hearing (if any), vision, and kinaesthesia are all co-related in presenting the speech to be read. The assumption underlying this approach is that the associated process among the senses reinforces each one of them individually. For example, even partial hearing of a sound serves to buttress its visual impression. The ear, it is assumed, assists the eye and vice versa. Hearing aids and motion pictures have been found to be extremely helpful in the practice of this approach. Motion pictures, in particular, aid associations, since they set the stage for situational speech reading. The speech reader not only gets his clues from observation of the speaker's face, but also from awareness of the particular situation in which the speech is taking place. It is obvious, for example, when someone has just received a gift that he will say "Thank you." The speech reader is aware that some such response is forthcoming, having taken his clue from his knowledge of the situation.

In order to assess the merits of the various methods of instruction, it would be necessary to have available an objective, valid, and reliable test of achievement in reading. The construction of such a text presents more than the customary number of variables which must be reckoned with. Among the more significant of these variables are the degree of hearing loss, the time of onset of impaired hearing, the language ability of the speech reader, the standardization of the test material and the test conditions, the mental ability of the speech reader and the difficulty of establishing norms for a heterogeneous population. Attempts have been made by Kitson, Conklin, Nitchie, Pintner, Mason and others to develop standardized tests of ability in speech reading which have contributed materially to the solution of the problem of evaluation of various methods. Of relatively recent development is a test devised by Utley, using motion pictures, as did Mason, to standardize the presentation of test material. Utley's test shows considerable promise and its hoped for widespread use should yield valuable information to serve as a guide in future undertakings in the area of evaluation. It should also lead to development of tests for aptitude and diagnosis of particular difficulties of the individual speech reader.

Since much depends on the training, personality, and ingenuity of the teacher and on the needs and motivations of the pupil it is difficult to lay down precise dicta concerning methods of instruction. Moreover, in actual practice most experienced teachers use an eclectic method geared to the particular needs of the speech reader as they reveal themselves in the course of instruction. However, certain basic principles are applicable regardless of the predilections which a teacher may have for any method. It is generally agreed that instructional material should be interesting, that it should be designed to improve ability in speech reading and that it should be within the educational attainments of the speech reader. In addition the speech should be clearly articulated but not exaggerated and the pupil should have an opportunity to practise with many teachers of both sexes. The teacher should be cheerful and encouraging particularly to beginners, since withdrawals from speech reading classes usually take place early in the course of instruction. Wherever it is possible pupils should be instructed in groups since social growth is thereby stimulated and the pupil has an opportunity to read the lips of others. It is needless to say that the physical situation should provide for cheerful surroundings and sufficient light. The light should fall on the face of the speaker and the speech reader must not have to contend with any form of glare in his eyes. Books and pamphlets are available from the American Hearing Society and the Volta Bureau, both located in Washington, D. C. to guide in home study those who do not have access to formal instruction.

Of course, special methods of instruction must be adapted to those children whose deafness antedates the acquisition of language. Along with speech reading these children are taught the meaning of words and they are introduced to the complexities of language structure. This type of instruction requires a teacher specially trained to cope with problems of deaf children.

In the long run speech reading is both a science and an art—a science because it involves certain fundamental principles and an art because it challenges the speech reader to creatively apply these principles.

REFERENCES

American Society for the Hard of Hearing, Washington, D. C.: New Aids and Materials for Teaching Lipreading, 1943.

Brhun Martha: Muller-Walle Method of Lipreading, Nichols Press, Lynn, Mass., 1947, (Revised Edition).

Bunger, Anna M.: Speech Reading—Jena Method, Interstate Printers and Publishers, Danville, Illinois, 1944.

Conklin, E. S.: "A Method for the Determination of Relative Skill in Lip Reading," Volta Review, Vol. 19, 1917, pp. 216-219.

Davis, H. and others: Hearing and Deafness: A Guide for the Layman, Murray Hill Books, New York, 1947, (In press).

DeLand, Fred: The Story of Lip Reading, The Volta Bureau, Washington, D. C., 1931.

Froeschels, Emil: "A Lip Reading Procedure for Adults," The Volta Review, Vol. 42, No. 6, June 1940, p. 369.

Kinzie, Cora Elsie and Rose: Lipreading for the Deafened Adult, John C. Winston Co., Philadelphia, Pa., 1931.

Kitson, H. D.: "Psychological Tests for Lip Reading Ability," The Volta Review, Vol. 17, 1915, pp. 471-76.

Mason, M. K.: "A Laboratory Method of Measuring Visual Hearing Ability," The Volta Review, Vol. 34, 1932, pp. 510-514.

Mason, M. K.: "A Cinematographic Technique for Testing More Objectively the Visual Speech Comprehension of Young Deaf and Hard of Hearing Children, reprinted from Abstracts of Doctoral Dissertations, No. 36, The Ohio State University, 1942.

Nitchie, Edward B.: "Tests for Determining Skill in Lip Reading," The Volta Review, Vol. 19, 1917, pp. 222-223.

Nitchie, Edward B.: Principles and Practice of Lipreading, Frederick A. Stokes, N. Y., 1930.

Pintner, Rudolf: "Speech and Speech Reading Tests for the Deaf," American Annals of the Deaf, Vol. 74, 1929, pp. 480-486.

Stowell, Agnes, Estelle E. Samuelson, Ann Lehman: Lip-reading for the Deafened Child, MacMillan Co., N. Y., 1928.

Whilden, Olive A., M. Agatha Scally: The Newer Method in Speech Reading for the Hard of Hearing Child, Harford Printing and Publishing Company, Aberdeen, Maryland, 1939 (Revised Edition).

Utley, Jean: "A Test of Lip Reading Ability," Journal of Speech Disorders, Vol. 11, No. 2, June, 1946, pp. 109-116.

Dorothy Doob, ED.D.

Instructor, Dept. of Speech and Dramatics, Hunter College, New York.

Chapter XII

RHINOLALIA

RHINOLALIA is voice quality characterized by too little or too much nasal resonance. The term rhinolalia includes the whole problem of pathological nasality and is generally divided into two classifications: rhinolalia aperta, or hyperrhinolalia, and rhinolalia clausa, or hyporhinolalia. Some voice authorities use the term rhinolalia only to cover the whole problem. They are unaware of the two classifications and neglect to mention the clausa part of nasality, although rhinolalia clausa is described in some texts as denasalization.

Hyperrhinolalia is synonymous with the term of that nasality which is the characteristic quality caused by too great a proportion of nasal resonance. Perhaps for the sake of clarity, the particular type of "New England twang" will help to create in the reader's mind the special kind of quality I wish to discuss at first, as differentiated from other types of rhinolalia which will be presented later. It is believed that the historical development of our country might offer an explanatory background for this voice problem. "As the melting pot of the world, we have and have had in large districts, great numbers of foreign born subjects. They try to learn our tongue but re-

152

tain their old articulatory habits, with a result of unsettled adaptation to the new language. The result is a conglomeration, and insecurity of the position and functioning of the articulatory organs, particularly the lips and tongue."[1]

A second contributing factor is believed to be due to a lack of exact articulation which could be avoided by appropriate speech training especially in the early age groups where articulatory habits are formed. The contention is that because the lips and tongue are not acting with fine precision, and since all the parts are to a certain extent interdependent, the nasal quality makes itself more evident.

As previously stated, rhinolalia can be classified under two types, rhinolalia aperta, or hyperrhinolalia; and rhinolalia clausa, or hyporhinolalia. The latter should be subdivided into an anterior and a posterior form. Hyperrhinolalia as well as hyporhinolalia may be either organic or functional.

The organic causes of hyperrhinolalia may be cleft palate, a hole or holes in the hard and/or in the soft palate, paralysis of the soft palate due to an injury, disease or malformation of certain parts of the brain, or to such states within the nerves supporting the motion of the soft palate, or to an underdevelopment of the muscles themselves.

The causes of functional hyperrhinolalia are the lack of the idea of how to use the soft palate or bad habits in the use of the soft palate.

In hyporhinolalia anterior, which is always organic, there is a relative stoppage of air in the anterior part of the nose due to anatomic abnormalities, (polyps, etc.). In hyporhinolalia posterior, organic, we find the causes due to adenoid growths, or other obstructions in the naso-pharyngeal area. The functional form is due to a permanent lifting of the soft palate during speech and to simultaneous contractions of some pharyngeal muscles (also sometimes of the tongue).

It is important to know that in hyporhinolalia anterior, the vowels and nasal consonants sound like the speech of a person who during speech, plugs his nostrils, but in hyporhinolalia posterior, the nasals are markedly distorted (*m, n, ng,* are very similar to *b, d, g.*)

Bender and Kleinfeld suggest three tests to determine nasal conditions. They are simple and easy to administer and herewith are presented.[2]

    a. *Object*: To determine whether there is a free passage of breath through each nostril.

       Directions: The examiner says, "Watch what I am going to do and do the same thing after me." The examiner then holds a piece of typewriter paper so that the upper right edge is removed by three inches from the left nostril. Then holding the right nostril closed with a finger of the right hand, breath is gently forced through the left nostril for two seconds. If the breath stream is steady and unimpeded, the upper right corner of the paper will be noticeably blown. The same directions should then be demonstrated for the right nostril.

    b. *Object*: To determine whether nasal resonance is used in the production of non-nasal sounds.

       Directions: Cool a small pocket mirror by running cold water over it. Wipe it dry. Then hold it an eighth to a quarter of an inch directly below the nostrils of the examinee just before he starts talking and ask him to say, "What will you say if Jack goes to the circus?" Because none of the sounds in the sentence is a nasal sound there should be no nasal emission—and hence normally no film appears on the mirror. If there is film on the mirror, there has been nasal emission.

    c. *Object*: To determine whether nasal resonance is withheld from nasal sounds.

       Directions: Same as for nasalization tests except that the examinee is instructed to say the sentence: "Now we will run for a long time." Because there are several nasal sounds in the sentence, there should be nasal emission of breath on each nasal sound. Hence there should be a film on the mirror. If there is no film on the mirror the examinee has denasalized the sounds. (This test, of course, if positive, indicates a high degree of hyporhinolalia, while in milder cases a small film may show.)

As to the treatment, it might be well at this point to state that practically all those who discuss rhinolalia aperta (if not due exclusively to a hole in the palate) recommend exercises for the soft palate. In general, the therapy would be exercises to enable the velum to operate properly by strengthening and training. The correction of rhinolalia clausa (hyporhinolalia) functionalis consists in training the patient to lower the velum during the production of nasal sounds *m, n, ng*. This is in direct contrast to the therapy used in rhinolalia aperta or hyperrhinolalia, where the patient has to learn to elevate the velum during the production of all sounds with the exception of *m, n, ng*.

Frequently after an adenoidal operation functional hyperrhinolalia still exists and the patient continues to speak with a denasalized quality. This sometimes occurs because the audiomotor pattern of the previous pronunciation of the m, n, ng, still persists. In these cases, the speech therapist must perform careful retraining along the lines indicated.

Since the subject of cleft palate will be discussed in detail in another chapter, I shall only present a brief discussion of the deficiency and some of the therapy that has been successfully used. The speech in cleft palate causes a great alteration of speech sounds. It is a physical defect and as the term suggests, the palate or roof of the mouth is cut or cleft. The cleft may extend through the soft palate, the hard palate or both, the gum and even the upper lip, the latter causing what is known as a harelip. The defect, of course is evidenced in speech by hyperrhinolalia. The column of air entering the mouth from the rear, finding no roof in the mouth to direct its course forward through the lips, rises into the nasal cavities and the major part of the air is emitted through the nose. These cases should be referred to a physician as early as possible because very little progress can be made until the defect is remedied. Froeschels indicates that "the surgical intervention may be carried out only where there is sufficient material at hand for covering the fissure. The speech specialist in particular will indicate this only when he can be convinced that the velum palatinum to be created by the operation will be long enough to reach to the posterior pharyngeal wall, or at least nearly so."[3] Morley[4] states that the "speech result obtained by the patient with the assistance of the speech therapist will depend to a great extent on the operative result obtained by the surgeon, who in turn will be unable to see the final result of his treatment until speech re-education has been completed." It has been observed in the clinic that often when an operation has been unsuccessful as to speech, the palate has not been able to touch the posterior pharyngeal wall. Sometimes swollen turbinates in the nose have made up for this deficiency and the patient gets in part the results he should have experienced, had the operation been successful. Experience proves that the earlier the case is treated, the better the prognosis for improving the patient's speech. Once the case has been properly treated by the physician, the speech therapist can then proceed to teach the correct positions of the sounds. Most cleft palate cases have difficulty with all consonants, especially *s, t, f, k, g,* and all vowels.

In presenting some of the therapy suggested by other voice authorities, it must be remembered that there are innumerable exercises and suggestions to be found. I have, however, selected only a few which I think are helpful and not too complex to apply.

Manser[5] suggests "contracts" for overcoming various voice and speech difficulties. She presents an interesting and clear "contract sheet" for both hyperrhinolalia and hyporhinolalia. Some of the more pertinent exercises are herewith presented.

NASALITY (CONTRACT)

1. Control breathing.
2. Control of soft palate.
3. Free tone on vowels.
   Free tone on syllables, then words containing these sounds.
4. Free tone in short phrases containing these sounds.
   Free tone in sentences and selections requiring energy.
5. Free tone in selections requiring conversational tone.

For controlled breathing, it is suggested that one use the counting exercises starting from 1 to 5, using a single inhalation and gradually increasing the numbers on one breath. Though important as a fundamental requirement for all good voice quality, the exercise she suggests for the control of the soft palate is more pertinent to our subject. First the patient must locate the soft palate by pushing back the tip of the tongue until it reaches the soft surface. Then, with a mirror, have the patient look at the throat and observe the uvula which is at the end of the soft palate. With the mouth open and looking into the mirror, say the sound *a;* notice how the uvula rises (if no total paralyisis is present!) Observe how when the uvula is raised, the soft palate spreads and forms a sort of block or curtain to the nasal passage. Now the patient must form the sound with the uvula lowered. There is a noticeable difference. All sounds in English should be made with the uvula held high with the exception of the nasals *m, n,* and *ng*. It is further suggested that the student yawn and get the sensation of how the throat opens. Panting like a dog is another simple exercise which will give practice in raising and lowering the palate. Gradually, one combines consonants and vowels trying to emit the sounds directly through the mouth. When this is achieved, the patient may attempt a combination with the nasals so that he may clarify for himself the difference in tone. Phrases and sentences including nasal and non-nasal combinations are added to the list of different exercises to fulfill the contract. The last phase is the reading of a passage with sustained clear tone.

Some of the same preliminary exercises are listed for the contract on denasalization or hyporhinolalia and so I shall present only those which seem especially helpful and applicable.

Denasalization (contract)

1. Control breathing.
2. Control of soft palate.
3. Sufficient resonance on the nasal consonants *m, n,* and *ng.* (For that purpose Froeschels suggests tactile control of the nostrils with the patient's index finger slightly touching one nostril).
4. Well distributed resonance on phrases and then sentences.
5. Well distributed resonance on sight reading and finally in conversational speech.

To insure proper resonance distribution on the nasal consonants, it is suggested that the patient hold the soft palate down for the *M* and raise it for *a;* then combine with M—*a.* Combinations of words with nasals are listed, but the real objective is to consciously control the raising and lowering of the soft palate.

Several exercises are suggested for hyperrhinolalia or rhinolalia aperta by Kantner[6]. Although there are four listed, I shall present only one exercise which I feel is not too involved for the average patient to follow.

Since the main cause of hyperrhinolalia is the escaping of the air stream through the nasal cavity instead of the mouth, one of the exercises suggested is designed with this difficulty in mind. It is called the modified balloon blowing exercise. We are familiar with the therapy of balloon blowing to strengthen and develop the muscles of the soft palate. Kantner suggests a slight modification of this exercise to give it still further value. "An ordinary balloon is blown up until the air within it is under considerable pressure. This air is then allowed to flow back through the lips into the mouth cavity where it is held dammed up by the closure of the vocal folds and of the soft palate. After a brief period of holding this position, the imprisoned air can be allowed to escape explosively through the nose by relaxing the muscles of the soft palate. If the patient is unable to make a complete closure of the naso-pharyngeal opening, the imprisoned air will leak out through the nostrils, either slowly or rapidly, depending upon the opening." In such a case you can indicate to the patient that the exercises serve as a clear demonstration of his lack of control. The author suggests that the exercises should not be practiced if there is evidence of a cold.

Because my first three case histories include other deficiencies in addition to hyperrhinolalia, I shall first present a classification of six types of voice hyperfunction according to Froeschels.[7]

First the hyperfunction of the muscles for closing the glottis, sometimes called the glottal stop. Second, the type called self-strangulation in which there is hypercontraction of the lower part of the pharyngeal cavity due to hyperfunction of some of the pharyngeal constrictors. Third, the hollow type of voice quality, sometimes called the "hot potato" speech, where the listener gets the impression of some mass obstructing the throat, which is due to a retraction of the back of the tongue to the pharyngeal wall. Fourth, the hypercontraction of the soft palate producing voice resembling a denasalized quality. Froeschels differentiates between this type of voice appearing only temporarily, and the permanent state of palatal hyperfunction known as functional rhinolalia clausa or functional hypo-rhinolalia. Fifth, voice quality affected by the stiffening of the anterior part of the tongue. Sixth, voice quality affected by the stiffening of the lips, sometimes characteristic of certain types of affected stage speech.

Since the major portion of the therapy I have used in over-coming hyperrhinolalia concerns itself with the "pushing" and "chewing" exercises, it seems appropriate to present the theory and concept as evolved by Froeschels. See Chapter XV.

To confirm the success of the above therapy, I should like to present three cases where hyperrhinolalia and hyperfunction of the voice were marked symptoms.

Case I. A young woman, E.F. about thirty-six years of age complained of her voice being tired continually, and also un-pleasantly nasal in quality. She had had these conditions as long as she could remember. At school, and later at college, she had been criticized for a whiny, nasal voice but had not been given any therapy to overcome it. She had been told to relax her voice by yawning and to place her voice forward. At the time of the interview, she held a position as a clerk in a city court. She also taught English to foreigners in evening school. After using her voice for a short time, she stated she could not be heard in the rear of the classroom, and it became tired and even more nasal in quality. She admitted that her real ambition in life was to become a school teacher. Recently, she had taken a written examination to qualify as a teacher in the grade schools and she now wished to prepare for the next part of the test which was a careful appraisal of her voice and speech. She was frankly worried that she would not qualify because of her poor inadequate voice. A diagnosis indicated marked hyper-rhinolalia and a hyperfunction of the self-strangulation type described on page 159. An explanation of the chewing method was carefully given to the patient. She came faithfully once a week for three months. Within a few lessons she had mastered the concept of chewing and began to chew syllables and short phrases. The hyperfunction gradually disappeared with only occasional errors noted at ends of sentences where the voice would break and have unpleasant quality. By the end of the third month, the hyperrhinolalia had disappeared (because in chewing the soft palate rises strongly) and the patient was discharged. The young lady incidentally passed her oral examination and is now holding a regular teaching position in the elementary schools of New York City.

Case II. A student G.H., twenty years of age entered my special speeech clinic course in September 1946. Her voice indicated a marked hyperrhinolalia and in addition a voice hyperfunction. Upon questioning, I learned the following data. She had her tonsils and adenoids removed when five years of age. There was no evidence of any voice change at that time though she had been continually criticized for high pitch both in elementary school and later in high school. One teacher stated that she had noticed frequent nasality. The patient complained of colds and admitted that she suffered from laryngitis regularly twice a year, sometimes completely losing her voice for a period of a week to ten days. During her first speech course at college, she was again criticized for abnormally high pitch, immature voice and marked nasality. Because of these deficiencies she was referred to my special speech clinic for remedial treatment. After a brief but careful explanation of the chewing therapy, we began the treatment. Almost immediately her pitch was lowered to its normal level. It took her almost two weeks to understand the actual concept of the therapy and apply it to her own speech, first in nonsense sounds and then in phrases. Within two months the hoarseness practically disappeared and almost all evidences of hyperrhinolalia were gone. The entire treatment lasted three and one half months, the student came twice a week and was discharged at the end of this period of time.

In addition to the chewing therapy for voice deficiencies as
well as for hyperrhinolalia, Froeschels has set up a series of
pushing exercises.[8] These exercises have been unusually successful in a variety of speech and voice deficiencies with hyperrhinolalia, also after operation of cleft palate and in cases of organic paralysis of the soft palate. In the following two cases this
therapy was used with excellent results.

These exercises consist of pushing down briskly both arms
with closed fists inward and towards the front of the thighs
beginning at about the height of the nipples. While the patient
says a single vowel or syllable the sounds are produced simultaneously with the arm movements. The patient must be careful not to emit the sound either before or after the pushing
movement, but simultaneously with it. Gradually, the patient
begins to learn to push at the beginning of a word and later a
phrase. The effect is noticed in the sounds that follow the downward thrust of the arms. By degrees, the patient learns to emit
the sounds without the physical movement by keeping the concept of the pushing in his mind. (This exercise should be performed 10 to 20 times a day, for about 30 seconds each time.)

Case III. B.D. was a student in my story telling course as well
as in a special voice course for prospective teachers. She was
interested in a radio career as well as becoming a teacher of
speech in the high schools. She was eighteen years old and
rather frail looking. In the first course, I noticed that her voice
was pitched very high and there was in addition to hyperrhinolalia, a marked waste of breath. The voice projection was inadequate. The radio instructor when testing her voice for
recording also criticized her for nasality and breathiness. Until
her entrance into these courses, she could recall no criticism of
her voice in either elementary or high school. She had always
been cast for leading parts in plays and seemed to make herself
heard without difficulty. Previous to her entrance into the voice
course, she had taken a six weeks intensive course in theatre

during the summer. She was cast in a play in which her characterization demanded a high, whiny voice and a rapid tempo in speaking. She rehearsed steadily for four weeks. The concentration upon this quality of voice only intensified her deficiencies so that by the end of this period, she possessed a marked hyperrhinolalia and an abnormally high pitch. Upon further questioning, she stated that an older brother did speak with some degree of nasality, but she did not believe that she had subconsciously followed his pattern of voice quality. First, we proceeded with an explanation of the chewing therapy. Again it was immediately noticeable that her pitch dropped to its norm. To eliminate the hyperrhinolalia, we used the pushing exercises. After three weeks of this therapy, there was a definite improvement. She practiced her chewing and pushing exercises conscientiously and the results were gratifying. The student attended class three times a week for three and one half months. Her last voice recording indicated normal pitch and almost complete absence of nasality.

The chewing brings the muscles into the optimal condition and therefore also serves the purpose of diminishing overcontractions which are present in cases of functional hyporhinolalia. Experience shows that in loud chewing the normal nose resonance which is missing in such cases, appears instantly if the patient chews meaninglessly. The effect can then gradually be transferred to meaningful chewing; that is to say, in words, phrases and finally sentences. The last case I wish to illustrate is one in which marked hyperrhinolalia was caused by paralysis of the soft palate and in which the pushing exercises were employed with unusual success.

Case IV. P.R. entered the Speech Clinic at Mt. Sinai Hospital in September 1946. He was five and one half years old. He could utter practically no normal sounds and those he emitted came only through the nose and were for the most part unintelligible. Upon examination, it was discovered that he had a high degree of paralysis of the soft palate. The pushing exercises were carefully explained to him and to his mother. Instructions and a demonstration were given as to how to perform them. The therapy was begun immediately, starting with the vowel *a*. In a few weeks he was shown a blowing exercise. He was asked to blow up a balloon and to get the feel of air emission through the mouth. He was also shown how to blow up his cheeks and release the air gradually and then open his mouth. A month later, he learned to massage his own soft palate very gently with his little finger. Now, the therapy began to include some new sounds. The consonants taught were *b, k, v*, and *l*, and, then gradually combined with a vowel, We were careful to observe that when combined with a vowel, the sounds were always emitted through the mouth. The patient has come twice a week and has practiced the pushing exercises faithfully at home. Steady improvement has been noted, the sounds learned are clearer and intelligible. Four months later for the first time, we were able to see some slight movement of the paralysed soft palate. Within the last month we have worked on the alveolar consonants especially *t* and *n* which seem to be most difficult to him. The pushing exercises will be continued and as clarity improves new consonants and vowels will be added. The prognosis is encouraging and it is our hope that the child will eventually speak with almost normal voice quality.

In conclusion, it is my belief that the cases illustrated in this chapter conclusively prove the effectiveness of the chewing therapy and the pushing exercises in connection with the different voice deficiencies indicated.

REFERENCES

1. *A. Bullen:* "Nasality: Cause and Remedy of our American Blight," Quarterly Journal of Speech, Feb. 1942, pp. 83-84.
2. *J. F. Bender and V. M. Kleinfeld:* Principles and Practices of Speech Correction, Pitman Publishing Corp., 1938, p. 48. New York.
3. *E. Froeschels:* Speech Therapy, Expression Company, Boston, Mass. 1933, p. 137.
4. *M. E. Morley:* Cleft Palate and Speech, The Williams and Wilkins Co., Baltimore, Md. 1945, p. VIII.
5. *R. H. Manser:* A Manual of Speech Correction on the Contract Plan, Prentice Hall, Inc. New York, 1938.
6. *C. Kantner:* "Four Devices in the Treatment of Rhinolalia Aperta," Journal of Speech Disorders, 1937, Vol. 2, p. 73.
7. *E. Froeschels:* Hygiene of the Voice, Archives of Otolaryngology, N. Y. August 1943, Vol. XXXVIII, pp. 122-130.
8. *E. Froeschels and A. Jellinek:* Practice of Voice and Speech Therapy, Expression Company, Boston, Mass. 1941, p. 236.

EUGENE SCHORR, M.D., D.D.S.
New York.

Chapter XIII

CLEFT PALATE

A. Surgery

EMBRYOLOGY

IN order to understand the malformations of the face, we must study its developmental anatomy and the way in which it is formed between the third and ninth week of fetal life.

At approximately the third week two thickened epithelial layers appear on the projecting surface of the brain above the primitive oral fossa. These layers are the olfactory placodes which later become depressed as olfactory pits. These pits are separated by a tissue called the frontonasal process which in the fourth week forms the upper boundary of the oral fossa. The opening of the fossa is surrounded laterally by 2 maxillary processes and below by 2 mandibular arches. These maxillary processes grow ventrally and later unite with the median and lateral processes. The mandibular processes fuse in the fifth week medially while the lower part of the frontonasal process divides itself between the pits into two lateral nasal processes and one median nasal process. Figs. 1 and 2.

166

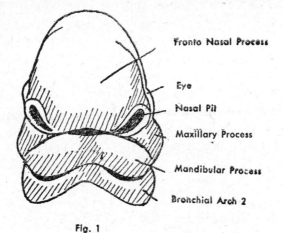

Fronto Nasal Process

Eye

Nasal Pit

Maxillary Process

Mandibular Process

Bronchial Arch 2

Fig. 1

DEVELOPMENT OF THE HUMAN FACE
(Adapted After Peter)

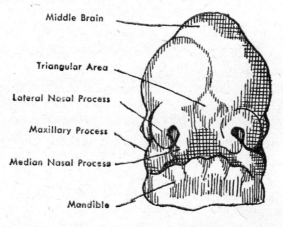

Middle Brain

Triangular Area

Lateral Nasal Process

Maxillary Process

Median Nasal Process

Mandible

Fig. 2

DEVELOPMENT OF THE HUMAN FACE
(Adapted After Peter)

The lateral nasal processes form the side and wings of the nose. From the median process 2 globular processes project out of which the following structures originate: the philtrum and the os incisivum or premaxilla. From the median process comes the septum. The palate has its origin in two folds which stretch from the maxillary processes towards the midline becoming fused in the ninth week starting from the front portion backward. If these processes do not unite or become incompletely coalesced, facial defects result, the causes and types of which we may now investigate.

Cause and Types of Cleft Palate

It is generally accepted, that the cause of cleft palate is inherited through recessive genes. It is held by some that malnutrition or infection is responsible; others blame intrauterin conditions such as pressure of the knees against the maxilla or those particular amniotic bands in the median cleft of the nose or lip.

The ordinary clefts which we observe occur generally between structures of normal development. There are, however, cases in which the maxillary processes are not normal: 1, when the individual shows other congenital defects and 2, when otherwise normal processes are combined with underdeveloped structures, as found in some forms of double hare lip. Here are organs single in their anlage, undersized as the premaxilla, philtrum and septum.

Because of their rarity it is unnecessary to discuss such anomalies as the median cleft and oblique cleft, in which no union has taken place between the median nasal process or maxillary process with the frontonasal process. The most common deformity is the single hare lip or cheiloschisis which is usually found on the left side. This condition is often complicated by a cleft in the bony parts, when the maxillary and median nasal processes have not coalesced. The next most common type is the double hare lip. Such cases in which this condition is complicated by a palatal cleft and projecting premaxilla are known as wolf snout.

ANATOMY AND PHYSIOLOGY

Before we enter into a description of the measures we are taking to help these unfortunate children, it is advisable to make some remarks about anatomy and physiology. We may best understand our goal in cleft palate if we compare our knowledge of these sciences with our experiences with the above mentioned anomalies.

The palatal muscles form a functional unit with the pharynx muscles and they are connected anatomically, functioning together at the beginning of the swallowing act.

The velum is attached to the hard palate by the palatal aponeurosis and by the continuous mucous covering. Directly under the surface of the velum in the midline is the azygus muscle, which starts at the posterior nasal spine and ends in the uvula. This muscle shortens the uvula; two other muscles originating partly in the palatal aponeurosis, partly at the pterygoid hamulus, and partly at the cartilagenous region of the Eustachian tube, form the anterior and posterior faucial pillars. These are known as: 1, the palatoglossal muscle which blends into the transversal muscle of the tongue; and 2, the palatopharyngeal muscle which spreads into the longitudinal muscles of the pharynx. The former holds the velum against the tongue during respiration and aids the latter muscle in forming the closure of the faucial isthmus. The palate contains also the tensor palatae muscle which arises from the region between the external and internal pterygoid plates of the sphenoidal bone. This muscle has in addition some inserting fibers on the external membranaceous wall of the Eustachian tube. Its tendon turns over the hamulus and ends in the palatal aponeurosis. The tensor opens the tube at the swallowing act and tightens the aponeurosis converting this tissue into a fixed point for all muscles inserting in it. The levator palatae muscle has its origin in the pyramidal process of the temporal bone. Its attachment goes far back to the proximity of the caroticus canal. The course of this muscle is inward and downward, approaching the inner surface of the tensor muscle and ending partly in the aponeurosis. Its major part blends with the corresponding muscle of the other side in the form of a sling. Its function is to shut off the entrance to the nasal cavity. The three constrictor muscles of the pharynx are not synchronically innervated; their continuous contraction is coordinated by their innervation. The result of this contraction is the formation of the Passavant pad by the pterygo-pharyngeal muscle which is the highest part of the superior constrictor muscle. The insertions of the pharyngeal muscles are fixed in the middle of the pharynx. When they contract a projecting ring is formed.

For the sake of completeness it may be said that the superior constrictor ends as cephalopharyngeus muscle on the sides of the head, the middle constrictor on the hyoid and the inferior muscle on the larynx. The closure of the nasopharynx is thus produced by the sphincterlike contractions of the pterygo-pharyngeal muscle, the levators, the palatoglossal and palato-pharyngeal muscles. Marcus Hajek proved that such cases in which the Passavant pad is not built up by these muscles, lateral contractions close the nasopharynx. The contact with the Passavant pad prevents the entering of food and air into the nose from the rear.

Man is born with two phenomena of coordination: breathing and sucking. For both phenomena certain muscles are innervated which are already coordinated. The cleft palate child cannot regulate its respiration and even if the child breathes through the nose, the air is not warmed up and falls quickly into the mouth. In a normal child the air meets resistance in the cover of the turbinated bones. This resistance makes the respiratory muscles strong. In the cleft palate child there is no resistance, since the air is sucked into the mouth; as a result this child has not proper training of its muscles.

The faulty vault of the hard palate does not assist in influencing the quality of voice and causes the function of sucking and mastication to be difficult.

Let us remember when the normal child sucks at the breast a coordination of the lip, tongue and mandibular muscles takes place. In the enunciation of certain sounds this identical innervation also comes into action. The breast-fed child sucks the milk out of the nipple in such a manner that the mandible uses the maxilla as resistance, pressing down the nipple in sliding over it. By doing this, it stimulates the future speech muscles into physiological activity. In the case of a normal bottle-fed child it presses its tongue against the palatal surface and squeezes milk out of the nipple, creating no muscular activity. The cleft palate child, however, cannot suck or press like a normal child. It is spoon-fed or nourished by suction plates or special teats. Feeding is difficult and the child is exposed to manifold dangers, even to the loss of its life. The disfiguration of the face and all these dangers make professional assistance imperative.

Time of Operation

Medicine took over the task given it by the inexplicable deviations in nature to create the proper condition for normal function of life. It is essential that an operation should be undertaken before speech habits have been formed before the end of the second year, at which age the bone is easily molded. Normal function is initiated when all structures have been correctly placed and the way paved for natural reflexes. The child will not acquire false habits of speech and thus may be saved from an eventual inferiority complex. Finally and of utmost importance is the elimination of all the dangers which jeopardize the child's life.

OPERATION OF HARELIP

It is impossible to pay due respect to all the splendid names who have made excellent contributions in this work. This anomaly has offered enough food for thought and a wide field of action for the skillful surgeon. Cleft palates are of different types and so is their treatment. And within the types no two cases are alike and so are the modifications of their correction. The objective of all surgical procedures. is the paring of the borders of the cleft, their union and holding together by suturing. That is rather easy with the correction of the single harelip. We have to see that no shrinking occurs and that with exact union the two tissues namely mucous membrane and skin meet in continuous line. That goal is reached by curved, angular or combined incisions technically worked out by Veau, Graefe, Nelaton, Malgaigne, Mirault, Blair, Ivy and Hudson Rose. The operation of Rose is simple and popular. He chooses curved incisions and removes from each side of the cleft semi-oval shaped pieces. The cuts are carried through the widest part of the vermilion border. The nasal alae are sutured, the flaps turned down and the margins of the vermillion exactly united. Figs. 3 and 4.

HUDSON-ROSE TYPE OF OPERATION

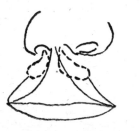

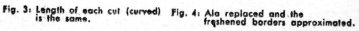

Fig. 3: Length of each cut (curved)   Fig. 4: Ala replaced and the
       is the same.   freshened borders approximated.

The real difficult part in these corrections is the repair of the flattened nostrils. Teachings of Brown, Mirault, Blair and Ivy are helpful. The essential procedure is to mobilize the base of the columella and nasal mucosa, to rotate the axis of the nostril, to adjust the alae and suturing of the floor.

We must relieve in all lip operations the lateral tension. The simplest and most efficient way is the application of the Logan bow.

The same principle as in single harelip is used in bilateral harelip, provided the philtrum has its normal length. The difficulty starts with the underdeveloped philtrum which is seen in most cases. In the correction the lips and the whole vermilion border of the prolabium are cut and flaps from each side are united to form the middle part of the upper lip. Figs. 5 and 6

OPERATION FOR DOUBLE HARELIP (After Ivy)

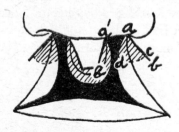 

Fig. 5

Fig. 6

Fig. 5: Tissue within the cuts (c, d, a) and border of the Prolabium removed.

Fig. 6: Completed operation.

show the standard procedure adopted by Ivy and Curtis. The premaxilla, however, is the real problem. A moderate prominent premaxilla is pushed back with digital pressure and kept in place by the lip, which is corrected in the first stage. If the intermaxillary bone projects too far and is attached only to the end of the vomer, the procedure is different. The bone is first replaced operatively and the lip repaired later. Bardeleben, Ivy and Pichler to mention a few names remove wedges from the vomer submucously and press the premaxilla to its normal position. Vaughan fixes the bone by a wire pulled through an area where no tooth buds are over the canine fossa. There are cases where the septum is lower than the borders of the cleft. Pichler in these cases elevates mucoperiostal flaps from the vomer and sutures the flaps under the elevated mucoperiostal margins of the front part of the cleft.

Closure of the Cleft in the Hard and Soft Palate

The principle for the palatal closure was worked out by Langenbeck and is still with some modifications the standard operation. Lateral incisions, parallel to the teeth are made through the palatal tissue down to the bone. The incisions start near the hamulus avoiding the palatal artery and are carried forward to the region of the cuspids. Mucoperiostal flaps are raised as far to the margin of the cleft. Its borders are freshened and sutured together. Figs. 7 and 8 illustrate the operation after Langenbeck modified by Pichler. Eventual failures are due to shrinking of the velum or ear trouble if the lateral cuts damage the levator muscle.

OPERATION AFTER LANGENBECK MODIFIED BY PICHLER

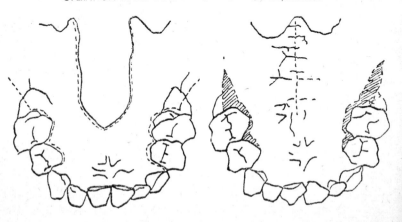

Fig. 7   Fig. 8

Lane recommends his operation in infants. He modified the method of Davies-Colley. A flap is turned over from one side to the other palatal half to bridge over the gap. Fig. 9. Failure may result in necrosis of the flap which is almost beyond correction.

OPERATION AFTER LANE

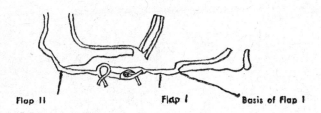

Flap II   Flap I   Basis of Flap I

Fig. 9

Brophy met strong opposition with his famous operation. But he had ardent followers too. The writer saw many cases operated with splendid results. The opponents claim damage to the tooth buds, retrusion and narrowing of the maxilla. Brophy closes the hard palate by twisting several wires over lead plates. The soft palate is closed at a second operation. Figs. 10 and 11.

BROPHY OPERATION

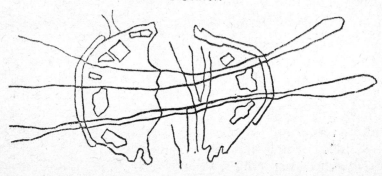

Fig. 10

Indicates insertion of silver wires through Maxilla and lead plates

BROPHY OPERATION

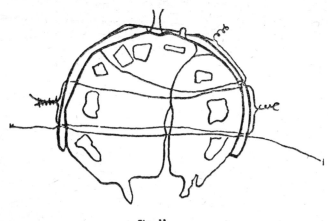

Fig. 11

Maxilla approximated by tightening the wires.

Ulrich compressed the palate by clamping, a procedure no longer in use. Warren Davis, Mears and Brown modified the old Ferguson operation and had remarkable results. The horizontal part of the palate with this soft tissue is detached from the maxillary process and moved medially. The suture is performed at the time the soft palate is closed.

LENGTHENING OF THE SOFT PALATE

One cannot expect good function if the palatal tissue is either poor in substance or shrunk following an operation. It is therefore obvious that attempts have been made to obtain better velo-pharyngeal closure.

Passavant tried to lengthen the palate and many famous surgeons followed him. Just a few names should be mentioned. They are Blakeway, Gillies, Veau, Ganzer, Billroth, Rosenthal, Wardill, Denis Brown and Dorrance. Dorrance's "push back" operation is today most popular. He mobilizes first the whole palatal tissue, raises and sutures it loosely back to be certain of adequate blood supply. The flaps are elevated at a second operation, pushed back to the posterior end of the palate and fixed by sutures. Hereby the cleft is closed. Figs. 12 and 13.

DORRANCE PUSH BACK OPERATION (I. B. Brown)

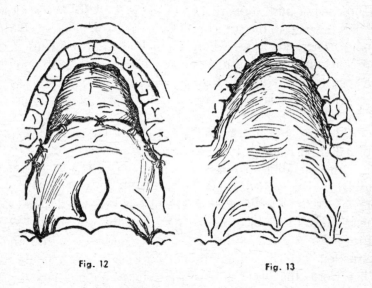

Fig. 12   Fig. 13

Fig. 12: First Act: The entire soft tissue is raised and pushed back and loosely sutured.

Fig. 13: Completed operation.

But there are cases, where no plastic operation can be performed or where failures occur after operation. Then we must resort to obturators which should replace the missing tissues for the physiological function.

ORTHODONTIC TREATMENT

Cleft palate is not very suitable for orthodontic treatment. The alveolar processes are movable and do not allow retention. Langenbeck and Brophy recognized this disadvantage and pleaded therefore for bony union. We can, however, apply orthodontics profitably to a certain class of cases. All that is needed is knowledge of how and when the work in question should be used. The orthodontist is able to retract a protruded premaxilla or push forward a retracted premaxilla. With adults he is a big help to the surgeon, if he narrows preoperatively the arches. There are cases where tooth buds and teeth are lost. Space retainers or small movements of the teeth may become a blessing for the child. Every surviving or duly restored tooth is an asset, especially in cases where the use of obturators is indicated.

Pichler stresses also the following point. The mandible in a normal child changes its position twice in embryonic life. At birth the mandible lies behind the maxilla. The cleft palate child has a very wide maxilla, its width is enlarged by the pressure of the lower jaw. If the child is not operated upon, the lower molars and bicuspids erupt lingually and this is combined with a distal occlusion of the mandible. In this malformation there is a slight mesio-occlusion of the maxilla. In other words the distance between velum and pharynx is enlarged. Here is a field where the orthodontist has an opportunity to be of service.

REFERENCES

1. *Arey, Leslie Brainerd:* Developmental Anatomy. W. B. Saunders Co., Philadelphia and London, 1945.
2. *Blair, Vilray P.:* The Why and How of Harelip Correction. Annals of Otology, Rhinology and Laryngology, 37; 196, 1928.
3. *Blair-Ivy:* Essentials of Oral Surgery. The C. V. Mosby Co., 1936, St. Louis.
4. *Brophy, T. W.:* Cleft Lip and Palate. Philadelphia, Blakiston Co., 1923.
5. *Dorrance, G. M.:* The Operation Stages of Cleft Palate.
6. *Davis, W. B.:* Ann. Surg. 87; 536. 1928.
7. *Federspeel M. N.:* Harelip and Cleft Palate. The C. V. Mosby Co., 1927, St. Louis.
8. *Ivy, R. H. and Curtis, L.:* Procedure in Cleft Palate Surgery, experience with the Veau and Dorrance Technic: Ann. Surg. 100: 502. 1934.
9. *Langenbeck Bernard, R. K. von:* Operation der angeborenen totalen Spaltung des harten Gaumens nach einer neuen Methode. Deutsche Klinik 8, 231, 1861.
10. *Lane, W. A.:* Cleft Palate and Harelip. London Medical Publishing Co., 1908.
11. *Pichler Hans:* Angeborene Lippen und Gaumenspalten. Scheff-Pichler Handbuch fuer Zahnheilkunde. Dritter Band. Hoelder-Pichler-Tempsky, A. G. Wien/Leipzig, 1927.
12. *Rosenthal, W.:* Zentralblatt fuer Chir. 51; 1621, 1924.
13. *Schorr, Eugene:* Sigmatism and Malposition of Teeth, A. J. of Orthod. and Oral Surg., St. Louis, vol. 25, pp. 1143-46, Dec. 1939.
14. *Vaughan, Harold Stearns:* Congenital Cleft Lip. Lea & Fiebiger, Philadelphia 1940.
15. *Veau, V.:* La Division Palatine, Paris, 1931, Masson et Cie.
16. *Wardill, W. E. M.:* Brit. J. Surg. 16:127, 1928-1929.

EMIL FROESCHELS, M.D.

President, International Society for Speech and Voice Science;
President, New York Society of Voice and Speech Therapy.

Chapter XIV

PROSTHETIC THERAPY OF CLEFT PALATE

Logopedic Contemplations Regarding the Construction of a Special Type of Obturator Against Hyper-Rhinolalia in Cases of Cleft Palate. (Meatus-Obturator)

IN order to understand hyperrhinolalia (open nasality) it is essential to possess knowledge of the physiology of sounds. Sounds consist partly of tones and partly of noises, that is, rhythmic and arrhythmic resp. oscillations of air. The former are caused by rhythmic movements of the vocal cords, while the latter are usually due to the fact that the articulatory air meets with and surmounts obstacles between the vocal cords, or in the resonance chamber (pharynx, mouth, nose). A mixture of surplus air with the sound is also a source of noises; in these cases exhalation exceeds the requirements of the volume of the sound. The obstacles are mainly closures or narrow passages; and so when the air is instantaneously released through the closure, a plosive results (B P T D K G); when it merely passes through a narrow passage, the fricative results—(F WH SH). Both plosives and fricatives are voiced or voiceless.—The obstructions in the resonance chamber also function in another way. They modify the tone and they do so in different ways. When a sound wave passes from one medium to a medium of

180

different density, a *reaction* consisting of the reflection of the waves into the first medium occurs. Such reflections occur from the walls of the resonance chamber, f.i. the tongue, its roots as well as other parts, the teeth etc., obstructing the path. It may happen that the reflected wave neutralizes part of the originally generated wave (*interference*). The direction in which a sound wave is reflected is determined by the direction in which the wave hits the reflecting medium. It is easy to visualize this process by observing the manner in which a billiard ball rebounds from the wall of the billiard table. *Reflection is one of the most essential components of the so-called "direction of tones,"* (f.i. a tone trending toward the skull, or a tone going strictly into the chest). Let us first consider some phenomena which are based on resonance. By this term physicists understand the intensification of a tone through the transmission of the vibrations of one (oscillating) body onto another body; the more numerous the oscillating particles, the greater the volume. The resonating bodies oscillate only as long as the oscillator does. All these phenomena may easily be studied through means of the Helmholtz resonator; these are spherical hollow bodies of various dimensions possessing two apertures, opposite each other; one of them is equipped with an ear-olive by means of which the resonating body can be connected with the ear. An oscillator (for example a tuning fork) is attached to the second opening and when a tone is produced to which that particular resonator is tuned, it resonates. Also adjacent tones and primarily the octave cause resonance although producing lesser volume. There are numerous hollow and compact parts in the human body which function as resonators. The entire resonating chamber (mouth, pharynx, nose), as far as it consists of cavities, and also its compact elements, soft parts, and bones and walls, and the sinuses of the nose, are all apt to be brought to resonance through certain tones created by the vocal cords; the trachea and the bronchial system[1] can be affected in the same way; the thoracic walls and even the extremities can be used as resonators in the production of certain tones. In fact, while highly trained singers produce a fully developed tone of medium high pitch, we can feel their fingers vibrate. Among the above mentioned parts of the body there are some adjustable in form, and others unchangeable. To the former group belong the mouth cavity and the larynx; to the latter the nose, the nasal sinuses, the skull, etc.

In order to realize the importance of the resonance for the human voice we would do well to bear in mind the vocal theory of Helmholtz which has been confirmed and completed by Stumpf². (See Chapter I).

The tone produced by the singing voice is a vowel or a voiced consonant. It is assumed that vowels differ from consonants in that the former contain tones, the latter tones and noises. Although it is true that we can always find noises in consonants, vowels are by no means always free from noises. In fact, lack of noise is the property of vowels only when produced by great artists; otherwise there are always noises in the tone. By this we do not mean the noises caused by "surplus air" only, but all those which come under the heading of "Hot Potato," "Squeezing," "Squeaking," etc. We will disregard these voice disorders however, and concern ourselves solely with the perfectly produced vowel. This, as we said before, in addition to the lowest tone (keynote) must contain a certain number of overtones. The number of overtones varies according to the vowel, and the pitch of the keynote. Where and how are they produced? They can only be produced by the vocal cords, since no other tone-generator exists in the speech organ of the human body.*

The shape of the pharynx and the mouth cavity can be considerably changed through contraction of certain pharyngeal muscles, approximation or deviation—of the palatine arches,

---

*We disregard the tones produced by whistling through the lips as they have no direct bearing on the subject.

raising and lowering of the soft palate, retraction or protrusion, raising or lowering of the tongue, and movements of the lower jaw and the lips. *Such changes of form not only create reso-nators for different tones, but also influence the conditions of reflection.* It is in this manner (reflection) only that "the tone," that is the aggregation of keynote and overtones at one given place, can be guided into different directions. When we bear in mind the fact that the direction in which the sound waves hit an obstacle, determines the direction in which they are re-flected, we shall readily understand that it is by no means in-consequential for the course they take, whether the tongue lies flat or is raised, or whether the soft palate is greatly arched or moderately raised, etc.

We know that in all sounds in the English language except M, N, NG, the air escapes through the mouth physiologically as the passage into the nose is obstructed by the elevation of the soft palate and the protrusion of the pterygopharyngeal muscle of the pharyngeal wall (Passavant's pad). When closure can-not be achieved, air penetrates into the nose during the produc-tion of all sounds, thus considerably distorting speech. This condition is called hyper-rhinolalia or open nasality although this term in no way explains the peculiar acoustic phenomena which are characteritic of this speech disorder.

In the 1945 *Year Book of Dentistry*[3] six types of cleft palate are distinguished from each other: "Class first, azygos; class two, uvula; class three, soft palate; class four, soft and hard palate; class five, soft and hard palate through the alveolar ridge, at the junction of the maxilla and premaxilla, usually accompanied by cleft lip on the same side; class six, soft and hard palate through the alveolar ridge, involving both sides of the maxilla and freeing the premaxillary bone, and usually ac-companied by a double cleft lip. The last four types are those in which treatment is sought, especially to correct speech diffi-culties."

I frequently asked myself why a mouth with a high gothic palate which closely resembles a mouth communicating with the nose due to cleft palate, never produces a phenomenon similar to hyperrhinolalia, and I am now convinced that the *meatuses* are responsible for the hyperrhinolalia; the shape of the actual nasal cavity varies only slightly from the mouth cavity, *but the mouth lacks similar canals.* It is therefore the peculiar type of resonators, namely the meatuses, which is responsible for the difference in sounds.

Before stating some conclusions about the relation between the meatuses and the hyperrhinolalia I want to quote Schalit[4] in order to remind the reader of the most frequently used forms of obturators: "Suersen chose for his palatal closure a hard rubber clot (Fig. 1) which he put into rigid contact with the pal-

FIG. 1

ate plate. The clot was as large in size so as to almost make it touch the so-called Passavant's pad. The clot then rose along the posterior pharyngeal wall as far as the torus tubarius upon which pressure was to be exerted. For breathing and nasal sounds only a small slit was left open when the pharyngeal muscles were relaxed. The Suersen obturator has the disadvantage of being too heavy and of being applicable only in cases of open cleft palate. If after an operative attempt at closing the cleavage the soft palate is too short to reach the posterior wall of the pharynx this obturator cannot be applied. The Schiltsky obturator[5] (Fig. 2) remedies this inconvenience. It consists of

FIG. 2

a hollow, air-inflated rubber clot which is attached to a palate plate by means of a spiral—or a band-spring. This obturator has great advantages over the Suersen obturator: the compression with each muscular movement; the low weight and, last but not least, the slight demand upon the supporting teeth. The high rate of decomposition of the rubber, however, causes new inconveniences. It was Warnekros who proved that the height and depth of the rigid obturator of Suersen could be considerably reduced (Fig. 3) if the rubber ball is required to

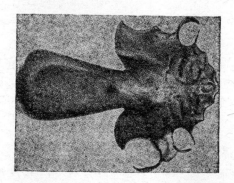

FIG. 3

close the cleft which remains after the *complete* Passavant pad has been formed. Warnekros also succeeded in constructing the

Schiltsky obturator for the too short velum rigidly of hard rubber (Fig. 4). In cases of good flexibility of the velum remnants Warnekros equips his obturator with a hinge (Fig. 5) or a

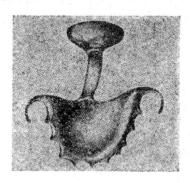

FIG. 4

FIG. 5

spiral spring so as to put this flexibility to its best advantages."

The 1945 *Year Book of Dentistry* distinguishes three main types of fixed obturators: "Solid obturator, Kingsley obturator and Fitz-Gibbon speech appliance. The solid obturator closes the defect by fitting into the nasopharynx and, by its walls, maintaining contact with the divided velum at all stages of phonation and deglutition. The Kingsley type has a flange contacting the divided velum, the portion attached to the palate being made of soft vulcanic rubber. The Fitz-Gibbon type is an all-metal appliance composed of a palatal plate, a tail piece that corresponds to the normal soft palate at rest and the bulb at the tail piece whereby palatal function is simulated.

"The movable, or pinlock hinge obturator is composed of the palatal portion, pinlock hinge and artificial velum. A vomer portion may or may not be included. This type is indicated only when an adequate flexible palato-pharyngeal musculature remains. A temporary type may be constructed for children, whose jaws are changing and who have few if any permanent teeth for clasping. This appliance consists of the palatal portion and clasps and must be adjusted or renewed periodically. A permanent type, to use after development has stopped consists of movable parts that close off the two cavities in speech and deglutition, the velum being hugged and lifted by remnants of functioning palatal muscles until its posterior border contacts Passavant's pad."

However, experience has proved that none of these different obturators improves the speech-defect in the majority of cases.

I attempted in cases of uranoschism to plug the meatuses with cotton and in doing so achieved an immediate change of the sound. The hyper-rhinolalia disappeared without damage to the nasal sounds (M, N, NG), and in some cases even changed into a hypo-rhinolalia (rhinolalia-clausa or "speech with clogged nose"). *Thus, my hope to attain proof that hyper-rhinolalia had its seat in a place other than that of the physiological nasality (M, N, NG) seemed fulfilled,* and new ways were opened for treatment through obturators. I therefore believed that a new approach must be made. If the rigid obturators heretofore in use, are made to achieve perfection of the non-nasal sounds, that is, when they are extended to reach the posterior pharyngeal wall, the patient will be unable to pronounce the nasal sounds (M, N, NG) and will be hindered in breathing through the nose. If, on the other hand, sufficient space is left to allow the air to enter the nose during the production of nasal sounds, non-nasal sounds too, will have a hyperrhinolalic quality unless the muscles of the pharyngeal wall during the pronunciation of the non-nasal sounds reach the obturator, which they rarely do.

As far as the movable obturators are concerned, the soft palate remnants, or rather the narrow mucous membrane muscle bridge which remains after the operation (Pickerill) and should be lifted, are much too weak to achieve the closure. Apart from this fact, the velum normally takes on a different shape in each sound (Haudeck and Froeschels) because it also assists in changing the resonator in order to enable us to resonate the constantly varying sounds in the compound supplied by the vocal cords. Therefore, the obturator should be constructed with a twofold aim in mind: to achieve best possible results for the production of the non-nasal sounds as well as the nasal sounds.

How can one determine the degree of hyperrhinolalia? The trained observer will be able to do this merely through listening, while the untrained observer will fail due to the fact that the speech of these patients shows various anomalies which are only partly caused by the pathological penetration of air into the nose and partly by the anomalous function of the articulatory organs, the tongue in particular. To give an example: The palatal sounds G and K are physiologically produced by pressing the back of the tongue against the border of the hard and soft palate. Since in a case of total cleft palate there is no actual palate, the patients usually replace these sounds by explosions which they produce by means of a powerful glottal stop, a phenomenon which is in no way comparable to the G and K. There are many similar mistakes and when one is not accustomed to perceive analytically the single components in the complex of speech all one hears is the general impression of more or less unintelligible speech without being able to determine what causes this impression at any one given moment. The untrained observer therefore will not be able to discern whether the disturbing factor is due to the penetration of air into the nose or to articulatory failures. For this purpose it is necessary to get used to the "analytic" work of our ears which asks for special phonetic studies.

The good results I achieved in plugging the meatuses with cotton suggested the construction of a new obturator. The idea was to put on a plate like that used for dentures a superstructure which, going up into the nasopharynx, hinders the air from entering *the meatuses only*. I therefore contacted in Vienna Dr. Schalit of the Kieferstation Clinic Eiselsberg (Prof. H. Pichler) suggesting that obturators be built with a crest, resembling a gothic roof, in order to obstruct the penetration of air into the meatuses.

The first step in making the meatus-obturator consists in constructing a plate, fixable at the teeth, as for a denture. A wire prolongation should be attached to the posterior end of the plate, the latter should coincide with the posterior end of the hard palate (respectively the line where this end would be if there were a complete hard palate). This wire prolongation should be loop-shaped. It has to carry the superstructure. A pile of softened rubber is vertically put upon the wire so that if the plate is fixed to the teeth the pile will lie in the naso-pharynx. The therapist with index finger presses the rubber against the posterior nostrils trying to cover *every* part of them with the rubbles. If one has fully succeeded in this respect the hyperrhinolalia will have changed into a hyporhinolalia, i.e. the patient will not say M or N but B and D instead. Still more reliable is the optic inspection by means of posterior rhinoscopy. If one detects *even the smallest* entrance to a meatus the obturator will be ineffective, and the hyperrhinolalia will persist. If an entrance into a meatus is visible one has to close it by smearing the rubber over that opening. If the closure of the posterior nostrils has been properly performed one lets the plug harden, before taking it out (with the plate) (Fig. 6). Then, one either drills a tunnel into the middle of the plug (Fig. 7), or one cuts out the whole middle part of it thus leaving only

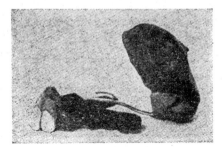

Fig. 6

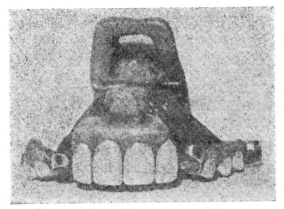

Fig. 7

Fig. 8

one pillar on each side (Fig. 8), corresponding to the end of the turbinates and the slight protrusions of the rubber where it has touched the posterior end of the meatuses. Afterwards one introduces the temporary obturator again into the nasopharynx (by fixing the plate to the teeth) to check the acoustic result. If the hyperrhinolalia has not completely or at least almost completely disappeared one must find out whether the two pillars are too far apart—and if so add some rubber at their medial ends. In a case of tunnel shape it sometimes is necessary to fill the tunnel again to drill the hole lower or higher into the plug. No general rule is possible. After the best result is achieved with the rubber plug it has to be vulcanized. Again posterior rhinoscopy proves necessary with the vulcanized obturator in place, because during the process of vulcanization the shape may change.* The whole procedure of forming the meatus-obturator after the plate has been made does not take more than two or three sessions.

The meatus-obturator, as I named the new type of obturator, of course, can be removed from the mouth and nasopharynx respectively whenever the patient wants. Dr. Schalit and I have reported on the manufacture and appearance of these obturators in several papers. The results as regards speech are most satisfactory.

If the meatuses are greatly narrowed through swellings, the meatus-obturator is superfluous. In certain cases in which the meatuses of one side only are narrowed an obturator might be constructed for one side of the nose.

The role which the width of the meatuses play in the speech of individuals with defective palates seems to be illustrated by the observations of two women who had been operated according to the Pichler method (septum-palate-suture). Although in both patients the velum did not reach the posterior

---

*Modern plastic-technique may be used.

pharyngeal wall, their speech was surprisingly good. Posterior rhinoscopy showed that the posterior nostrils due to the use of the mucous membrane of the vomer to cover up the original defect of the palate, had shrunk in size and the turbinates apparently had been pressed upward. Due to this pressure the meatuses were considerably narrowed. With all due caution I therefore presume that the septum-palate-suture, due to these effects, favorably influences the speech.

The meatus-obturator hardly ever fails in removing the hyperrhinolalia. Since I first described the meatus-obturator different writers have published excellent results achieved with it. Staude[5] e.g. has treated five cases in this way. In all his case histories one phrase indicates typically the result achieved, namely: "The meatus-obturator removed the hyperrhinolalia immediately and perfectly."

Needless to say that articulatory defects cannot be influenced by any obturator and therefore a systematic training is needed.

FIGURES IN SCHALIT'S PAPER

Fig. 1. *Suersen* obturator of hard rubber.

Fig. 2. Pharyngeal obturator of rubber after *Schiltsky,* with spiral spring for operated and contracted soft palates.

Fig. 3. Rigid obturator named after *Warnekros* for non-closed cleft palates.

Fig. 4. Pharyngeal obturator named after *Warnekros,* with clot made of hard rubber and inflexible gold fixture for operated, closed and contracted soft palates.

Fig. 5. Obturator for open cleft palate with hinge named after *Warnekros.* (The five figures from *Partsch-Kantowrowicz:* Handbuch der Zahneilkunde).

LITERATURE

1. *Froeschels-Stockert:* Ueber Auskultationsphaenomene am Brustkorb. Wien. Arch. f. klin. Med. 1923.
2. Die Sprachlaute. Berlin. J. Springer. 1926.

3. The Year Book Publishers. Chicago. See also: Beder, Oscar E.: Obturators, A review. J. of Oral Surg. 1944, 2, 356-368.
Fitz-Gibbon, J. J.: Prosthodontist to orthodontist. Int. J. Orthodont., oral Surg. 1937, 23, 337-50.

4. On a new Obturator (Meatus-Obturator) for cleft palate. Dr. Albert Schalit. After a report given in the Verein Oesterr. Zahnaerzte. May 2, 1928.

5. Die Therapie der Sprachstoerungen bei Gaumenspalten, insbesondere durch den Meat-Obturator (Froeschels-Schalit). Doctorthesis. University of Cologne. 1931.

EMIL FROESCHELS, M.D.

President, International Society for Speech and Voice Science;
President, New York Society of Voice and Speech Therapy.

Chapter XV

PATHOLOGY AND THERAPY OF STUTTERING

1. SYMPTOMATOLOGY

STUTTERING in the great majority of cases starts in child-hood. However, there are a small number of cases of "traumatic" stuttering. These are cases in which someone starts to stutter after suffering any kind of injury. For the present, I am dealing only with cases in which stuttering began in childhood.

In a study I made with my assistants we found that in the early stages, stuttering consists in word and syllable repetition; pressure does not occur. When pressure appears, the intial stage is over. I might add that in our series of 700 cases, we found one case where pressure symptoms seemed to be the original sign. Most authors[1, 2] agree with our findings.*

Children begin to stutter most frequently between the ages of three to five years, and never at the start of speech! That is the period when the child accomplishes the tremendous task of

---

*Johnson's[3] attempt at refusing the expression physiologic stuttering for these initial symptoms seems to be due to a misunderstanding. On the one hand, he tries to show how hard it is to form the right concept of stuttering at all; while on the other hand, he refuses the expression physiologic stuttering for the initial iterations. Only if one forms a concept of stuttering that involves the awareness of the patient of his difficulties, can one possibly exclude the initial iterations from that concept. But even granting such an explanation of the meaning of the term stuttering, could anybody rightly interfere with the attempt to trace back the trouble to its initial symptoms, if the latter also occur without special awareness of the patient? Why those initial symptoms then should not be covered with the same name as the symptoms developing from them does not seem plausible to me.

194

acquiring skill in speech. The child's inner drive is frequently greater than his speech skill, and that seems to be the cause of word and syllable repetition*; the repetitions represent a kind of filling-in material for missing words or even sentences. They are originally a device to gain time. It is worthy of note that these repetitions are spoken at the same rate of speed at which the child talks normally. They are neither faster nor slower. This indicates that the child's difficulty is not of motor origin, as some writers believe it to be. Whenever motor functions are disturbed, the speed of the motor response is affected.

With the help of several pediatricians, I counted the number of children in Vienna who went through a period of repeating. The result was surprising: 80% of the children tested were "repeaters." A study by Davis[4] confirms our findings. Vivacious and intelligent children seemed to be most affected. Despert[5] showed that by stimulating the emotional expression of children, we frequently obtain repetition of a speech sound or a group of speech sounds. Between three and five years of age, many children are not able to keep pace with their own "speech temperament." Gradually, their speech skill increases and after a few months, the great majority—all but about 2%—stop repeating. The remaining 2% who may be indistinguishable from the normal children up to that point develop into either stutterers or clutterers.

If word or syllable repetitions show too often they should be considered signs of a beginning nervous speech disorder. Other signs of this kind are drawling vowels[6]; speaking in a whisper, or refusing to speak altogether.

After the initial state the child uses pressure in the speech muscles, apparently in an effort to check the repetitions. "Ba-ba-ba" is no longer spoken with normal pressure, but the lips are firmly compressed before the b's are pronounced. This de-

---

*A momentary confusion may have the same effect.

vice produces a delay in articulation and obviously fails in its purpose completely. That stuttering symptoms are, at least in part, the outcome of a reasoning process, is corroborated by the difference of findings regarding morons and idiots: Dersjant[7] found many stutterers among morons, but among 500 idiots, Kennedy[8] did not find a singe stutterer.

To clarify our terminology, it should be mentioned here that we use the terms "clonus" for repetition and "tonus" for pressure and the terms "clonotonus" and "tonoclonus," for a combination of both in one sound depending on which sign is more prominent.

Parents and nurses frequently do not understand that the reason for the repetitions is the child's immature speech skill. They should try to enrich the child's vocabulary, and help him increase his skill in forming sentences. Instead, they ask the child to repeat the "difficult word," or to speak slowly, or even to take a breath, and in this way lead him on the wrong track. He begins to think there are difficult words, and searches for ways to pronounce them better. As a result, his attitude toward speech may become one of anxiety, or he may develop tonic symptoms. However, the fault does not always lie in the environment. Undoubtedly, some children arrive at the same point by self-observation.

When tonic symptoms arise, then breathing must begin to show abnormalities, since air cannot escape during the blockage. Blushing and grimaces as well as reflex contractions of muscles remote from the mouth may appear. Invariably, these signs arise only after tonus develops. Seth[9] found abnormal breathing in stutterers, even when they were not talking. Mohr[10] could not corroborate these findings, and Steer[11] states that normals show breathing patterns similar to those of stutterers. Robbins,[12] however, found breathing and blood circulation of stutterers similar to breathing and blood circulation in shock. Clonotoni and tonocloni delay the flow of speech. In older stutterers, we find these symptoms much accelerated. Invariably, fast tonoclonus and clonotonus occur as a late sign.

A finding which is difficult to explain is the fact that gradually, syllable repetition diminishes in frequency and the tonic component becomes dominant (clonotonus and tonoclonus respectively). Finally, there is pure tonus, without repetitions, and with blockage in the muscles of the larynx, pharynx and mouth. All the older symptoms show occasionally along with the newer ones. Accompanying movements and various disturbances of breathing (such as talking on inspiration, waste of air, etc.) are usually associated with pure toni. These toni remain slow for years.

After the initial stage of stuttering is over—but never before a tonic component has developed—the child may begin to accompany his speech by movements of other parts of the body. Some of them are: looking sideways, shaking or clenching his fists, tapping or stamping his foot. A peculiar type is the embolophrasic-sounds, syllables or words which the patient intersperses in his speech or uses as aids when he starts speaking.

Accompanying movements probably originate as reflexes. They distract the patient's attention from his speech and thereby break the vicious circle: the patient is able to speak more fluently for the moment. When stutterers become aware of the relief they have accidentally found, they may employ these movements deliberately. After a while, however, a given movement loses its suggestive power. The stutterer, ever resourceful within the confines of his neurosis, usually invents a new movement. In addition, the old one often persists, and may become automatic.

The muscle movements which are found to accompany stuttering, may be either of the tonic or clonic type. For instance a patient may shake his head, look upward, or clench his fists.

A striking observation in this respect is a negative finding.

Stuttering is never accompanied by nystagmus (vacillation of the eye-balls), while other eye-ball movements are frequently associated with stuttering. The reason for the absence of nystagmus (which is the clonic movement of the eye-balls) is that nystagmus is a pure reflex and therefore cannot be produced at will.* (Nystagmus may occur in stutterers as well as in normals as spontaneous nystagmus, or as nystagmus due to a labyrinth or optic disturbance). In all the other voluntary muscles also clonic accompanying movements may show. It follows that only those muscles are involved in the clinical picture of stuttering which are controlled by will. If muscle action in stuttering is controlled by the patient's will, it follows that we are not dealing with real muscle spasm, but with movements simulating spasm.

Over a period of time, a stutterer's toni, cloni and tonocloni may change in speed. They frequently become accelerated, but they may also become exceedingly slow. It seems as if the patient is trying out a different tempo in an effort to overcome his difficulty. (Schick[13]).

In the advanced stage, the voice of stutterers is frequently very low and monotonous (Scripture[14], Rothe[15]). Speaking during inspiration is another sign of advanced stuttering. Twitching of the alae nasi frequently occurs and is sometimes found even after a stutterer is cured (Mohr[16]). Although as a rule stutterers are able to sing and whisper without blocking, Bristove[17] and others agree that there are exceptions to this rule.

As the stutterer matures, he becomes more embarassed by the dramatic manifestations of his affliction. While he is unable to overcome his blocking, he tries to suppress the more conspicuous symptoms or replace them by less dramatic ones. I call this phase concealed stuttering. An early and very com-

---

*12 cases of voluntary nystagmus are known in the world literature. Such extraordinary findings, none of them concerning a stutterer, cannot be used against the theory drawn from my observation on stutterers.

mon manifestation of the concealing tendency is at work when the stutterer avoids difficult words by substituting other words. Frequently, he prefers not to speak at all. It is evident that such an attitude must have a detrimental influence on the entire personality. Hoepfner[18] pointed out that a tendency toward antisocial behavior may result from it. Van Riper[19] acknowledges, as common to all cases, only tonic and clonic signs; other signs are only individual modifications of the clonic and tonic. It is worthy of attention that stutterers in Europe usually begin to conceal their symptoms at an earlier age than stutterers in America do.[20]

We have now traced the development of the signs of stuttering—from the beginning phase of syllable repetition to the late one of concealed stuttering. It seems to me that the progress from one sign to the next is due to an inner logic.

Pichon and Borel-Maisonny[21] objected to this description of stages as too rigid, but did not propose specific modifications.

Our classification provides a means for recognizing one specific type of stuttering which is not at all uncommon, namely stuttering due to imitation.

Imitation stuttering is chiefly characterized by a modification of the tonic component. It is a physical necessity that the more violent and the more prolonged the overcontraction of the muscles of articulation has been, the more powerful is the acoustic impression of the start of the sound. The imitation stutterer does not watch every detail; he reproduces syllable repetition and prolonged articulation; but when he opens his mouth for the explosion the strong acoustic impression characteristic of true stuttering fails to show. Similarly, when accompanying movements occur and there is no tonus we are dealing with imperfect imitation of true stuttering.

The picture of imitation stuttering resembles to a certain degree a phase of stuttering which we may call incomplete cure. The patient has learned, usually with the help of a therapist, to control his violent muscle contractions but is still troubled with stoppages in articulation. I have named this type of tonus "incomplete tonus."

As to the traumatic type of stuttering the reader is referred to my book "Sprachaerztliche Therapie im Kriege" (Speech Therapy in War[22]).

Finally, a group of functional disorders undoubtedly related to stuttering must be mentioned here. It comprises disturbances in writing and in playing a musical instrument. They also are characterized by clonic and tonic symptoms (Van Dantzig[23]).

2. THE NATURE OF STUTTERING

The main theories regarding stuttering hold it to be due either to organic or psychogenic causes.

Some proponents of the organic basis believe that interference with the dominant brain hemisphere causes stuttering. Such interference is said to take place if a left handed person is forced to use his right hand constantly instead of his left. (Orton[24] and Travis[25, 26], Rutherford[27], Subert and Kapustin[28], Wahl and Cotte[29]). English authors saw stuttering arising in soldiers who received brain injuries during the first world war, when they were shifted to the sound hand.

Among critics of the sidedness theory we cite Spadino[30] and Meyer[31]. Spadino says: "The difference found between the groups of stutterers and non-stutterers was so small that if any relationship between stuttering in children and any of the factors enumerated exists, it must be a relationship that is operative only in rare cases." Meyer found that "in more than three quarters of the total number of stutterers studied there was no evidence for the assumptions that a dominant cerebral hemisphere had not been established."

An observation of mine which has not been recorded in the literature also tends to refute the sidedness theory. In Europe, there are very few left-handers compared to the number in the

United States. However, statistics indicate that the percentage of stutterers on both continents is about the same, between 1 and 2% of the population.

In order to discuss the findings among British soldiers with brain injuries, I wish to submit my own experience with hundreds of similar cases. In my hospital, not one case of stuttering resulted from shift of handedness.

My hospital was the central hospital of the Austro-Hungarian monarchy for soldiers with brain injuries as well as certain nervous disorders, such as speech disorders.

I consider stuttering as a neurosis. A man who has to undergo a shift of handedness after battle injury may well be subconsciously ready to develop a neurosis. Our patients may also have been ready to develop one; but it never turned out to be stuttering. These men saw stutterers being treated at the hospital, and were able to observe some favorable results of the treatment. The British soldiers had no opportunity for such observation. It seems to me that my patients subconsciously steered clear of a neurosis which they saw treated and sometimes cured in their immediate environment.

One striking fact is that deaf children very rarely stutter. Harms and Malone[32] found eight cases among 14,458 deaf; four of them became deaf only after the onset of speech; for the other four, no history was available. Else Voelker[33] described stuttering in a 12 year old deaf boy. I personally have not seen a single deaf stutterer in all my life. The explanation, I believe, is to be found in the speech habits of the deaf. Whenever their emotions are stirred, they resort to sign language; that is why they rarely find themselves in those speech situations which cause syllable repetition in the normal hearing child.

Many authors have investigated psychosomatic aspects of stuttering. They describe abnormalities of body function observed in stutterers without, however, claiming an organic basis for stuttering.

P. Moses and I[34] studied 194 stuttering children to determine their body type according to Kretschmer's classification. We found about the same number of pyknic and asthenic children, while other authors believe the asthenic type to be preponderant among stutterers.

Palmer and Gilette[35] describe deviations from the normal respiratory cardiac arrhythmia in stutterers, and Stratton[36] found diminished creatine and creatinine output in their urine. More recently, however, Beard and Jacob[37] reported wide fluctuations in the creatinine output of both normal and neuropathic individuals. Studies of the serum calcium and blood sugar of stutterers have been made by Kopp[38], however it is possible that the disturbances of metabolism are the result of the neurosis. Seeman[39] studied the breathing of stutterers and found that it is compared with normal breathing—shorter in orthosympathirotonics and longer in vagotonics.

Cross[40] states that stutterers are less skillful bi-manually than normal individuals. Travis, Tuttle and Bender[41] found that normals react to complicated stimuli more promptly and with the "dominant" hand, while stutterers react less promptly and as ambidexters. Madame Kopp[42] observed that stutterers over 12 years of age generally show less motor skill than normals. Blackburn[43] reports similar results for tongue and jaw movements. West, Kennedy and Carr[44] found slowness of diadochocinesis; Shackson[45] observed shortened latency of muscle contractions in stutterers.

Jasper and Murray[46] as well as Moser[47] concluded from photographs of the cornea light reflex during oral reading that the eyes of stutterers stop more frequently than those of normal readers. Abnormal eye movements during reading in addition to abnormal breathing and abnormal masseter movements were described by Mozley Alonzo[48]. Gardner[49] found that the balance between the dilators and constrictors of the pupils was disturbed. Peters[50] and others found that there were relatively more mirror readers and writers among the stutterers than among the normal.

Travis and Knoll[51] and Freestone[52], recording brain potentials saw unequal reactions of both hemispheres, and out-of-phase reactions were observed, especially in severe cases. Rheinberger and his co-workers[53], however, could not verify those findings.

We now turn to authors who assume stuttering to be of psychic origin and attempt to define the personality traits of stutterers, for instance Bender[54], Ingebretsen[55] and Freund[56]. A self-description by Johnson[57] is of considerable interest.

While many of these studies help to clarify the concept of stuttering as a neurotic manifestation, it would seem that the findings contained in them do not apply to stutterers exclusively, but to other neurotics as well. What is lacking are control groups consisting of non-stuttering neurotics.

A few authors have studied, quantitatively, as it were, the amount of stuttering that occurs under controlled conditions. (Johnson, Larson and Knott[58], Brown[59], Hahn[60] and Brown and Moren[61]).

In presenting my own concept of stuttering as a neurosis, I draw in part on the observations of other authors, too numerous to mention. I believe that children passing through a period of word or syllable-repetition may or may not fix this sign, and that a subconscious desire for abnormal behavior is the decisive factor. Such widely divergent situations as sibling rivalry, antagonism toward one parent, emotional insecurity, and over-protectiveness on the parents' part are found again and again as the background of stuttering. Problems of sex are certain to play a part in a number of cases. Psychoanalysts consider these problems as the underlying cause of all stuttering (Coriat[62], Blanton[63], and others). However, I do not share their belief.

Stuttering alters the balance of the family situation in favor of the stutterer and, therefore, becomes a means for achieving satisfaction.

3. THERAPY

All methods of stuttering therapy except psychotherapy are directed toward the symptoms of the disorder; they are surface methods.

Pure psychotherapy has been tried, but psychoanalysis, in particular, has not proved successful in curing stutterers. Sigmund Freud himself acknowledged this fact in a personal communication to me. Fletcher[64] says that the stutterer has in his mind many conscious associations regarding his speech which tend to inhibit normal function. It is, therefore, logical that treatment be directed toward the symptoms.

One of the oldest methods of working on the symptoms of stuttering is Klencke's method[65]. With certain modifications, it is still in common use. It begins with breathing exercises and continues with voice and finally articulation exercises. Psychotherapeutic measures, however, are also part of the treatment.

The drawling method, introduced by Liebmann[66], uses a different approach. By prolonging the vowel sounds in reading and conversation, many stutterers are able to speak without blocking. Reading in unison and singing are also advocated by some authors. However, it is doubtful whether there could be a carry-over from these exercises into speech. The psychological set-up is quite different when a person has to express his own ideas in a normal tempo.

Most stutterers can speak fairly fluently when they are by themselves. In order to condition his patients to the presence of an audience, Liebmann had them speak in a dark room. When the room was lighted afterwards, they found out that there had been people listening to them. Use of a house telephone that can be interrupted has been described by Carhart[67]. The purpose is similar to Liebmann's use of a darkened room. Bryngelson[68] trains his pupils first to stutter voluntarily. By this device, he believes, the pupil learns to control his own speech impulses so completely that later on he can avoid stuttering. Donath[69] and Levbarg[70] advocate hypnotism combined with speech training. Hahn[71] and Kopp[72] suggest that therapy be flexible and adapted to individual differences.

It now remains for me to outline my own system of therapy, which I developed after trying all recommended methods for years. In very young children, however, I follow Liebmann's ideas.

If the patient is a young child still in the stage of syllable repetition without tonus, it is important that no one draws the child's attention to his speech. By telling stories, which the child repeats phrase after phrase, his vocabulary should be enlarged, and his skill in forming sentences increased. When there are signs of tonus, however, the drawling method, both in reading and conversation, may be indicated. Since the appearance of a stutter constitutes neurotic behavior, the therapist must gain insight into the child's emotional problems. It is part of his task to help the child to readjust himself. This is usually possible only by educating the parents to an understanding attitude.

For older children and adults, I found a way I believe in which I can convey to the stutterer the inner knowledge that speech is easy. If the method works, the stutterer will lose his preoccupation with the speech function. The method which I propose and have been using for the past fifteen years, is the chewing method.

Chewing, I am convinced, is the origin of human speech, and chewing and talking are largely identical functions. In the chewing of primitive peoples, considerable movement of the lips and jaws takes place and a variety of sounds is emitted at the same time. During the babbling period, infants move their lips, tongues, and jaws as if they were chewing, while they in the same way also exercise their vocal apparatus. Observations in the field of speech pathology also confirm the close link between chewing and talking. Certain aphasic patients when trying to speak only manage to chew and produce unarticulated sounds. The picture of epileptics awakening from a seizure is similar. Further discussion of the development of speech may be found in the book "Practice of Voice and Speech Therapy"[73] and an article on "Hygiene of the Voice"[74]. It is apparent that the same set of muscles, innervated by the same nerves, is used in chewing and speaking. Since we can chew and talk at the same time, the two functions must be identical.

The chewing method should be used in the following manner. First an explanation of the identity of chewing and talking is given to the patient. The fact is mentioned that neither he himself nor any other stutterer has ever experienced difficulty in chewing. Then we teach the patient to chew "like a savage."

Next, the patient learns to use his voice while chewing. Although consisting of nonsense syllables, this voiced chewing sounds like human language. (If, on the other hand, monotonous sounds like "ham-ham-ham" are made, he does not move tongue and lips as it should be done). We have the patient chew with voice, do the same ourselves, and so pretend to carry on a conversation. The stutterer experiences no difficulty in this speech activity, which is of psychological value. After a number of "chewing" conversations, the patient becomes aware of the fact that there is no fundamental difference between this kind of language and his native tongue, as far as use of the muscles is concerned.

When we finally let the patient talk, we direct him to keep chewing constantly in mind. Every so often during the day, he must set aside a few moments for voiced chewing. This is done not as a matter of practice but only to serve as a reminder. During conversation with the therapist and while reading aloud, the patient is told to intersperse a few nonsense syllables of chewing in his talking. How long it takes a patient to make the idea of chewing part of his speech function, depends on various circumstances. However, it is certain that many stutterers overcome their fear of speech to a remarkable degree by following the chewing method.

In many cases the patient needs a fundamental psychological reorientation. As a neurotic individual, he has subconsciously abandoned speech as a normal outlet, and made speech in the form of stuttering a defense against his environment. But his weapon has turned into a boomerang. Therefore it is necessary to remove his preoccupation with himself and to release constructive forces within him.

REFERENCES

1. Johnson, W., J. Speech Disorders, Vol. 7, No. 3, 1942.
2. Paikin: L'analyse du phénoméne clonique et son rôle dans la pathologie du bégaiement. Revue française phonetique, VII.
3. The Indians have no word for it. Quarterly J. of Speech XXX. No. 3, Oct. 1944, pp. 330-337.
4. Repetitions in Speech of Young Children. J. Speech Disorders 4: 303, 1939.
5. Despert, J. L.: Emotional Aspects of Speech and Language Development. Monatsschrift fuer Psychiatrie und Neurologie. 104, 4-5, 1941, p. 193-227.
6. Flatau in (2) Versamml. d. dt. Gesellsch. f. Sprachh. Leipzig, 1929.
7. Voordrachten en Besprekingen, 11, 13. X, 1937.
8. Speech of the Feeble-minded. Yr. Bk. Am. Speech Correction Assocaion, 1930.
9. Seth: Brit. J. Psychol. 24: 375-388, 1934.
10. Atmungsuntersuchungen an Stotterern. Monatschr. f. Ohrenh. 69: 149.
11. Symptomatology of Young Stutterers. J. Speech Disorders, March 1937, p. 3.
12. Comparative Shock and Stammering. Am. J. Physiol., vol. 48, p. 285.
13. Schick, A.: Statistisches zur Entwicklung des Stotterns. Wiener klinische Wochenschrift, 1921.

14. Das Stottern. Arch. f. Psychiat. 1924, p. 814.
15. Die Sprachheilkunde. Vienna 1913.
16. Beobachtungen ueber Nasenfluegelsymptom und Stottern. Kongress (5) d. internationalen Gesellschaft f. Logopaedie und Phoniatrie, Vienna 1932.
17. Bristove: Voice and Speech, London, 1880.
18. Zur Klinik und Systematik der associativen Aphasie. Ztschr. f. d. ges. Neurologie und Psychiatrie, 93: 178, 1922.
19. Van Riper: Speech Correction. New York, Prentice-Hall, 1939. Preparatory Set in Stuttering. J. Speech Disorders, V, 3, p. 49.
20. Froeschels, E.: Differences in the Symptomatology of Stuttering in the United States and Europe. J. Speech Disorders, March 1941, p. 45.
21. Le bégaiement, sa nature et son traitement. Paris, 1937.
22. Berlin and Vienna, 1919.
23. Dantzig, van: Logopaed. e. Phoniat., Vol. 11, No. 3.
24. Orton: Reading, Writing, and Speech Problems in Children. New York, Norton, 1937.
25. Studies in Stuttering: Studies of action currents in stutterers. Arch. Neurol. and Psychiatry, Vol. 21, 1929.
26. Speech Pathology. New York, Appleton-Century, 1931.
27. Speech re-education for the birth-injured. J. Speech Disorders, III. 4, p. 190, 1938.
28. Zentralbl. f.d. ges. Neurol. u. Psychiat., Vol. 52, p. 338 (review).
29. La gaucherie et le bégaiment. Ann. med.-psychol. 97.5. April 1939.
30. Writing and Laterality Characteristics of Stuttering Children. New York, Teachers College, Columbia Univer., 1941.
31. Psychosomatic Aspects of Stuttering. Jour. of Nerv. and Ment. Disease, Vol. 101, p. 137, 1945.
32. Relationship of hearing acuity to stammering. J. Speech Disorders, 4: 363, 1939.
33. Spasmophemia in dyslalia cophotica. Ann. Otol., 46. Sept. 1937.
34. Ueber Konstitution associativ-aphasischer Kinder. Wien. Med. Wochenschrift, Vol. 76, No. 29, 1926.
35. Respiratory cardiac arrhythmia in stuttering. J. Speech Disorders, 4: 133, 1939.
36. Factor in the etiology of a sub-breathing stammerer. J. Comp. Psychol., Vol. 4.
37. Physiologic significance of the creatine coefficient and the creatine tolerance test. Arch. Neurol. and Psychiat., Vol. 42, p. 67-87.
38. Metabolic studies of stutterers. Speech Monog. I, 1, Sept. 1934.
39. Sur la régulation neurovégétative de la durée de la phonation. Folia Phoniatrica. Vol. 1, 1947, pp. 22-37.

40. Motor capacity of stutterers. Arch. Speech, March 1936.
41. An analysis of precedence. Arch. Speech, 1936.
42. L'évolution psychiatrique, vol. 2, 1936.
43. Psychol. Monog. 41: 1, 1931.
44. Rehabilitation of Speech. New York. Harper, 1931.
45. Action study of muscle contraction latency. Arch. Speech, March 1936.
46. J. Exper. Psychol. 15: 528, 1932.
47. Qualitative analysis of eye movements during stuttering. J. Speech Disorders, 3: 131, 1938.
48. Analysis of associative and congenital factors in the symptomatology of stuttering. Studies in Clin. Psychol., Psychol. Monog. vol. 3. Studies in psychol. (Iowa) Vol. XXII.
49. Study of the pupillary reflex with special reference in stuttering. Psychol. Monog. Studies in Clinical Psychol. Vol. III. Studies in Psychol. (Iowa) Vol. XXII.
50. Study of mirror reading. Arch. Speech Disorders, March 1936.
51. Bilaterally recorded brain potentials from normal speakers and stutterers. J. Speech Disorders, 1938.
52. University of Southern California Thesis, 1941.
53. Electroencephalographic and Laterality Studies of Stuttering and Non-Stuttering Children. The Nervous Child 2: 117, 1943.
54. Personality structure of stuttering. New York, Chicago, Pitman, 1939.
55. Some experimental contributions to the pathology and psychopathology of stutterers. Am. J. Orthopsychiat., Vol. 6, No. 4, 1936, p. 630.
56. Monatsschr. f. Ohrenh. Vol. 71, No. 6, 1937.
57. Because I stutter. New York, Appleton-Century, 1930.
58. Studies in the pathology of stuttering. J. Speech Disorders, March 1937.
59. Influence of grammar function of the incidence of stuttering. J. Speech Disorders, 3: 195, 1937.
60. Study of the relationship between stuttering occurrence and phonetic factors in oral reading. J. Speech Disorders, 7, 2, June 1942, p. 143-151.
61. Frequency of stuttering in relation to word length in oral reading. J. Speech Disorders, 7, 2: 153-159, 1942.
62. Nerv. and Ment. Disease Mong., 1928.
63. Ment. Hyg. 15: 281, 1931.
64. Problem of Stuttering, New York, 1928.
65. Heilung des Stotterns. Leipzig 1860.
66. Vorlesungen ueber Sprachstoerungen. Coblentz. Berlin, 1900.

67. Two-room technique in the treatment of stuttering. J. Speech Disorders, June 1938.
68. J. of Abnormal and Social Psychology, Vol. 30, 1935, p. 194-198.
69. Therapie der Gegenwart. 73: 456, 1932.
70. Potent therapy of certain disorders of voice and speech. Arch. Otol., No. 30, 1939.
71. On integration of stuttering therapy. J. Speech Disorders, 2: 87, 1937.
72. Proc. Am. Speech Correction Association, Sept. 1939.
73. Froeschels and Jellinek, Boston, Expression Co., 1941.
74. Arch. of Otolaryngology, Vol. 38, Aug. 1943, pp. 122-130.

ADDITIONAL BIBLIOGRAPHY

75. *Kennedy and Williams:* Association of stammering and the allergic diatheses. Brit. Med. J., Dec. 24, 1938.
76. *R. E. Card:* Study of allergy in relation to stuttering. J. Speech Disorders 4: 223, 1939.
77. *B. Bryngelson: Investigati*on in the ethiology and nature of dysphemia and its symptoms, stuttering. J. Speech Disorders 7: 15, 1942.
78. *S. Flatau:* Psycho-physiology of voice and speech coordination. Internat. Conf. Speech Training, London 1927.
79. *S. Meyer:* Stuttering as an emotional and personality disorder. J. Speech Disorders, 4: 347, 1939.
80. *C. S. Bluemel:* Stammering and inhibition. J. Speech Disorders, 5: 305, 1940.
81. *Moore:* Conditioned reflex study of stuttering. J. Speech Disorders,
82. *Molhant:* Hyg. Ment. 29: 101, 1934, pp. 101-118.
83. *C. S. Bluemel:* Jour. A. M. A. 96: 1846, 1941, pp. 1846-1848.
84. *E. L. Kenyon:* Etiology of stammering. J. Speech Disorders, 7: 97, 1942.
85. *Stinchfield-Hawk:* Speech Pathology. Boston, Expression Co., 1928.
86. *D. Weiss:* Ztschr. f. Kinderforschung, Vol. 38 to 44 (reviews).
87. *Martha Vié:* Cong. (6) Internat. Soc. Logopaed. and Phoniat., Vienna 1934.

ANNIE MOOLENAAR-BIJL
Speech Clinic, Laryngological Department,
University Hospital of Groningen, Holland.

Chapter XVI

CLUTTERING
(Paraphrasia praeceps)

HISTORY

IN an extensive description of a speech defect one usually
starts with the history of the defect: its first recognition, the
development of views and therapy from the former ages until
the present day. In dealing with the historical knowledge of
cluttering however, which in short consists of that speech defect wherein excessive rapidity, slips of the tongue, iterations
and indistinctness predominate, we may be brief, for it has
not been mentioned as a distinct speech defect until the second
half of the 19th century. Before then a differential diagnosis
with stuttering was not yet made. Already *Hippocrates* concerned himself with stuttering, and looking back with the
knowledge of cluttering we now possess, we come to the conclusion that his idea of stuttering included cluttering for the pictured stuttering as arising out of an incongruity between
thought and speech. Even in the greater part of the 19th century we find cluttering being considered at its best as a certain

211

form of stuttering, as is apparent from *Klencke's* "temperamental stuttering" and "habitual stuttering" (1860). In the great strides which the science of logopedics made in Europe towards the end of the 19th century (*Kussmaul, Gutzmann, Berkhan, Liebmann*), cluttering began to be distinguished from stuttering, the terms "Tumultus sermonis" and "Paraphrasia praeceps" arose, and the affinity and rather frequent combination with stuttering were still clearly recognised. But nevertheless presumably many patients were still considered stutterers, whom we should today call clutterers—whether or not stutterers at the same time. The authors mentioned above considered stuttering to be a functional speech defect and their statements on its aetiology (hastiness, lack of attentiveness) and symptomatology (rapid, irregular, speech tempo, slips of the tongue, iterations, omissions, indistinct pronunciation) still were terse.

AETIOLOGY

Liebmann[1, 1a] already penetrated more deeply into the phenomena, and he saw the cause of this speech defect in a special acoustic and also motor inattentiveness and in an incongruity

FEEBLE MEMORY

between thought and speech. *Nadoleczny*[2] says there is a weakness of memory for word forms caused by inattentiveness. This view, based on intuition, has been confirmed in a more exact way later on by the investigations of *Saunders* and *Robbins*[3]. In 53% of the clutterers they examined, they found a subnormal "auditory memory span," i.e. ability to repeat faultlessly a number of meaningless syllables or figures, which number they fixed for normal individuals as 4 for children of 4, 5 for the age of 7, 6 for the age of 10, 7 for the age of 14 and over. In this respect it is interesting that *D. Weiss* found about the same values and also a defective memory for the sequence of syllables in children suffering from paragrammatism with a delayed speech development. This feeble memory for small series of syllables need not be correlated with the quality of the intellect; it is only related with the acoustic receptivity.

INATTENTIVENESS

Clutterers pay little attention not only to their own speech but also to that of others: they are inattentive, hear and take up only half of what others say (*Froeschels*[4]). So the idea is obvious that these children do not belong to the acoustic imagery type. In this respect one might also think of an enfeebled "figure-background-relation" (*Goldstein*) with regard to expressions of speech, as has been elaborated magnificently by *Florensky*[5]. Clutterers are very little or not at all conscious of their abnormal speech which causes other people much trouble, and this is the reason why in general only few clutterers appear for treatment in speech clinics. Consequently one can very rarely have large numbers at one's disposal for investigation and conclusions.

IMAGERY TYPE

This drawback is also attached to *Froeschels and Kallen's* publication on the clutterer's imagery type[6]. Their aim was to ascertain whether the clutterer in observing and reproducing has clear images, perhaps restricted to one sensory zone, or rather vague, unclear, changing ones. As might be expected, no definite imagery type emerged from this very small number of experimental subjects. It was important however that on the whole, clear, sharply defined images were absent, regardless in which sensory zone. Maybe exactly this absence of a mainstay in the flow of thoughts is the cause of the unbalanced and stumbling speech. (See also *Froeschels and Jellinek*[7]).

Many clutterers give by their extremely quick, badly differentiated speech the impression that their thinking progresses in a disorderly way and with abnormal speed, more rapidly than the motor system can keep pace with. This becomes evident at once in the repeating of a story which they have heard or read, in which whole sentences or parts of the plot are omitted and the chronological sequence is garbled. They probably do think on continuously in the meantime, but fail to transmit these parts logically into words because of rapidity of their thinking; they do not notice themselves to what extent gaps and absurdities must arise for the listener in this way. From which it is again evident that the acoustic observation of their own speech is extremely feeble.

MENTAL SPEECH

That on the other hand, loud, slow and precise speaking diminishes the rapidity of thinking (and therefore has a favourable effect on cluttering) is supported by the expositions of *Schilling*[8], concerning the "mental speech." There are certain relations between the course of the thinking process and the dynamics of speech, so that for the most favourable development of the former a well defined degree of intensity of the latter, corresponding with age and intellect, is most beneficial. This correlation mainly bears upon the function of speech as an aid to thinking (directed towards the "Ego") and not upon other functions of speech such as communication and self-expression. Only when after the acquisition of a certain vocabulary the ability to speak becomes important for the infant, does the introverted action set in. This function is accompanied by an ever decreasing amount of dynamics: first loud, then whispering, next mute-motoric and eventually mental speech. At first therefore strong acoustic and motoric stimuli are necessary to evoke an understanding; later on, as higher demands of speed and precision are made on thinking, the phonetic ballast begins to act as a hindrance. Mental speech forms, as it were, a link between thinking and speaking in both ways: observation—assimilation and thinking—expression.

There are clutterers who skip the link of mental speech totally or partially; their thoughts are not yet ripe for speech and they already set their motorics going. (Cf. *Froeschels,* and *Koukol & Poray-Kochitz*[10]). It is advisable in taking the anamnesis to pay some attention to the question, whether the clutterer may not have talked and read aloud little in his childhood (whatevery may have been the reason) and thus may have not attained clear images of the words.

But in the case of grown-ups too the aid given to thinking by talking aloud must not be underestimated; there are e.g. people to whom in an important conversation a certain thought only occurs when they are speaking, or who at any rate can only then formulate sharply, or realise a vaguely present idea. They belong to the so-called "dictional" type. (Cf. also *Gomperz's* three stages between thinking and speaking). Secondly, in performing activities like typewriting, many people read their text aloud, softly or with mute articulation, and here too peculiar scriptural cluttering symptoms occur (*Branco v. Dantzig*[11]), in case of a too rapidly progressing thinking process, i.e. if the digital motorium cannot keep up with the formulation of the thoughts or if the mental sound-analysis is not transformed into finger movements precisely.

On the one hand therefore the excessive rapidity of the clutterers' thinking process exerts an unfavourable influence on their speech, on the other hand the speech deviations will also influence their thinking process less favourably, as speech loses its secondary function as an aid to thinking.

READING SYMPTOMS

Most clutterers exhibit in their reading the same phenomena as in speaking; above all an all too hasty and irregular tempo, a neglect of punctuation marks and correspondingly an incorrect partition of breath and a very poor intonation; furthermore omission and insertion of words or syllables, the reading of words other than the text contains and the transposition of letters in the sense of metathesis, prolepsis and postposition. (Examples see *A. Moolenaar-Bijl*[12]). Just as the speech deviations recall forms of aphasia, so the disorders in reading suggest forms of alexia. (See also *David P. Boder*[13]). With clutterers however the basal function of reading, i.e. the recognition of the shapes of letters and the ability to join up letters into words is intact, but the visual attentiveness and the transformation of optic stimuli into adequate forms of movement is insufficient. By establishing these sensory and sensomotor uncertainties and defects we are making for the direction to which all publications on cluttering issued in the last fifteen years are pointing: the organic foundation of cluttering.

ORGANIC FOUNDATION

The pioneer's job in this respect was done by a particularly deeply penetrating article of *Florensky's*[5]. Cluttering strictly taken, the getting entangled in details of speech, need not necessarily be accompanied by an excessively rapid tempo, but the latter may be an idiopathic phenomenon which she called

TACHYLALIA

tachylalia. Two pictures therefore arose out of the complex of symptoms up till then regarded as an entity: firstly tachylalia, which may involve as secondary phenomena slips of the tongue

PARAPHRASIA

and repetitions, and secondly paraphrasia, essentially based on difficult word-finding and sometimes carrying with it through its "hunt for word-forms" an acceleration of tempo, slips of the tongue and iterations. Tachylalia is the plainer defect of the two, and may be cured by simply regulating the tempo. But all symptoms of paraphrasia on the other hand: hesitating choice of words, uncertainty of syntax, insertion of irrelevant elements, garbling of speech sounds, may be fully explained ac-

"Figure-Background"

cording to *Florensky* from the viewpoint of a disturbed "figure-background-formation" as elaborated by *Goldstein*[14]. A correct distribution of stimuli and a correct differentiation of reaction processes in the central nervous system are indispensable conditions for a correct action. The active process, momentarily predominating, *Goldstein* calls the "figure"; that which is going on in the background forms as it were a setting. If the differentiation of stimuli diminishes, the relation between figure and background changes; the demarcation between the whole and the component parts, and between one part and another becomes less sharp and less stable. This stands out clearly in the case of paraphrasia by the vagueness and slight intensity of the idea which ought to stand in the focus of attention. Thus a levelling and mutual exchangeability of the parts of speech is caused, and as a result of the absence of logical pauses there is an apparent acceleration of tempo. We see how under the influence of this decreased differentiation a telegram-style originates in motor aphasics, and in case of paraphrasia whole sentences or parts of them are shortened or dropped out, which may be established best by making the subject repeat a story.

All this may be formulated too as *Froeschels* has suggested. Language is built up horizontally and vertically. A disturbance in the horizontal structure (the mutual relations between the component parts) may consist of the premature appearance of a part (before or during the pronunciation of a preceding part) or of the perseveration of a part already pronounced. In the vertical structure the idea of a less important part may displace that of the whole, which ought to dominate, or vice versa. Externally these disturbances may manifest themselves in pauses in speaking, stop-gaps ("embolophrasias"), iterations of syllables, words or sentences and the premature appearance of parts of words or of sound-units.

MORE SYMPTOMS

If *Florensky* penetrates into the depths, *Weiss* exposes the syndrome of cluttering more broadly[15], stressing the importance of a sharply made differential diagnosis between stuttering and cluttering, and of the hereditarily fixed feeble speech constitution, evident from a positive family anamnesis. He often found delayed speech development, word deafness, audimutism, dyslalia, cluttering and stuttering in the family. The most important symptom of cluttering *Weiss* considers to be the predomination of the "cloni" (pure iterations). In addition to the symptoms already recorded in this article when dealing with other authors, *Weiss* mentions i.a.: the inability to split up in syllables, the so-called "phobic attitude" with suddenly distended mouth and eyes and tightly shut glottis, the repeated inspiration in the middle of a sentence (*Froeschels* too has paid attention to defects in block forming[9]), a monotonous or stereotype intonation, a much too soft or loud speech, sometimes related with this a paretic hoarseness. The symptoms become clearer in case of fatigue and falling off of concentration. Therefore one should not content oneself in examining a patient with letting him answer questions with short replies or making him read aloud a short passage, for the symptoms of cluttering often only become apparent after some time. If we may add *Saunders'* observation[3] that children with an "auditory memory span disability" are unable to supply rhyme words; that, according to *Nadoleczny*[2], small words are often omitted (just as in retarded development of speech) and that the clutterer gets the more mixed up as the pronunciation, structure or meaning of the sentences become more complicated; that inspiration often is audible because of the hastiness (*Froeschels*[4]), and that clutterers often are so-called "saliva sprayers" (*Nadoleczny*[2], *Florensky*[5])—then we have an already awe-inspiring list of symptoms, all of which are reducible to either difficult word finding or a lack of attention to the details of speech in the acoustic or motor zone, while in addition the tempo of thought and that of speech do not keep pace.

RELATION TO STUTTERING

The combination of stuttering with cluttering occurs rather frequently. Both *Weiss*[15a], and *Freund*[16] regard the cluttering in such a case as the primary disturbance (abnormal speech constitution) and the stuttering part of the speech defect as a neuropathic superstructure growing rampant on it, liable to occur especially during puberty. In the cases he describes *Freund* sees a genetic relation between this recent stuttering and the already longer existing cluttering ("Balbuties e paraphrasia praecipe"). Concerning the essential difference between cluttering and stuttering, viz. the absence of a continuous dread of speaking, of consciousness of a defect and also of toni and concomitant movements in the former, unanimity existed from days of yore, even though the clutterer may by his continuous uncertainty in choice of words or word-forms develop a vague fear in the end, causing symptoms of stuttering at the same time. *Scripture*[17] already formulated this: "The cluttering child is ridiculed or made anxious in other ways until the "stutterer's fear" is produced." Others too vented similar opinions.

The well-developed stuttering involves a narrowing of consciousness with regard to one's own expressions of speech and therefore tends to be aggravated if the patient's attention is focused still more on his speech. In the case of cluttering the reverse applies: "The clutterer speaks better the more he thinks about his speech, the stutterer often speaks better the less he thinks about it. The clutterer shows negligence and lack of self-control; the stutterer cannot release himself from anxiously watching over his speech." (*Scripture*[17]). *Freund*[16] has facilitated the survey of this difference by the following table:

	Stuttering	Cluttering
I. Consciousness of defect	present	absent
II. Calling attention to speech	aggravates defect	improves defect
III. By unrestrained speaking	better	worse
IV. Speaking to strangers	worse	better
V. Giving short reply is	difficult	easy
VI. Making repeat causes	no improvement	improvement
VII. Therapy embraces	distraction of attention from speech	focusing attention on speech

FEEBLE SPEECH CONSTITUTION

From all this we must conclude, that the "difficult word finding" and the memory-gaps, held responsible for the developmental stuttering by the Viennese school, may indeed count as the cause of initial stuttering (*Hoepfner's* "primary ataxia," *Froeschels'* "physiological stuttering," which *Freund* therefore prefers to call "physiological cluttering"); and secondly that these factors in addition play their part in causing cluttering, if they do not act as more or less casual momentarily occurring forces, but as the constitutional basis of the "speech temper" and its forms of expression. For genuine stuttering a neurotic predisposition must be present as a matrix, while the organically feeble speech constitution must be considered as the substratum for cluttering.

TEMPER

The speech temper reflects the personal temper. Many authors noticed qualities in clutterers such as hurriedness, restlessness, inattentiveness, uncertainty, lack of balance, and indifference. To determine the correlation between speech temper and personal temper (e.g. according to *Kretschmer's* typology —which has often been done with stutterers—or according to *Heymans'* classification of characters), the former would have to be analysed and defined more precisely. Then one would have to fasten down characteristic habits of intonation, tempo, accents, pronunciation, motorics, use of the voice etc. in objective measures. A first step in this direction was done by *Trojan* with regard to recitation[18] and in like manner surely more points of contact might be found in the field of speech pathology.

In individual motorics two sorts of accompanying movements are distinguished in speaking just as in some other forms of expression, differing in intensity and degree of consciousness. Some are "directing, picturing and creative" (*Herz*[19]) and lie on rather a high level of consciousness; others are more primitive and playful, and do not appear to take part in building up the communication. The latter, unconscious, movements probably have a supplementary function in the need of expression. In case of an investigation of the temper, attention would therefore also have to be given to the clutterer's gestures, in order to be able to picture the structure of his personality as completely as possible.

THERAPY

From the foregoing expositions it is evident, that the treatment of cluttering must aim at slowing down the rate of speaking and at the same time at cultivating clear images in the acoustic and motor-kinesthetic sphere, as we may assume that these will influence the processes of thought and speech favourably.

When making the clutterer repeat words or sentences one may regulate the tempo with a metronome or pendulum, by marking time with the hand or by making the patient beat with his fingers on the table (*M. v. Dantzig*[20]). The secondary symptoms like iterations and slips of the tongue disappear with the slowing down of the speech. If we desire that the patient make this unusually slow tempo his own—in the long run a new automatism of speech must originate—then it must be supported by clear images of speech movements, which we may cultivate by articulation exercises, in which the clutterer must form a clear idea of every movement of his mouth. We may help his kinesthetic imaginative faculty with visual images, such as e.g. have been indicated by *Froeschels* in his phonetic script (which may be modified to suit other languages[21]).

We exercise the memory for the sequence of syllables by making the patient repeat a gradually increasing number of meaningless syllables, proportionate to his memory span. Numbers too may serve well in this respect. Thus at the same time the acoustic attention is directed toward the speech, and this may also be done very consciously by varying one sound unit at a time in a certain syllable. Later on this may alternate with series of figures and short sentences, modified continually; questions must first be repeated before they may be answered. The latter kind of exercises are very beneficial too for those clutterers, in whom not so much the rapid tempo but rather a difficult and uncertain word finding is the cause of the speech defect. One should above all never forget to exercise reading very systematically from the beginning: first senseless syllables, then words—sentences—stories. A piece of paper with a slit in it suiting the unity which must be read is moved over the text. In this way the attention is being prevented from straying away. Simultaneously with this reading one should exercise writing the same units, so that the patient may learn to combine impressions gained by vision, hearing, speaking and writing. (Cf. the treatment of certain forms of aphasia). It is very useful to make the patient read and write numbers, both in figures and in letters. As soon as the patient is able to repeat longer sentences at the right speed, one passes over to making him repeat stories. In the beginning short pauses for thinking are inserted (*Stein*[23]) and the therapist must go on keeping a severe eye on the right speed and a clear pronunciation. As much as possible exercises in foreign languages are included, and finally free conversation.

If a clutterer has a dyslalia at the same time (sigmatismus seems to occur rather frequently), he should be taught a correct articulation first with the aid of a mirror. Here one will already find occasion to call the patient's attention to some details of speech.

PROGNOSIS

In not too serious cases without complications the prognosis is quite favourable for children and young adults. But in spite of an often amazingly rapid improvement in the beginning, one must count on a rather lengthy treatment, demanding much perseverance from the patient and much patience from the therapist.

In the case of a combination of cluttering and stuttering treatment is more difficult and the prognosis less favourable. To start with, the tempo has to be slowed down; this influences the cluttering favourably and does no harm to the stuttering. But we may not spend too much attention on the details, for the improvement of stuttering demands a broader, unconstrained state of mind with regard to speech. So the therapist will have to set to work carefully and treat the cluttering and the stuttering in turn in those cases where the stuttering factor has not only arisen out of the uncertainty in word-finding and fear of tripping, combined with a focusing of the attention on these phenomena, but is rooted more deeply. This demands a sharp observation of the symptoms and a psychologic feeling, as one has to reckon with the patient's temper and internal resistances, and the mutual influence of the two different speech disturbances.

REFERENCES

1. *Liebmann:* Vorlesungen über Sprachstörungen. 1900.
1a. *Liebmann:* Poltern, Paraphrasia praeceps. (Z. Neur. 127, 1930, 274).
2. *Nadoleczny:* Kurzes Lehrbuch der Sprachheilkunde. 1926.
3. *S. D. Robbins:* Relation between the short auditory memory span disability and disorders of speech. (Laryngoscope 1935, 545).

3a. *D. Weiss:* Test untersuchungen an normalen u. sprachgestörton **Kindern.** (Wien. med. Wschr. 1930, nr. 35).

4. *Froeschels:* Lehrbuch der Sprachheilkunde (Logopaedie). 1931. 3. Edition.

5. *J. A. Florensky:* Zur Frage der funktionellen Sprachstörungen Paraphrasie und Tachylalie. (Z. Neur. 148, 1933, 159).

6. *Froeschels & Kallen:* Vorstellungstypen von Polterern. (Wien. med. Wschr. 1930, II, 1162).

7. *Froeschels & Jellinek:* Die Bedeutung der Vorstellungstypen für den Sprach- und Gesangsunterricht. (Wien. med. Wschr. 78, 1928, 956).

8. *R. Schilling:* Die Bedeutung des inneren Sprechens für die normale und gestörte Sprachentwicklung. (Med. Klinik 1934 I, 289).

9. *Froeschels:* Zur Psychologie der Sprachstörungen, die auf mangelhafter Übereinstimmung von Wortfindung und Sprechtemperament beruhen. (Tijdschr. Log. en Phon. 11, 1939, nr. 5).

10. *Koukol & Poray-Kochitz:* Sur le battarisme. (Rev. franç Phoniatr. 3, 1935, 171).

11. *Branco v. Dantzig:* Schrijven, typen en spreken. (Tijdschr. Log. en Phon. 11, 1939, nr. 5).

12. *A. Moolenaar-Bijl:* Nieuwere inzichten omtrent broddelen en initiaalstotteren. (Voordrachten Amersfoort 1937).

13. *David P. Boder:* Fortschritte der Behandlung der Lesestörung. (Mschr. Ohrenheilk. 71, 1937, H. 9).

14. *Goldstein:* Über Aphasie. 1927.

15. *D. Weiss:* Über die Frage des Polterns und seine Kombination mit Stottern. (Mitt. Spr. u. Stimmheilk. 1, 1935, H. 4).

15a. *D. Weiss:* Das Poltern und seine Behandlung. (Mschr. Ohrenheilk. 70, 1936, 341).

16. *H. Freund:* Über die Beziehungen zwischen Stottern und Poltern. (Mschr. Ohrenheilk. 68, 1934, H. 12).

17. *E. Scripture:* Stuttering and Lisping. (New York 1912).

18. *F. Trojan:* Psychologischer Typus und reproduktives Sprechen. (Verh. Int. Ges. Log. u. Phon. 1935, 100).

19. *E. Herz:* Beitrag zur individuellen Motorik. (Mschr. Psychiatr. 89, 1934, 97).

20. *M. v. Dantzig:* Het lettergreeptrommelen, een nieuw hulpmiddel voor hakkelaars. (Tijdschr. Log. en Phon. 12, 1940, 1, 2).

21. *Froeschels:* Cluttering. (J. Speech Disorders, 1946, 11, 31).

22. *Leopold Stein:* Sprach- und Stimmstörungen in der täglichen Praxis. 1937.

22a. *A. Moolenaar-Byl:* Bydrage tot de therapie van het broddelen. (Tydechr. Log. en Phon. 1947, m 12 & 20, 1948, m.1).

MARY WOOD WHITEHURST
Formerly Supervisor of Auricular Training of
Hoff General Hospital, Santa Barbara, Cal.

Chapter XVII

HEARING REHABILITATION

IT has taken a ruthless war to shake us into the realization
that successful rehabilitation for the average hard-of-hearing
individual is not an impossibility. On the contrary, it is a very
real possibility, as the Army and Navy Rehabilitation Centers
for the Hard of Hearing have demonstrated. The results obtained at these centers have been unquestionably successful and
are recognized as accomplished educational undertakings.

The four military centers were unified in a common purpose,
common objectives and a more or less common method of approach. At the same time, however, each was permitted a free
hand in setting up its own program and working out its own
individual problems. This chapter is a specific report of one of
these centers, Hoff General Hospital, and, therefore, will differ
somewhat in detail from reports of the other centers.

No one subject or phase of a subject could claim sole responsibility for the complete rehabilitation of our servicemen. Each
part of the program fitted together neatly like pieces of a jig-
saw puzzle, so that at the end of an eight weeks' course each
man went out with a confidence in his ability to resume his

This chapter is based on "Auricular Training at Hoff Hospital" by Mary Wood
Whitehurst, published in The Volta Review, May, 1946.

place in a society from which he had withdrawn. He felt equipped to compete with his normally hearing friends with less strain and with more assurance than ever before.

How was this accomplished? Briefly the procedure can be outlined as follows:

1. Each soldier was given an ear examination by a staff otologist and otologic treatment was administered, if necessary.

2. He was scientifically fitted with a hearing aid if his degree of loss warranted it.

3. He was taught how to use this hearing aid and given 30 hours of auditory training which enabled him to get the maximum efficiency from his hearing.

4. He was given 6 weeks of intensive instruction in lip reading which taught him to follow conversation by watching the faces of people, particularly their lips. He learned to synchronize sound and sight.

5. He was given speech correction and taught how to place his voice with the assistance of his new hearing aid.

6. He was given vocational aptitude tests to determine what particular skills he had and what type of job would permit him the best utilization of these skills.

This chapter describes only one phase of the rehabilitation training program, namely auditory training—sometimes called auricular or acoustic. Such training is a means of re-educating the hearing that remains—the so-called residual hearing—so that the residue may function at its maximum capacity. The end results are better understanding of speech, and better adjustment to a hearing aid and to the world of sound in general.

At the military centers it was generally agreed that the first step in rehabilitating the deafened soldier was to restore him to this world of sound of which he had been such an integral part, and the second was to help him adjust to it so that he would never deliberately choose to withdraw from it again. This, it was believed, was the natural and normal course to pursue. Accordingly, when the need was indicated, each man was carefully fitted with a hearing aid, then sent to the auditory training department for a personal interview and a test for the intelligibility of speech. This test attempted to measure each individual's capacity to understand speech with his hearing aid. The test consisted of the following parts:

1. Recorded instruction (diagram type), including at least three specific ideas in each sentence of instruction.
Aim: Accurate and quick interpretation of speech amplified through the loudspeaker.

2. Live voice test.
    a. Short, conversational phrases.
       Aim: Quick recognition.
    b. Proverbs and parodies on these proverbs.
       Aim: Subtle meaning.
    c. Word perception test.
       (1) Single words arranged according to frequency.
       (2) Pairs of words for vowel and consonant contrast.

The scores of this test were recorded and later compared with the final scores on the same test. In this way a percentage gain for each pupil was determined. The results of the test decided the type of training the patient was to have. If this score was low, or if he was unable to endure the new and unpleasant background noises that came through his aid, or if he had one markedly poorer ear which might improve with training, he was given individual instruction. If the score was good and neither of the other two symptoms apparent, then the patient was given group instruction. Regardless of the score, each man was required to have 30 hours of training. There were no exemptions because it was believed that a speech intelligibility test merely revealed the individual's capacity to use his hearing aid under one controlled condition, namely, a quiet background.

There were many other situations with which he would be

confronted and which, in turn, would confuse him unless he was trained to cope with them. A hearing aid amplifies all sounds. The person learning to use one, therefore, must be trained to listen for the important sounds and to disregard the unimportant ones. Auditory training would teach him how to listen and what to listen for—and, conversely, what *not* to listen for.

And again, the new user of a hearing aid must adjust not only his hearing but his whole nervous system to the noisy sound world into which he has been admitted. Frequently this sudden impact of sound is devastating. Little by little he must build up a tolerance for loud, unexpected, startling noises so that ultimately they cease to disturb him. Also he must learn to endure such minor, but no less annoying sounds, as the friction of clothes over the microphone.

A further reason for requiring auditory training of every deafened soldier was the belief that such training would not only bring about better understanding of speech but also would quicken the mental processes which so often begin to slow up with on-coming deafness. Keen auditory alertness can be attained and maintained only with continuous practice.

INSTRUCTION

I. Types of Instruction

Individual Instruction carried with it all that the term implies. First, the pupil's hearing was tested on two types of instruments—close-coupling headphones and a point-contact receiver. (His hearing aid as a training medium had already been ruled out as a result of the test for the intelligibility of speech). The pupil listened through each type of receiver to recorded speech, recorded music and to live voice heard through a microphone, and chose the instrument through which he obtained the clearest hearing. With this choice made, his training began. He was kept on special training equipment until he began to recognize sound patterns. There was no specific time allotted to this individual training. In each case the instructor decided when the pupil was ready to continue the training with his personal hearing aid.

Class Instruction. The classes averaged 12 to 15 in number, grouped so far as possible according to educational background. The first two weeks headphones were used for the hearing of speech sounds. The reason is obvious. Certain speech sounds, particularly high frequency consonants, are difficult to pick up with a hearing aid unless the instructor speaks closely and directly into the microphone of the aid. With 12 or more pupils in a room such a condition could not prevail; therefore one common microphone was used to which were attached headphones. After recognition of these speech sounds through headphones and subsequent drill, the transfer to hearing aid was made.

II. Length of Instruction

The minimum length of instruction for all pupils was 30 hours. Some individual pupils needed more and were given it. The success of the work was largely due to the concentration within the allotted time. In this type of training, 30 lessons on successive days were considered much more beneficial than twice that many extended over an indefinite period of time.

III. Levels of Instruction

The first week was used to introduce the group to hearing aids before fitting; to instruct and give practice in the use of individual aids; to teach how to operate and adjust controls, etc.

Weeks 2 to 4 were given over to basic instruction in auditory training.

Weeks 5 to 7 emphasized advanced work in auditory training.

IV. Breakdown of Levels of Instruction
  A. Basic Course

1. Speech intelligibility
   a. Listening to live voice
      (1) Voiced and breath consonants
          Recognition of initial, medial and final consonants in words, followed by sentences using predominating consonant sounds.
      (2) Short orientation talks, combining sound and sight.
      (3) Graded devices for quickness and accuracy of perception.
      (4) Jokes, anecdotes, short human interest stories for content by members of class in order to provide them with opportunity to hear different dialects.
   b. Listening to recorded speech
      (1) Slow narrative without sound background

2. Gross sounds

3. Recorded music, amplified through the loud-speaker
   a. Listening to instrumental music
      (1) Recognition of various solo instruments for pitch and timbre discrimination.
   b. Listening to vocal music
      (1) Recognition of solo voices for pitch discrimination.
      (2) Emphasis on word content. Scripts were used freely in basic course.

B. Advanced Course
   1. Speech intelligibility
      a. With live voice
         (1) Vowels and consonant combinations in single words. Sentences.
         (2) Further graded devices for quickness and accuracy of perception.

(3) Narratives read by:
2 and 3 voices in unison, 2 and 3 voices with attention to one voice while others tell different narrative softly, using sound and sight. (Simulating background of conversation).
(4) Stories for content told by individual members of class.
(5) Short dramatic skits with group participation.
(6) Distance listening as at lectures, church, etc., using both sound and sight.
(7) Informal conversational groups typical of home living-room set-up. Sound-sight.

b. Recorded speech
(1) Narrative with sound background.
(2) Narrative using 2 or more characters.
(3) Plays, skits, etc.
(4) Radio broadcasts.

c. Recorded Music
(1) Instrumental
(a) Recognition of outstanding instruments as they solo in bands or orchestras.
(b) Combination of 2 or 3 instruments with concentration on one at a time.
(2) Vocal
(a) Recognition of 2 voices in combination with concentration on one at a time.
(b) Listening to separate lines of melody by concentrating on one voice at a time. (Attempted only with 2 voices)
(c) Solo over chorus.
(d) Emphasis on word content. Without script, if possible.

Throughout the course emphasis was always on better speech perception. However, all material chosen was not speech. A liberal amount of music was used in our training because we felt there was a very definite place for it. First, it was used for its therapeutic value. Unquestionably music (some form of music) is enjoyed by practically everyone. It relaxes the individual; it permits him to forget, for the moment those maddening head noises, which after all seems to be the only practical solution to the problem.

Second, music is diverting. It would be too fatiguing (and this we guarded against) to sit for 50 minutes and listen to nothing but speech. Music affords an interruption and makes possible better concentration when speech is introduced again.

Third, not only is music diverting, it is also educational. By having his attention directed to certain instruments or lines of melody, the pupil is gaining in concentration and in the ability to listen over and through something else. This is particularly true in listening to song material. In extracting the words of a song through a background of accompaniment, the hearing-aid user is coping with a situation comparable to one he experiences every day when he is trying to sift out the speech of one person through a background of sound.

RESULTS

The results of this auditory training program were quite conclusive. With rare exception every pupil showed a definite gain in speech perception. This was exhibited by his ability:

(1) to "hold his own'" in a conversation.

(2) to understand speech through a background of noise.

(3) to make a practical correlation of sound and sight— auditory training and lip reading.

(4) to accomplish all the above with increased mental quickness and alertness.

Again, with few exceptions, the pupils who were fitted with hearing aids learned to adjust comfortably to these devices; became accustomed to the new background sounds; and gradually were able to extend the wearing time.

Finally, the training restored the man's confidence in himself. When once he realized he could both hear and understand, he knew that he could go out and resume his place in a society from which he had withdrawn.

The following statistics and case histories are submitted as confirmation of these results.

Percentage Gains on Speech Intelligibility Test for 61 Pupils Receiving Private Instruction (Test administered before and after training. Period of 6 months represented)

Percentage Gain	—	0	2	3	5	6	7	8	10	11	12	13	14	15	
No. of Cases	1	2	2	3	1	2	5	1	4	2	4	5	2	6	
Percentage Gain	16	17		18	20		21	23		25	27	29	31	33	36
No. of Cases	1	1		4	2		2	2		3	2	1	1	1	1

CASE HISTORY 1

Medical Report:

Diagnosis—Nerve Deafness.

Cause—TNT Explosion.

How Long Deafened—5 Months.

Total number hours of training—14.

Hearing aid—Bone conduction for right ear—90-volt battery.

I. Condition of hearing at beginning of training.

A. Speech through hearing aid very distorted.

B. Response to special training equipment:

(1) Speech Perception Test Score:

Left ear—100 words correct out of 150.

Right ear—110 words correct out of 150.

(2) Music

Right ear—all sounds distorted.

Left ear—fair.

Could follow words of songs only when pointed out by instructor.

II. Stages of Progress:

Progress at first steady. By tenth lesson began to notice decided improvement in speech reception, both to live voice and to vocal recordings. Beginning eleventh lesson he was given two daily periods of instruction (40 minutes each). From this point his progress was rapid. Final tests showed no distortion in right ear for music. Heard the highs of piccolo and the lows of bass violin. He was able to follow the words of songs without any scripts.

Final Speech Perception Test Score:

> Left ear—143 correct out of 150.
>
> Right ear—142 correct out of 150.

Voltage on hearing aid reduced from 90 volts to 45.

Case History 2

Medical Report:

> Diagnosis—Mixed Deafness.
>
> Cause—Undetermined.
>
> How Long Deafened—8 Years.

Total number hours of training—18.

Hearing aid—Air conduction for left ear.

I. Condition of hearing at beginning of training.
>   A. Left ear.
>>   (1) Doing all the work. In good condition.
>>   (2) Speech and music very clear.
>>   (3) Required very little volume.
>   B. Right ear.
>>   (1) Useless for all practical purposes. Had been this way for about 8 years.
>>   (2) On special close-coupling training equipment could hear sound but could not understand speech. Music badly blurred. Use of right ear spoiled the clear reception of left when taken together. Maximum volume required.
>>   (3) No response at all to hearing aid in this ear.

II. Stages of Progress:

A. Seven days from beginning of training right ear began to clear.

Much exercise with right ear alone after first hearing it with left ear to get correct concept of tone.

B. At eighth lesson began to hear speech with right ear alone (left ear plugged up). Maximum volume.

C. (1) At fourteenth lesson perfect balance between two ears. Right ear able to hear with same amount of volume as left.

(2) Speech perception given on close-coupling instrument to right ear alone, with left ear plugged. Score—119 correct out of 150.

(3) Tried hearing aid in right ear. Left plugged. Able to converse across table without reading the lips.

CASE HISTORY 3

Medical Report:

Diagnosis—Nerve Deafness.

Cause—Undetermined. Deafness greatly increased by shell explosion. Left ear completely shattered.

How Long Deafened—10 Years.

Total number hours of training—16.

Hearing aid—Air conduction in right ear.

I. Condition of hearing at beginning of training.

Left ear—no hearing.

Right ear—a great deal of sound but no clarity to speech.

Speech Perception Test Score—100 correct out of 150.

II. Stages of Progress:

A. At eighth lesson everything began to clear.

Music and speech suddenly became "clear as a crystal."

B. From this point until end of training hearing in right ear of superior quality. Developed ability for fine detail in listening.

C. Speech Perception Test Score—140 correct out of 150. *Right ear only.*

WILLIAM G. PEACHER, M.D.
Philadelphia, Pa.

Chapter XVIII

DISORDERS OF ARTICULATION DUE TO GUNSHOT WOUNDS OF THE HEAD AND NECK IN WORLD WAR II

INTRODUCTION

DURING World War II speech disorders in the U. S. Army were treated in clinics at the nineteen specially designated neurology-neurosurgery centers[14, 19] located strategically throughout the United States. Due to the extent of hostilities and magnitude of the casualty load necessitating medical and surgical treatment of an emergency nature together with associated neulrological and physical residuals which often required prolonged reconstructive measures, formal speech therapy was restricted within the confines of the United States. Facilities, however, for detailed neurological and psychological studies were available at the neurosurgical centers in the communications zones but not in the theaters of operation. In fact, investigations were instituted, not infrequently, at this point but were not completed for the reasons mentioned above as well as army policy stating that cases needing more than ninety days hospitalization were to be returned to the zone of the interior for extended management.

The speech clinics were under direct medical supervision in all instances. Consultation with the various specialties pertain-

236

ing to language problems (otolaryngology, psychiatry, etc.) was available and used as necessary. On completion of all essential diagnostic data, and depending upon the etiology, pathology and need for further medical and/or surgical therapy, the patient was seen by the speech pathologist who was also well grounded in psychology. Additional specialized analyses were then initiated as indicated, such as phonetic transcription of articulatory errors, vocal recording etc. Recommendations for treatment were then outlined by the attending physician and speech clinician correlating all current findings and adapted to the individual. These measures were coordinated with general rehabilitation of the patient in order that he might be able to return eventually to civilian life in the best possible condition from physical, mental, educational, economic and social standpoints. Service men remained in the hospital until the responsible neurologist was satisfied that a plateau of improvement had been attained even though this might take a year or more.

All types of speech disturbances were encountered and although the great majority were due to wounds or exposure to enemy action, other organic neurological and structural lesions more commonly observed in civilian life were studied (tumors, inflammatory and degenerative processes, cleft palate, etc.). Further, even though many functional disorders included with the dyslalias such as those due to articulatory deviations on the basis of inadequate educational standards and training, regional differences, psychological variations, imitation, short auditory memory span, poor sound discrimination etc. were seen, the main emphasis was on the organic etiological factors due to obvious wartime circumstances and the fact that minor speech defects alone were not disqualifying for full military duty.

From the standpoint of incidence, the dysphasias were encountered most commonly and together with the dysphonias and stuttering have been described elsewhere.[9, 10, 13, 14, 16, 17, 19] Disorders of articulation also were observed frequently[9, 10, 11, 13, 14, 18, 19] and will be reviewed from all aspects at this time. Several other papers have appeared[2, 4, 5, 6, 7] on this subject during the war years (World War II).

DYSARTHRIA

Disorders of articulation are divisable into various sub-groups depending upon certain anatomical, semeilogical and etiological factors. Lesions of the central or peripheral nervous system are productive of either dysarthria or dysarthro-phonia as noted in Table I. The latter term has been suggested[19] in lieu of dysarthria as the majority of these types of cases have associated problems involving phonation as well as articulation. Complete loss of both of these functions has been observed occasionally and has been designated as anarthro-phonia. Although defects in the motor sphere are more common, an occasional sensory form with parietal lobe localization (bilateral lesions more often than unilateral) has been seen. Further, even though it is beyond the scope of this presentation to discuss the problems and theories of dysphasia and dyspraxia[1], lesions of areas 44 and 6 (Brodmann) respectively in the dominant hemisphere can produce changes in articulation and phonation independent of the usual pathology resulting in dysarthro-phonia. In this connection, it is interesting to point out that other forms of dysphasia (sensory, amnesia, mixed) in addition to the motor variety alluded to above can result in similar alterations in speech due to injuries, tumors, etc. involving different areas of the brain. Appropriate examination usually can identify the type present.

TABLE I

Classification of Neurological Disorders of Articulation
1. Dysarthro-phonia
   A. Central Nervous System

a. Motor
  1) Pyramidal tracts
  2) Extra-pyramidal system
  3) Fronto-ponto-cerebellar tracts and associated cerebellar pathways.
  4) Area 44 (Brodmann)—see text
  5) Area 6 (Brodmann)—see text
b. Sensory
  1) Parietal lobe
B. Peripheral Nervous System
  a. Motor
    1) Vagal paralysis—palatal branches
2. Dysarthria
  A. Peripheral Nervous System
    a. Motor
      1) Facial paralysis
      2) Hypoglossal paralysis

Dyslalia

Dyslalia is the term preferred to denote disorders of articulation due to structural lesions involving the peripheral speech mechanism. As palatal defects are associated commonly with both articulatory and phonatory problems, rhino-phono-lalia has been used to designate this condition[19] rather than rhinophonia or rhinolalia. Functional forms of dyslalia are relatively frequent and have been alluded to previously (q.v.). The various types of dyslalia therefore include:

I. Organic etiological factors
  1. Pathology involving the lips, tongue, teeth or alveolar margins, such as trauma, carcinoma etc.
  2. Palatal lesions—rhino-phono-lalia.
    a. aperta—due to congenital, traumatic and inflammatory causes with resulting nasality or hyper-rhinolalia.

b. clausa—due to tumors, malformations etc. with production of de-nasality or hypo-rhinolalia.
1) anterior
2) posterior
II. Functional etiological factors
1. Regional differences
2. Psychological variations
3. Poor sound discrimination etc.

Anatomically, dyslalia resulted from structural damage to the
articulatory apparatus following gunshot wounds most commonly under the following situations:

1. Soft tissue wounds such as the lips and cheeks.
2. Varying degrees of loss of the tongue.
3. Destruction to the floor of the mouth and tongue.
4. Lesions of the soft and hard palate.
5. Maxillary and mandibular fractures with deformity.
6. Dental loss, particularly the incisors.
7. Trismus.
8. Cicatrices involving the organs of articulation, especially
between the tongue and floor of the mouth.

Due to the peripheral courses of the facial and hypoglossal
nerves, neurological implication was not uncommonly observed with structural damage to the articulatory apparatus.
Further, the necessity of emergency tracheotomy in many of
these battle casualties resulted also in disturbances of phonation
which was not always due to actual laryngeal lesions[17]. Finally,
with the multiplicity of modern wounds, intracranial trauma
often co-existed, occasionally with symptoms of dysphasia.[14, 19]

In some instances, speech therapy was instituted during surgical management. However, many maxillofacial wounds
caused severe destruction to the peripheral speech mechanism
necessitating often one to two years for satisfactory restoration.
In such instances, language training had to be postponed until
all such procedures were completed. At that time, adequate

compensation from the articulatory standpoint often had been accomplished. Occasionally, additional re-education was required particularly in the following types of cases:

1. Loss of varying portions of the tongue.
2. Adhesions between the tongue and floor of the mouth. Release of such scar often resulted in increased lingual mobility with amelioration of the subsequent speech problem.
3. Associated speech defects such as the dysphasias and dysphonias.

DYSAUDIA

Articulatory problems associated with hearing impairment were classified as dysaudia. Cases in this category were treated at the three specially designated Hard of Hearing centers (Borden, Hoff and Deshon General Hospitals) in the army.[20] They were transferred to speech clinics at the Neurology-Neurosurgery installations only in the presence of other language defects such as dysphasia, dysarthro-phonia, dysphonia etc. The U. S. Naval Hospital at Philadelphia was selected to assume care of all casualties of this type occuring in the navy.[8]

The following etiological factors were found to contribute to the production of hearing disturbances with associated speech defects: acoustic trauma, cranio-cerebral injuries, otitis media, systemic diseases such as mumps, pertussis, meningitis, scarlet fever; chronic progressive deafness etc.

Vocal and articulatory changes were not unusual in these types of cases and depending upon the degree of hearing loss and accompanying pathology necessitated speech reading and exercises, auditory training for adequate sound discrimination, fitting of a suitable hearing aid, control of co-existing symptoms such as headaches, vertigo, tinnitus and other neurological sequelae, psycho-therapy, fenestration procedures for patients with chronic progressive deafness, medical and surgical measures to control infection etc. (See Chapter IX).

DYSLOGIA

This group includes the various disorders of articulation observed in cases of neurosis, psychosis, and mental retardation. Symptoms, however are more characteristic of the underlying psychiatric problem rather than the accompanying speech disturbance. Therapy is directed therefore along these lines at the various Neuropsychiatric centers[14, 19] rather than specific speech re-education. The principles of examination and treatment here outlined have been applied, however, in some favorable instances.

METHODS OF EXAMINATION

Complete examination of the individual from all standpoints is prerequisite to successful therapy. These principles have been outlined in detail elsewhere.[12] A general summary of the various methods utilized is listed seriatim below, and these are adapted to the needs of the patient. It is important to emphasize the use of words and sentences weighted with the individual sound to be tested rather than employing the long, unwieldy test phrases such as "Round the rugged rock the ragged rascal ran. Methodist Episcopal. Third riding artillery brigade," which are often difficult for the normal person. In this way an accurate and permanent account was maintained. It also facilitated concentration on the faulty sound during re-education. Of additional significance is the recording of the patients' responses following the principles of the International Phonetic Alphabet rather than notation according to the examiners interpretation, use of diacritical markings etc. This system was extremely valuable due to its universal application, and it further enhanced the recounting of progress during recovery. It is also necessary to consider both articulatory and phonatory factors during the examination due to their frequent association.

METHODS OF EXAMINATION

1. Case history—medical, neurological and speech.
2. Physical, neurological and psychiatric examinations.
3. Laboratory studies:
   a. Blood and urine analyses.
   b. X-rays.
   c. Electro-encephalography.
   d. Lumbar puncture.
   e. Spinal fluid chemistry.
   f. Audiometry.
   g. Laryngoscopy—indirect and/or direct.
   h. Photographs and plaster models of deformities.
4. Psychometric analyses.
5. Experimental phonetic methods—pneumography etc.
6. Consultations: Otolaryngology, oral surgery, occupational-therapy, physiotherapy, plastic surgery etc.
7. Surgery:
   a. Encephalography.
   b. Ventriculography.
   c. Craniotomy with inspection of the cortex.
   d. Exploration and examination of peripheral courses of the facial and hypoglossal nerves.
   e. Reconstructive procedures with investigation of maxillo-facial defects and deformities.
8. Observation of spontaneous speech.
9. Vocal recording.
10. Use of weighted words, phrases and sentences with the individual sound to be tested in the initial, medial and final position.
11. Phonetic analysis to include sound additions, substitutions, omissions and distortions.
12. Sound discrimination tests.
13. Speech perception examinations.

14. Oral reading studies for articulatory errors:
    Gates Primary Reading Tests.
    Gray's Oral Reading Paragraphs.
15. Description of the voice to include intensity, quality and and pitch.
16. Discussion of rhythm in speech.
17. Photography of the laryngeal apparatus as indicated.
18. Investigation of associated speech defects: dysphasia, dysphonia, stuttering etc.

THERAPY

Numerous therapeutic procedures are available in the management of the various disorders of articulation. Phonatory factors have also been considered due to their frequent association. These are summarized below and must be adapted to individual requirements. Specific re-education was postponed usually until all medical and surgical problems' primarily or secondarily implicating the language mechanism' structural and/or neurological had been clarified. Muscle exercises (tongue, lip, palate etc.) if indicated usually initiated the speech program. Both individual and group therapy were given. The type and length of training depended upon the patients' tolerance, response, presenting and associated defects (physical and/or neurological) etiology pathology etc. Sessions were limited to fifteen to thirty minutes twice daily, occasionally longer. It is to be remembered that all service men participated in the general rehabilitation of the organism on an eight hour daily basis. Some material on this subject has appeared elsewhere.[2, 3, 6, 7, 15]

TREATMENT

1. Treatment of associated physical defects, surgical and/or medical.
2. Specific reconstructive surgery following maxillofacial wounds including repair of soft tissue deformities, man-

dibular grafts, local and distant pedicle flaps in the presence of palatal perforations, facial defects, resection of cicatrices involving the tongue, floor of the mouth etc.

3. Orthodontal and oral surgical therapy, particularly with extensive jaw and dental traumata due to gunshot wounds.

4. Fitting of an adequate extra- or intra-oral prosthesis or obturator. The majority of perforating wounds with resulting defects, particularly of the palate, however, have been repaired successfully.

5. Treatment of accompanying neurological residuals affecting the speech apparatus. A. Peripheral exploration of the facial and hypoglossal nerves. Depending upon the etiology and pathology present, neurolysis, neurorrhaphy, transplantation, anastomosis (facial-accessory etc.) etc. may be necessary. Under these circumstances, physical therapy (see 7) and exercises as indicated in 13, 14 and 15 are instituted following satisfactory wound healing. Occasionally, irreparable damage is found. In these instances, nerve grafting has been of occasional value. If all methods fail, a facial transplant may be used in seventh nerve lesions, but even here results are not always entirely adequate. In these cases, compensatory techniques as outlined in 15 must be initiated. B. Resection of cerebro-dural and cortical scars. The necessity of such procedures depends upon previous diagnostic records, such as neurological, physical and psychological examinations, electro-encephalography, encephalography, ventriculography etc. These, together with the operative findings demonstrate the presence of intracranial damage and the need of re-education along the lines of residual cortical function and associated pathways (e.g. in the dysphasias) in addition to the therapy outlined in this section.

6. Psychotherapy and mental hygiene.

7. Physical therapy. Heat, massage and electrical stimulation

have been particularly useful in lesions of the seventh and twelfth cranial nerves. Local manipulation has also been of value in some structural injuries of the soft palate and tongue.

8. Occupational and diversional therapy.

9. General reconditioning of the entire organism: physical, mental, social, educational and economic, rather than emphasizing the neurological or physical disability alone.

10. Treatment of associated speech problems such as dysphasia, stuttering etc.

11. Psychiatric therapy particularly in the dyslogias.

12. Speech reading and acoustic training especially in the dysaudias.

13. Routine tongue, lip, palate and breathing exercises as well as those to promote relaxation as indicated.

14. Chewing and cork exercises for cases of dysarthria and dysarthro-phonia, and pushing technics for paralysis of the soft palate as recommended by Froeschels[3] have been useful in some instances.

15. Phonetic stimulation for adequate sound production. Compensatory movements are occasionally necessary in the presence of irreparable neurological and/or structural damage to the peripheral speech apparatus. When the correct sound is obtained, it is strengthened by appropriate methods including the use of nonsense syllables, combinations of vowels and consonants, discrimination exercises, familiar rhymes, poems, proverbs etc. Imitation, mirror practice, mechanical and kinesthetic guidance and ear training are helpful during this process.

16. Visual, auditory and tactile stimulation are valuable in the development of associated pathways particularly with the articulatory problems accompanying the dysphasias.

17. Negative practice was of value in occasional cases. In such instances, the individual was instructed to repeat and con-

centrate on his own deviations that he may become more aware of such errors thus gaining additional insight for their correction.

18. Use of the mirrophone has facilitated the patients' detection and correction of his own errors.

19. Permanent recordings allow continued re-evaluation and are helpful to the individual as a comparison and to demonstrate his progress.

20. Records demonstrating phonetic discrimination to the patient.

21. Methods to improve easy initiation and production of voice, stress and melody pattern.

22. Drills to illustrate changing inflection and rhythm in speech.

BIBLIOGRAPHY

1. *Bucy, P. C.:* The Precentral Motor Cortex. The University of Illinois Press, Urbana, Illinois, 250, 268, 420, 1944.

2. *Freud, E.:* Treatment of Disorders of the Voice and Speech Caused by War Wounds. Ann. d'oto-laryngol. 14-16, (Jan.-Feb.), 1940.

3. *Froeschels, E.:* A Contribution to the Pathology and Therapy of Dysarthria due to Certain Cerebral Lesions. J. Speech Disorders, 8: 301-321, 1943.

4. *Loebell, H. A.:* A Half Year's Experience in the First Division for Voice and Speech Disturbances in the Armed Forces. Deut. Militararzt. 6: 148-152, 1941.

5. *Michaelson, N. M.:* Tongue Wounds. Am. Rev. Soviet Med. 1: 216-219, 1944.

6. *Panconcelli-Calzia, G.:* Uber die Wiedererlangung der Sprechfaehigkeit nach Zungenverletzungen. Deut. Militaerarzt 8: 270-271, 1943.

7. *Panconcelli-Calzia, G.:* On the Activity of the Speech Station of Military District X. Die Med. Welt. 14: 1220-1221, 1940.

8. *Pauls, M.D., Haskins, H. L. and Hardy, W. G.:* Speech Reading, Auditory Training and Speech Correction in the Re-education Program. Supplement to the U. S. Naval Med. Bull. 232-248, (March), 1946.

9. *Peacher, W. G.:* Speech Disorders in World War II. J. Speech Disorders, 10: 155-161, 1945.

10. *Peacher, W. G.:* Speech Disorders in World War II. II. Further Studies. J. Nerv. and Ment. Dis. 102: 165-171, 1945.
11. *Peacher, W. G.:* Speech Disorders in World War II. III. Dysarthria. J. Speech Disorders, 10: 287-291, 1945.
12. *Peacher, W. G. and Peacher, G. M.:* Speech Disorders in World War II. IV. Dysarthria and Dyslalia. Methods of Examination. J. Nerv. and Ment. Dis. 103: 484-493, 1946.
13. *Peacher, W. G.:* Speech Disorders in World War II. V. Organization of a Speech Clinic in an Army General Hospital. J. Speech Disorders, 11: 233-239, 1946.
14. *Peacher, W. G.:* Speech Disorders in World War II. VI. Survey of Speech Clinics in the U. S. and British Armies. J. Nerv. and Ment. Dis. (In Press), 1947.
15. *Peacher, W. G.:* Speech Disorders in World War II. VII. Treatment of Dysarthria. J. Nerv. and Ment. Dis. (In Press), 1947.
16. *Peacher, W. G. and Harris, W. E.:* Speech Disorders in World War II. VIII. Stuttering. J. Speech Disorders, 11: 303-308, 1946.
17. *Peacher, W. G.:* Speech Disorders in World War II. IX. Dysphonia. Arch. Otolaryngol. (In Press).
18. *Peacher, W. G.:* Speech Disorders in World War II. X. Speech Defects Resulting from Maxillofacial Injuries. J. Plastic and Reconstructive Surg. (In Press).
19. *Peacher, W. G.:* Speech Disorders Resulting from Gunshot Wounds of the Head and Neck. Medical History of World War II. Neurosurgery. U. S. Government Printing Office, Washington, D. C. (In Press).
20. *Truex, E. H.:* Chronic Deafness, Its Treatment in the Army. Ann. Otol. Rhin. & Laryngol. 54: 466-482, 1945.

O. R. BONTRAGER
Director of the Reading Clinic, State Teachers
College, California, Pennsylvania

Chapter XIX

REMEDIAL READING
AND GENERAL SEMANTICS

A RECENT index to the literature on reading contains over 8,000 entries, representing chiefly writings done in the past 20 years. Approximately one-half of the productions dealt with eye movements (roughly 140 in number), vision (260), auditory factors, word 'blindness', and similar 'remedial' topics. The recent Army draft provides one measure of the effectiveness of this great reading crusade, representing tons of ink and paper. *One in seven adult Americans was found to be functionally illiterate.* Recently, 52 per cent of the citizens looked blank when asked on a Gallup poll: what is a filibuster? This proportion of illiteracy becomes frightening when we remember that one-seventh of the population of the United States represents a figure greater than the majority by which most of our Presidents were elected to office.

This discussion is based on a careful evaluation of four recent books and extensive readings selected from about 400 articles published since V-E Day. An examination of these post-war writings recalls Hawthorne's Mr. Gascoigne, whose 'mind seemed to run on political topics, but whether relating to the past, present, or future, could not easily be determined, since

249

the same ideas have been in vogue these fifty years.' Aristotle would be unable to understand the assumptions and language of modern medicine or nuclear physics; however, the assumptions and undefined terms in 1947 works on reading would sound familiar to him.

2.

Dead men tell no tales. They don't read, either. What are the happenings that take place under the skin of a living being when he reads? In what way do the happenings under the skin of a *remedial* reader differ from those under the skin of a *successful* reader in a given situation? On these issues, the writers provide no diagram. One writer (who, incidentally, does not come to grips with these questions in several thousand pages) recently discovered, after surveying what came out of his typewriter, two additional 'types' of reading: *corrective* and *developmental*. Thus is 'confusion worse confounded.'

In millions of words, I can find no scientific basis for determining when a reading performance has been successful. By *scientific basis,* I represent a state of affairs analogous to what happens when two physicians *independently* diagnose Mr. X as having type B pneumonia and *independently* prescribe the treatment that will save his life. In an age when our physicians act on the basis of blood counts, X-ray, and other *non-verbal* findings, reading authorities act on *verbal* definitions. One writer states repeatedly that reading is a *facet* of something. Webster defines *facet* as a small plane surface. By this token, the discoverer of *facets* is on the surface of things. Had he announced that reading is a *faucet,* he would have relieved the shortage of plumbing fixtures to the same extent that his invention of *facet* comes to grips with anything in this world, reading included. This writer also makes the remarkable discovery that reading problems are ordered as a continuum. The *alexias* are to be found at one end of the array, and the *dyslexias* at the other. Here is the etymology of these terms: ALEXIA

(N. L. *a* — not + Gr. *lexis* — speech, reading, etc.); DYS-LEXIA (Gr. *dys* — bad, difficult, etc. + *lexis* — speech, reading, etc.). Thus, poor readers are seen to be distributed along a continuum, at one end of which are poor (or *not-*) readers, and at the other end of which are poor (or *bad, difficult*) readers. This is where we came in. Here is demonstrated the correctness of the mathematical conclusion reached by the leading actor in *Lost Week End*: 'A circle is a perfect geometric figure; it begins no place, and it ends no place.' This authority made his discovery, not by using the laboratory and surgical techniques of modern medicine, but by probing his convolutions for Greek synonyms for poor reading. Other authorities, quick to recognize that a new word has been added to the vocabulary of 'remedial' reading, set forth on a new assault against the windmills: a new crusade on behalf of the 'dyslexiacs'. Without as much as looking into a single skull, they have discovered brain *'conflict'* or *'twist'* (see *Colliers*: November 30, 1946; *Life*: September 2, 1946; *Time*: March 24, 1947) as accounting for 'dyslexia'. Which part of the brain is 'twisted' or in 'conflict' we are not told. To provide diagrams would possibly be too difficult, since no one in 1947 knows all that happens under my skin when I crook my finger.

3.

In over 400 articles on reading and 'remedial' reading, written since the atomic age began, one finds no operational account of what happens in a living being when he reads. There are no hints that the specialists are even aware of this. Yet, every paper I have read states or implies this verbal postulate: *reading is getting thought from the printed page.* Different writers employ different synonyms for 'get' and for 'thought'. Thus, for 'get' one finds 'grasp', 'gain', 'acquire' 'derive', 'extract', 'obtain', 'take', 'gather', 'comprehend' (L. *cum* + *prehendere*), 'apprehend', etc. For 'thought': 'sense', 'essence', 'meaning', 'spirit', 'concept', etc. They 'torture one poor word ten thousand ways.'

No one tells us what we *do* when we *get* 'thought', and no one diagrams for us *what* we 'get'. *A reader gets nothing from a printed page.* Anyone who will honestly face the full implications of the preceding sentence will be compelled to discard practically every line that has ever been written about reading or 'remedial' reading as logical nonsense. Surgeons will understand this; reading authorities, in the main, will not. They are lost, to paraphrase Porter Sargent, in the mazes of their own convolutions.

4.

P. W. Bridgman has said that 'the true meaning of a term is to be found by observing what a man does with it, not what he says about it.' The activities carried on in 1947 under the label, 'remedial' reading, provide interesting clues as to what the experts mean by the word, reading. With few exceptions, the specialists center their attention on the poor reader's 'getters': his eyes. They photograph the 'getter' (eye) movements. One writer justifies this procedure by making reading analogous to what happens when marbles are transferred from Box A to Box B. The marbles can be moved by taking one marble at a time. They can be moved by grabbing whole handfuls at once, in which case the transfer is effected more rapidly. This author is by no means unusually naive. He only reduces to an absurdity the nonsense to which scores of other authorities devote entire articles, chapters, or volumes. The latter dignify the nonsense by the use of terms like *fixations, regressions,* and by employing mathematical calculations. As I indicated earlier, a recent index lists approximately 140 books and articles on eye movements alone.

In addition to photographing the 'getter', tests are administered to determine whether or not the 'remedial case' can 'hold thoughts' after he 'gets' them. The examiner exposes a series of words, such as: HERE BOY TREE RUN THIS ROAD. The 'case' is then asked to repeat in correct order as many of the words as he can recall. Thus is established the extent of his 'thought holding power,' otherwise known as *visual memory span.*

The sponge ('getting', absorption, etc.) theory of reading, when translated into current practices in remedial reading, results in the use of various kinds of gadgets to improve the 'thought-getters', commonly known as eyes, and the 'idea holder'. Photographs show how many stops the 'getters' make in traversing a line. The eyes see only when they stop. They do not see when in motion. Therefore, the fewer stops per line, the more 'getting' can be accomplished on each stop. Printed matter on paper rolls is fed through mechanical engines involving a system of shutters that expose fixed lengths of line at controlled speeds, thus forcing the remedial guinea pig to 'get' at a pre-determined rate. A third of a line is exposed at a time, and immediately thereafter covered with a shutter, to compel the 'getter' to 'hold the thoughts.' The speed of the engine is gradually increased, so that the 'patient' gradually does 'better and faster' whatever it is that he does. Whether or not this turns out to be reading, I shall consider later. At this point it is necessary only to observe that the theory that the eyes see only when at rest would force the conclusion that all the 'dog fights' waged by airmen in World War II were fought by blind men. *The blind can read; horses cannot.* Ernest Horn, one of the very few *scholars* dealing with reading problems today, dismisses this 'thought grabbing' nonsense as follows: 'The classroom teacher needs to be concerned with movements of the eyes little more than with the movement of the bones of the middle ear.'*

5.

A second series of practices that suggest a belief in 'thought-getting' employs various puzzles to train what is called *visual*

---

* Horn, Ernest, *Methods of Instruction in the Social Studies.* New York: Charles Scribner's Sons, 1937, p. 202.

discrimination. A child who has been talking for years, and can tell his dog from his cat, his mother from his father, a glass of water from a glass of milk, his house from his neighbor's house, — in short, can discriminate visually in hundreds of ways — is, in terms of these practices, suddenly found to have a faulty discriminator. He is given puzzles that require him to: find the monkey whose tail is missing; find the picture of the cow with only three legs; draw a line around the two letters that look just alike; find two words that begin with *r;* find the parts of two words that look alike; find the words that begin with *d* (these are mixed with a list of words beginning with *b*); draw a circle around *saw* (other words in the line are *sat   son   was*). If he should select a word that begins with *b* instead of *d,* or if he encircles *was* instead of *saw,* hurried conferences are called to discuss another *reversal,* otherwise known as twisted brains (*Time:* March 24, 1947). No one in the world thinks of calling a conference when Brown mistakes Smith for Jones, or when he picks up Watson's pencil by mistake, or accidentally passes out a two-dollar bill to settle a one-dollar debt. But not so with the modern phrenologists in reading. Prefix and suffix wheels are brought into play to train the discriminators. Puzzles are concocted to train in 'word discrimination,' 'letter discrimination,' 'sentence discrimination,' 'left-to-right progression' (in China it would have to be up-to-down-progression), and so on. Papers and books are written on 'omission of words,' 'addition of words,' 'substitution of words,' 'guessing,' 'laterality confusions,' 'peripheral confusions,' and 'central confusions' — confusions to which no more significance should be attached than to the confusion that takes place when Smith picks up Brown's hat. Anyone who asserts the contrary is asked to demonstrate, *with diagrams,* the difference in the neurological structures involved in 'lateral' and 'central confusions.' Even after the visual discriminators have been 'conditioned,' to use the garage mechanic's terminology, it still remains to be shown that the 'discriminator,' *without confusions,* reads at all. Pavlov trained his dogs to discriminate visually between a circle and an ellipse—possibly as difficult a performance as discriminating between *b* and *d*. Is there a reading authority who can demonstrate that puppies can read? Pavlov measured the results of his dogs' performance in drops of saliva. What evidence, other than noises, have 'remedial' specialists to offer that the good visual 'discriminators' read at all? *Reading is not as simple as making noises,* as I shall presently show.

6.

A third series of remedial practices involves the diagnosis and training of the hearing 'getter', known as *auditory discrimination.* Willie Brown, who can carry on a conversation and is immediately on the alert when he hears mama say *candy,* is heard saying *wich* for *which* or *singin'* for *singing.* It makes no difference that in some sections of the country (e.g., western Pennsylvania) readers and non-readers alike say *wich* for *which.* Willie's auditory discriminator is remedial trained by putting him through stunts like these: closing eyes and counting taps as teacher taps desk; pointing in the direction of the clock when blindfolded; giving words that rhyme with *cat;* listening while the trainer pronounces lists of words beginning with *f* (or *b, c, d,* etc.); listening for words that end in *-ing,* and so on. He is trained on digraphs and diphthongs. He swallows large doses of syllables, disyllables, trisyllables, and polysyllables. He learns word 'un-locking' in phonics, where he wrestles with surds and sonants; with plosives, fricatives, labials and dentals; with consonant blends and murmur diphthongs. All this in a language that gives us: *cow, bow* (and arrow), *cough, bough, trough, rough, out, ought,* and *slough.* Heaven forbid that some authority discovers that before future Willies can talk, they must analyze *tree* before they can say *tree,* or that they must take the *clock* apart before they can say, *clock.* If the analyzers are correct, then the Chinese cannot learn to read; one cannot sound out a hieroglyphic. The deaf learn to read; parrots, though they can hear the sounds and reproduce them, cannot. History provides many illustrations of the fallacy of: *post hoc ergo propter hoc.* People frequently die in bed; however, it would probably be inappropriate, in most instances, to say that beds cause people to die.

7.

A fourth practice in remedial reading is employed when the visual and auditory 'discriminators' of *talking* people apparently cannot be trained to 'get thought' from ink marks. In such cases, the kinaesthetic 'getter' is developed. Words are printed with a crayon on a large piece of cardboard. The remedial reader traces the word with his first and second fingers until he is able to reproduce it without looking. Later, he is taught to look at a word in script, pronounce it, then to copy it (without the preliminary tracing) as he speaks each part of the word. Still later, he learns to look at a *printed* word, pronounce it, close the book and write the word without looking. Finally, he is able to make the noise that corresponds to the ink mark without copying it. What goes on under the reader's skin as he makes the noises is not known. This, in a world with atom bombs loose in it, may turn out to be of some importance. The paper tests of the remedial specialists do not provide an answer.

8.

It appears that reading investigators have not yet explored the possibility of developing the olfactory and gustatory 'getters' as a 'remedial' technique. Kinaesthetic, olfactory, and gustatory 'memory spans' have yet to be discovered. They no doubt will be as the cerebrations of specialists continue to spiral. As new fields of research are explored, it may be that the phonetic blends will some day be taught through the olfactory approach of an amalgamation of Evening in Paris and Djer Kiss. Possibly, too, it is not too much to hope that future gustatory training methods will make it possible to teach the non-reader by feeding him noodle soup made of consonants, vowels, and murmur diphthongs.

9.

I have described some 'remedial' reading-assumptions-in-action. Current practices illustrate many others, of which I will consider only two. The first I call the salt and pepper theory in reading. Following this theory, 'remedial' classes are organized for pupils whom the teachers report as unable to read *The Spectator,* a theorem in geometry, or some ink marks in history. These pupils are segregated, and taught how to do something called 'reading', apparently on the assumption that reading *The Spectator* equals reading geometry. They are equipped with the salt and pepper with which they can sprinkle ink marks, wherever they may be encountered, and then read them. It has never been clear to me what any teacher of *The Spectator* can possibly do other than teach people how to read it. If pupils enter a history class *already knowing how to read the history under consideration,* what else can the teacher possibly teach them? *No one ever learns, finally and completely, how to read.* I am aware of no parallel to current exhibits of arrant sophistry that differentiate between *teaching* reading and *remedial treatment* in reading. If techniques have been produced for teaching a pupil to read in a 'remedial' room *after* failure, then it is not impertinent to ask why such techniques are not used to *prevent* failure. If mathematics teachers, and others, cannot teach children how to evaluate the ink marks in *their* classes, how can it be assumed that anyone else can? *One does not read reading.* The *something* that we read invariably turns out to be some history, science, and so on.

A second assumption merits brief consideration. It suggests that the person who can read possesses an unconditional asset.

In the United States, 'readers' purchase 180 million comic magazines yearly. The publishers of 'Superman' report an annual profit of $1,500,000. Roughly two per cent of our people read books, mainly fiction. Recent history shows that acts of psychical violence committed in wars of words become the chief weapons used by dictators to forge their way to power. A society devoted to *Tarzan* and *True Romances,* and exposed to the double talk, propaganda, and quackery of the prints, may soon discover that reading can become a short-cut to destruction. Reading authorities appear not to recognize this as a remedial problem.

10.

Assumptions govern behavior. When the earth was regarded as flat, men did not venture out of sight of land. When I use the term, 'reading', I refer to what happens in a living being when he evaluates ink marks, hieroglyphics, etc. Figure 1 represents some of the factors that I assume to be involved in every reading situation. If these factors are accepted as relevant, then programs of reading instruction and 'remedial' reading must automatically emphasize what is now disregarded.

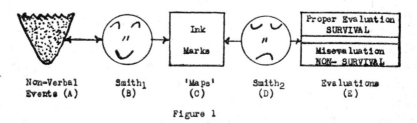

Figure 1

It appears that every situation in which reading is done involves: (A), some non-verbal events; (B), Smith$_1$ who in some way becomes familiar with or 'knows' something about (A); (C), some ink marks made by Smith$_1$ to represent what he has discovered about (A); (D), Smith$_2$, who undertakes to arrive at a proper evaluation of (A) by an examination of (C); and

(E), whatever follows Smith₂'s evaluation of (C). Included in (A) are the non-verbal happenings constantly taking place under the skin of Smith₁ as he evaluates (A). Included in (E) are the non-verbal happenings, reactions, etc. under the skin of Smith₂ as he evaluates (C). Throughout this discussion, I will use the letters, (A), (B), (C), (D), and (E) to refer to the corresponding parts of the diagram.

A careful evaluation of Figure 1 suggests origins of reading problems that were almost entirely unsuspected before Alfred Korzybski formulated his system of *general semantics* in *Science and Sanity*. Even in 1947, no recognized writer on reading methodology deals with all the issues suggested by the diagram. Those who set the pattern of reading instruction in America today assume that reading problems arise solely in (C) and (D). The factors involved in (A), (B), and (E) are disregarded. Future events may show that this is *the* reading problem of our time. Human survival, in an atomic age, may depend upon its solution.

11.

Scientists describe the non-verbal events that comprise the universe, ourselves included, in terms of order, relations, and structure. Human progress and survival (E) thus far can be accounted for in terms of man's proper evaluation of order, relations, and structure. Thus Hogben, in *Mathematics for the Million,* shows how man in the millenia before the dawn of civilization became aware of *order* in the apparent movements of the sun, moon, and stars. He further noted *relations* between these movements and the seasons. From the observed order and relations, he reached conclusions about the *structure* of the universe. Agriculture and navigation became possible.

When Leeuwenhoek looked for the first time into a new world filled with thousands of kinds of microscopic beings, he established new *structural* characteristics in the environment. When Spallanzani afterwards found that microbes have parents, he discovered something about *order* and *relations*. When Pasteur learned that microbes can kill people, he discovered additional information about *relations*. Every discovery of man —fire, the steam engine, the circulation of blood, anesthesia, the electric lamp, radio, atomic power, etc.—is a monument to his discovery of some structure in the non-verbal world of which he is a part. Today, the researches that are being carried on to eliminate cancer, polio, heart disease, and so on will succeed as new relations and structure are properly evaluated. Indeed, as Korzybski has shown, the basis of all knowledge is structural.

12.

Smith$_1$, who makes the hieroglyphics, stands between Smith$_2$ and the non-verbal events. This makes for an as yet unrecognized source of reading difficulty for Smith$_2$. For Smith$_1$, unaided, sees no microbes. He does not see the ultra-violet, the vitamins, the cosmic rays, or the atom; he mistakes poison gas on the battle field for apple blossoms; he does not translate into sounds the waves in the supersonic range, nor can he hear without an instrument the radio signals that reach him from all over the earth; he evaluates the room as 'hot' at the moment his wife announces it as 'cold'. In this condition, he appraises the non-verbal universe and proceeds to make ink marks about it. Still more: to his seeing, hearing, feeling, etc., Smith$_1$ brings his dogmas, creeds, notions of cause and effect, 'right' and 'wrong' —in short, his notions of relations and structure that often date back to the cave man. To him, the non-verbal world *is* what it appears to be; yet, it is not.

Smith$_1$ becomes inseparably involved in (C). Ink marks do not make themselves. The relations and structure in (C), as represented by Smith$_1$, will include *his notions* about relations and structure in (A). Dissimilarity in the structure of (A) and (C) can come about through Smith$_1$'s ignorance, his deliberate misrepresentation, the structure of the language he inherits, or through all of these. *We have no methods by which we can scrutinize (C) alone that will enable us to ascertain the degree of dissimilarity between (A) and (C); and (C) will not tell us.* Only a comparison of the structures of (A) and (C) will disclose the similarities and dissimilarities between them.

But who will make the comparisons? Smith₁ can see no microbes, atoms, or electrons. He sees what he sees. History has shown that his opinions cannot be accepted as an accurate guide to a correct evaluation of the structural characteristics of (A). Modern astronomy has shown that the sun he sees as 'rising' in the east and 'setting' in the west *is not* as seen. The wave theory of energies has shown that the 'red' he sees as in the flower *is not* as seen. The radio has shown that the 'space' he sees as 'empty' becomes fullness, involving fields. Electric refrigerators do not screen out the 'heat' that he feels as in the water. They reduce dynamic, molecular structures to smaller volumes. Heat *is not* as evaluated by Smith₁.

The structure of the non-verbal world, (A), is not established by opinion. It *is not* as reported by the so-called 'senses'. Structure can only be inferred; no one has ever seen an atom. *The test of the accuracy of the inference is predictability (E)— not opinion.* Anyone who believes that the book he now holds in his hands is a 'solid', static, unmoving kind of thing is asked to produce a non-verbal atomic bomb on the basis of his theory. To the extent that we can test our opinions and produce empirical, predictable, non-verbal results, we establish their validity for the time being.

13.

In 1947, science provides the only method we have for the evaluation of the structure of (A). The method, as already shown, is the empirical, non-verbal verification of inferences. Predictability, (E), is *the only* test we have that gives us *any clues whatsoever* as to the accuracy of the opinions we hold regarding relations and structure *in any connection.* And it should never be forgotten that *the beliefs, opinions, etc. that we hold,* whether on reading, war, race, taxes, climate, behavior, 'good', crime, 'problems', 'false', or what not, imply some relations and structure in the non-verbal universe. Moreover, unknown structural factors, entirely unrepresented in our beliefs, dogmas, and opinions, may nevertheless wreck our most 'logical' generalizations. In life we cannot escape the consequences of disregarded structural factors. The biscuits will kill us, despite our verbalizations about 'how delicious they are,' if some unsuspected structural factor, say insect powder, accidentally becomes mixed into the flour. We live by the non-verbal events in the universe; we die by them, too, if they are not properly taken into account. Today, millions of children in our schools learn what they learn about reading by following methods and materials sponsored by reading authorities who disregard the relationships between correct evaluation of structure in the non-verbal world and what becomes, in the final analysis, human survival (E).

14.

The empirical tests of science (1947) have established predictability for these (among others) inferences regarding the structure of non-verbal events, ourselves included: A dynamic, ever-changing, electronic, *process* state of affairs; nothing is identical, in all respects with anything else. Even the structures of two atoms differ, for they comprise different portions of dynamic fields. Everything is related in some way to everything else. We find here infinities of characteristics, possibilities, and combinations of events.

Empirical investigation establishes no 'properties' in the non-verbal world: no 'color', 'heat', 'taste', 'sound', 'good', 'wrong', 'hardness', or any other 'qualities' or 'attributes'. There are no classes—only absolute differences. Empirical fullness is found in what is seen as 'empty' space.

Science establishes no two-valued causality, but infinite combinations and processions of order-relations: events following other events, that we erroneously regard as fixed, cause-effect relationships. Finally, as noted above, structure is not as seen.

These are some inferences that have been validated for the time being. It is necessary to say 'for the time being,' for unexpected factors may invalidate a generalization. Extending a theory, or inference, to make it account for more phenomena, may render it untenable. Newton's accounts of structure appeared valid as long as they were applied only when erecting skyscrapers or building bridges. But they do not explain the atom. *Science does not stay fixed,* widespread notions to the contrary notwithstanding. The entire history of science records change after change in what was 'known'. Today, much of what was 'known' about atomic structure as recently as 1941 has already been discarded. It may be, too, that a Schrodinger, in 1947, has produced a generalization more inclusive than the theory of Einstein.

15.

It remains now to examine the structure of (C), the ink marks Smith₁ makes about (A). Korzybski has demonstrated the importance of similarity in structure between (C) and (A) with his map-territory analogy:

Territory	SF		C		NY
	*		*		*
Map	C		SF		NY
	*		*		*

FIGURE 2

If the structure of some actual territory is such that Chicago is between New York and San Francisco, and we should try to travel by a map that located the cities as indicated in Figure 2, we would go astray, meet with 'disappointments', perhaps inconvenience others, and so on. We could not get where we want to go by following a map that misrepresents the structure of the territory.

It happens that Smith₁ inherits a language that differs in structure from the structure of the non-verbal events. His language *compels* him to emphasize similarities but *permits* him to ignore differences. By ignoring differences, he can classify a million unique individuals under the label, farmer, and talk about what farmers want, overlooking completely the fact that what farmer₁ wants is not what farmer₂ wants. His language permits him to represent unique individuals as identical in a universe where there is no identity. In a similar manner, he can talk about 'labor', 'business', 'Russians', 'Germans', and 'Americans', representing with one label thousands, or even millions of *different* individuals. In language he can equate Hitler and Goethe, Pavlov and Stalin, Edison and Dillinger.

It is true that without recognition of similarities, intelligent behavior and language would be impossible. However, human survival has depended upon the recognition of *both* similarities and differences. Detecting differences between mushroom₁ and mushroom₂ has spelled survival as long as men have eaten mushrooms. Differences incorporated in 'booby traps' killed soldiers on the battlefield. Following a language that does not structurally show differences, and that represents differences as identical, inevitably leads to lowered predictability and eventually to non-survival (E).

A second structural characteristic of the language we inherit enables Smith₁ to put a 'property' or an 'attribute' into a nonverbal event where science finds no properties or attributes. When he uses the *is* of predication to say, 'the rose is red,' he creates a language that no scientist can follow and produce an ultra-violet lamp. When he said, 'Germans are superior,' he created a language that was followed by millions, but for which no predictability was established, as some of the millions must now understand. A language structurally similar to the chain of events that preceded the statement, 'Germans are superior' would reveal something like this: I, Smith₁ (not some Omnipotent), who sees what he sees, and believes what he believes, have examined *a few* non-verbal events belonging to the human class of life; after my examination, I, Smith₁, divided *all* the individuals belonging to the human class of life into two classes: Germans and non-Germans. From my *limited* examination, *I* conclude that *all* (unlimited) individuals whom *I* classify as Germans are exactly the same in all respects, forever and ever, amen; *I* reach the same conclusion regarding *all* non-Germans; I have compared *a few* individuals in the German class with *a few* individuals in what I am pleased to call the non-German class; I am therefore able to conclude that *I* would find absolute differences which establish a superior-inferior relationship (my beliefs and seeing apparatus operating as they operate) if I were to make every possible comparison between *all* the individuals in the two groups. I am now able to state that *each* individual belonging to the 'German' class is 'superior' (whatever *I* represent by the term, 'superior') to *every* individual in the non-'German' class in *every* situation in which *anyone* can compare them.

Today it is not difficult to find, in Germany and elsewhere, empirical evidence of what happens when we follow a language that is structurally false to fact. In the end, the non-verbal relations and structure prevail, *no matter what we say*. But reading methodologists do not recognize structure as a problem. Events of the future will establish whether or not such omissions are justified. From this there is no escape.

A third structural characteristic of language enables Smith₁ to represent a non-verbal something as something verbal. In short, he can say in language that map is the same as the territory. When he uses the *is* of identity to say, 'Water is a drink,' or, 'Schmidt is an Aryan,' he not only makes nonverbal water₁ equal water₂ equal water₃, etc., but he equates all these to the ink marks, d-r-i-n-k. One does not drink ink marks. Non-verbal typhoid germs may also make it clear to Smith₁ that water₁ is not water₂. In the second sentence, a living fellow called Schmidt is made the equivalent of the ink marks, A-r-y-a-n. Or, if you please, Nimitz equals Doenitz equals ink marks, A-r-y-a-n, equals Schmidt. Words are not what they represent, no matter what the language permits us to say. *A map is not the territory*. Any soldier who participated in D-Day can testify that a verbal description of D-Day is not the same as what happened. Every 'surprise' and every 'disappointment' can testify for the reader, better than anything I can say, that the map (what we believe, expect, 'think', etc.) *is not* the territory (what happens).

Someone has said that words can become 'triggers to action'. They *can* if we do not understand that the map *is not* the territory. For millions of people everywhere, it is sufficient only to know the label (map) that is attached to an event to 'know' *all* about the event. *Is* he a 'democrat'? A 'republican'? A 'capitalist'? A 'labor leader'? For those who identify map as territory, behavior is automatically determined as soon as someone supplies a label.

Not many years ago, the *map, Deutschland Erwache!* (Germany Awake), and many other maps shouted through loud speakers and plastered on billboards, produced some behavior in millions of Schmidts. When they 'awoke' some years later to find their homes heaps of rubble, they discovered, a little late, that the map is not the territory. As the American army entered Nuremberg (95 per cent in ruins), a German doctor told a reporter, 'We listened to too many words.'

To meet this 'remedial' problem, the very first reading books we place in the hands of our children train them to make false-to-fact identifications. I have recently analyzed 20 pre-primers; without exception, they employ the *is* of identity. The structural issues I have indicated are disregarded. If tomorrow another ex-corporal should appear, where in the reading methodology of 1947 can we find the basis on which we can operate against him?

A fourth characteristic of language enables Smith₁, either by design, or ignorance, or both, to make ink marks that represent nothing that can be empirically established as in the universe at all. This can be a source of unsuspected danger to Smith₂, who would then be following a map for which there is no territory. The yearbooks and textbooks that urge Smith₂ to 'get thoughts from printed pages,' deal 'reflectively' with the 'thoughts', determine 'meanings' from context (the method of determining what a word represents by examining the *words* surrounding it), equip himself with spectacles so he can see words, or perform other verbal gymnastics, do not help him at all. *The existence or non-existence of the territory cannot be established by scrutinizing the map. In an atomic age it becomes a matter of extreme urgency that Smith₂, who has to rely on verbal maps for almost everything he 'knows' about the world, understands this. His survival depends upon it.*

16.

I have hinted, in an extremely fragmentary way, at only a few of the structural factors involved whenever we read. No reader should conclude after scanning these lines that he knows all about general semantics. *Science and Sanity* contains nearly 800 pages. Even a brief inspection of that volume will show that the problems I have merely touched here are extremely complicated and cannot be solved except by a *study* of literally every branch of human knowledge. The problems will not be solved by writing another yearbook of synonyms about what to do with ink marks; they cannot be ignored out of existence.

In a world of catacylysmic *change,* the main connection we

have with the dynamic, non-verbal events is through *static* ink
marks. Today the statesmen undertake to confine within the
straight jackets of a *static* language the *dynamic relations that
will not stay fixed*. Concurrently, reading experts advise us to
build 'concepts', 'backgrounds of information', 'get', 'make', or
'bring meanings' to pages, etc.—all *static* notions about how to
deal with *static* ink marks. They do not tell us how to "build
backgrounds' for the new events and relations to come. These
are the events with which we will have to reckon, no matter
what 'meanings' we 'bring' to the pages. General Eisenhower
recognized this when he suggested that the 'atomic bomb mentality' may eventually prove to be our nemesis, just as an older
'Maginot line mentality' proved to be the undoing of the
French. The 'Report on the International Control of Atomic
Energy' similarly exposes the tragic inadequacy of notions of
'background', 'concepts', etc. for survival in an atomic age:
'Only a constant re-examination of what is sure to be a rapidly
changing technical situation will give us confidence that the
line between what is dangerous and what is safe has been correctly drawn; *it will not stay fixed'* (italics mine).

17.

Descriptions of current programs of 'remedial' reading do
not show that the specialists understand that *to read requires
constant checks on not-words*. They continue to train future
generations of Erewhonians, who believed that 'we are drawn
through life backwards': *words come first; events, afterwards,
if at all*. This may be *the* remedial reading problem of our time.

As we near the end of Year of Atom Bomb II, we may well
consider the possible consequences of misevaluating the ink
marks of 1947 and project ourselves a million years hence,
when the archeologists of a new order of life probe into what
may be the atomic ruins of our present 'civilization'. They fit
together the artifacts of twentieth century man, revealing

knowledge of relations and structure in the technological world. Their most puzzling problem may be to understand how, during this age, it was possible for authorities on symbolism to devote hundreds of pages to descriptions of operations to be performed on words: seeing, syllabizing, pronouncing, dicing, mincing, shredding—in short, doing everything but french-frying them—and to ignore completely problems of structure and the relations between words and the non-verbal events. The events of the future *will* test the words of today, no matter what score the 'remedial' reader makes on a paper test.

CHARLES H. VOELKER, M.A.

Private practice: Clinical physiology and biophysics; Professor and Head, Department of Physics, Washington College, Chestertown, Maryland.

Chapter XX

EDUCATION OF THE SPEAKING VOICE

A FRAME OF REFERENCE

IN order to discuss the education of the speaking voice, it is first essential to offer a description of the speaking voice. Both the selection of scientific field and the terms used should be determined by the historical perspective the twentieth century offers.

It is not yet possible to describe the speaking voice in acoustic nomenclature. This does not mean that good acoustic oscillographic curves are not available. Instead, we do not yet know what in these curves is the voice quality. In contrast to this, the physical approach to phonetics has made tremendous strides since the times of Helmholtz, Willis, Wheatstone, Hermann, et al., to today's work of Dudley[1], Potter[2], et al. These researchers have made one of the few advances in acoustical methodology since the nineteenth century, in that, their work was neither described nor suggested by Lord Rayleigh[3].

The field of physiology offers today the avenue of choice for

270

a description of the speaking voice, because, due to the French, more information is available. Certainly twentieth century phoniatry is based on physiological or biophysical conceptions. Physiological training therefore is today important for the physician or psychologist who would enter the field of phoniatry.

Pedagogical approaches still show today the same grimacing as formerly on the part of the vocal coach or professor of interpretation. This is a technique of education that requires no scientific background, and as a result, it is the coaching method for the artist who offers his pupil an experienced ear and refined taste. Much of the language of interpretation is not to be taken as seriously semantic, but instead, only as incantations leading to the desired result. Many of the introspective gymnastics are good fun and exercise for the talented pupil, but may do permanent psychological damage to a patient suffering vocal pain or inadequacies.

It must be remembered that dramatic talents, like musical talents, can never be taught, but instead only allowed to develop in a favorable environmental milieu. Therefore, voice therapy is not concerned with the manufacture of a talented artist. It is instead confined to amelioration of the disorders and discomforts of the voice user.

It is necessary early to eliminate the voices of tussis, sobbing, laughing, etc., and restrict this discussion to the speaking voice. The singing voice should be differentiated so as to cast it out of this article. This difference was examined by varying only one attribute of the voice at a time. The psychophysical judgments of audiences were evaluated by a statistical summary of their voting as to which was singing and which was speaking. The only significantly different attribute was vibrato. This isolated report leads one to believe that a vibrant voice is a singing voice and that there is no vibrato in the speaking voice[4]. It is true that tremulous voice does appear in dramatic and psychogenic states, but tremulo is not considered singing by artists.

Tremulo and vibrato must not be confused because the tremulous voice of the anxieties disappears as does the anxiety when the tremulous voice becomes vibrant, as in singing to keep from being afraid. It is held then, that the same melody pattern and cadence will be changed from speech to song by the addition of a vibrato. Vibrato is defined as a musical ornament also by Seashore[5]. It is characterized by a fairly constant frequency variation extending a semitone on the musical scale and averaging 6.5 of these frequency variations each second.

One should be conscious, of course, of creating a dichotomy which is entirely artificial, when one considers voice quality as if it were distinct from the phonetics, etc., but the departure here from a description of the individual as holistic is in order to emphasize an attribute by differentiation.

Emerging Conceptualities

There is not space to offer a historical description of the evolution in our thinking step by step, nor to list the constructs that have been left behind, nor is there space to point out the misconceptions still persistent in vocal literature. These are discussed at length by Stanley[5]. Of that which has done most to clarify our concepts, Tarneaud's physiological researches[7] and Cotton's biophysical researches[8] stand out. The results of their work describe in physiological terms how the speaking voice is produced, and their descriptions include the bulk of the twentieth century's beliefs and advances. The plan of this article is to link their descriptions to education and therapy. This article further suggests that the new physiological descriptions do naturally indicate the therapy that Froeschels developed in the ambulatorium and based on clinical observations. This is important because it offers an opportunity for an alternate description. One's description could be either in terms of the physiology or disease syndromes. This chapter could be confined to reiterating Froeschels' hyperfunctional theories, which are the conclusions for education of the speaking voice, for voice therapy reached by twentieth century vocal researchers.

At the outset, the Froeschels classification should be epitomized, from his several reports[9], perhaps as follows:

1. hyperfunctions of the laryngeal adductors.
2. hyperfunctions in the laryngeal vestibule (here I substitute Canuyt's vocabulary[10]).
3. hyperfunctions in the oropharynx.
4. hyperfunctions in the nasopharynx.
5. glossal hyperfunctions.
6. labial hyperfunctions.
7. pneumono-hyperfunctions.
8. hypofunctions such as Jackson's myasthenia laryngis[11].

Hypofunctions are very common and may be due to abuse, simple imitation, or general dysintegrated vocal coordination[12]. Tarrasch has reported both action current and roentgenographic studies of these breathy voices[13].

Hyperfunctions and sequelae are seldom single in occurrence. The manifestations may be so complex in a particular patient that a single label would be misleading. Even certain forms of asthma seem to be related (Schmitz-Svevo).[14]

Thus it is apparent why Muckey's book[15] is an important landmark in the first quarter of the twentieth century. He wrote for both singers and speakers, and his keynote was interference. By interference, Muckey meant that the glottal sounds must be produced and reach beyond the speaker's lips with as little muffling or attenuation by constriction as possible.

In order to describe physiologically what has been found by Tarneaud, Cotton, et al., this article will employ an anatomical organization to show non-organismically what each topographical body part contributes to voice quality. A similar description is given by Curry.[16]

Glottis vocalis. Today it is held that phonation is a product of the puff aerodynamic phenomena which originate at the rima glottidis. Whereas the sonant consonants of the several languages are analogous to the interference found in defective voice quality, the vowels locate the present considerations of voice quality. Froeschels' description is more fortunate in that he does not need to make this distinction for therapy, since his conception has ontogenetic and perhaps phylogenetic backgrounds.

Which aspects of vowel pronunciation are vowel quality and which are voice quality are not today known. Our newest concept of the two combined is not to list mean frequencies as did Fletcher.[17] We have departed somewhat from Ohm's Law of Acoustics in this. Instead, one describes Crandall's work,[18] or better Paget's work,[19] in similar terms to what Hermann in the last century called formants. Today, when we think of formants, we speak of "bars" in describing the speaking voice and thus adopt the nomenclature of Potter's "Visible Speech" soon to be published by Van Nostrand.

As to which is voice and which is vowel, my own guess is that vowel quality may yet come to be described as the interaction of what Kopp[20] listed as *Bar 1* and *Bar 2,* whereas acceptible voice quality may in time be described as producing *Bar 3* as distinct from *Bar 2* or even *Bar 1.* The *Voice Bar* is also a vocal consideration since it results in the speaking voice in indistinctness when it rises above *Bar 1.* Besides the bars, one should mention the "voiced fill" and the "voiced stop-gap-spike fill." The fact that the speaking voice is generally concerned with language is the sine qua non for speech, but on the contrary if these fills were extensive they would be most similar to poor voice. Fortunately these fills are very brief moments in articulatory gesticulation. So brief are *stop-gaps* that they may have no psychophysical auditory function directly.

Today it is held that glottal puffs are quite loud without any resonant amplification whatever. This was first indicated at the very beginning of the twentieth century from an observation on a suicide patient whose glottis was exposed by means of a razor. It was later demonstrated by a syphilitic similarly exposed as a result of the progress of his disease. The laryngeal microphone, too, would seem to verify that the glottal sound has the greatest energy, and at all other body sites and even in the ambient atmospheric ocean, the sound is weaker than at the source. One needs only to learn to "finger" a freshly excised larynx to reproduce lifelike qualities with great volume. The audience will even accuse you of faking blowing by substituting your own voice.

One can observe in sound high speed roentgenographic motion pictures (Menserath) how the supraglottal areas interfere with the efficiency of the acoustic coupling. Stroboscopic and especially high speed 4000 frame per second motion pictures[21] of the glottidean activity demonstrate how the puffs are produced. The energy of these puffs is dissipated downward in subglottal tubes, and upward through supraglottal tubes, and further dissipated in parasitic vibrations of structures anatomically linked to the larynx.[22]

The acoustic coupling of the glottidean puffs is determined by the proportion of sound energy in the larynx which reaches the speaker's ambient atmospheric ocean beyond the labial orifice. In physics and in engineering, we attempt to describe what happens to the total energy available. Just as the number of B.T.U.'s available for tractive work in a steam locomotive is a small fraction of the B.T.U.'s created, so in voice we must wonder how minute is the fraction of the glottidean acoustic energy which becomes available for communicatory purposes. The message, theme, or theory presented here is that much that is created is wasted, that more is wasted in defective voices than in superior voices. When too little of the acoustic power or energy created at the glottis reaches the ambient atmospheric ocean, then there is a voice disorder. It is not possible at this writing to give a numerical value for normal voices and defective voices. Perhaps the twentieth century will yet indicate its order of magnitude in watts, ergs, or some appropriate units. In a healthy voice, merely an estimate would be that for 1.5×10^{-8} watts at the glottal source, only 3×10^{-7} watts are made available for communicatory usefulness. Thus what were formerly called resonating magnifiers, in this interpretation, probably reduce the glottal energy 1200 ergs per second, or if you like, an amount equal to 750 million Mevs of nuclear energy.

Furthermore today it is held that the laryngeal puff mechanism is a very efficient acoustic generator. This means that the puff itself is effective acoustically without dependence on superimposition of vibrations which in time build up natural cavity or free vibrations by correctly timed pulses. In contrast to the singing voice, in the speaking voice there is very little temporal opportunity for this to take place. Actually, now it is supposed that the puffs themselves provide the brilliance and what was formerly called resonance in the voice.

Fletcher (*ibid.*) suggests that the vocal puffs provide a pressure spectrum designated by $F(k)$ for the kth component. If f_0 is the natural frequency of the supraglottal tube, f the fundamental glottal frequency, and Δ the damping constant, then as a first approximation the amplitude of the kth component

$$A_k = \frac{C\,F(k)}{\left[\left(k - \frac{1}{k}\frac{f_0^2}{f^2}\right)^2 + \left(\frac{\Delta}{\Pi f}\right)\right]^{1/2}}$$

where C determines the particular scale of amplitude selected. Fletcher gives

$$F(k) = \frac{1}{k^{3/2}}$$

which indicates that the intensity of the kth component

$$I_k \infty \, n^{-3.0}$$

Tiffin[23] studied stroboscopic pictures of one complete opening and closing of the glottis. The glottal area in each frame was measured with a planimeter. Using these area values as ordinates and successive frames as abscissae, a curve was drawn to represent area of opening as a function of time, which curve is regarded as revealing the form of the glottal pressure variation. A Henrici analyzer would then determine from this curve the harmonic constitution of the glottal tone. The experimental value of the exponent for these physiological glottal spectra averaged 3.07, when a straight line was fitted by the method of least squares to the sequence of harmonic magnitudes.

However, microscopically within this microscopic generalization there was noted by Cotton and can even be seen in the physiological spectra high frequency bars of the order of 2.5 to 3 kilocycles per second which we know to be characteristics of puff sources generally. This is the region of *Bar 3*, which may in time become a salient describer of voice quality. Thus again it is suggested that much we think of as voice quality may be glottal. We know that human hearing is particularly sensitive in this region. Cotton thinks that the contribution of the supraglottal regions is, among other things, attenuation of *Bar 3*. One of the theoretically effective acoustic air filters, though seldom practical for industrial noise, follows in gross anatomy the shape of the supraglottal duct from the glottis to the labial orifice. Engineers use it to attenuate definite frequency bands, but if this is its effect in the flesh, then its influence must be very complex, since steel or brass differs from flesh in that in the latter several rather than a few bars would be affected. Cotton considers the supraglottal areas a special tube, the side walls of which, in the oropharynx, vibrate. This might possibly function as an acoustic air filter such as Stewart's low-pass design.[24] Applying the Heaviside impedance method to acoustic air filters yields an attenuation close to the Helmholtz-Kirchoff law. Once the phase of these vocal wall vibrations is determined it may be possible to evaluate them as series capacity or shunt inductance. We are fortunate mathematically, since the equations have been solved for systems where the wave length is long compared to the dimensions of the acoustic air filter.[25]

A trained laryngologist can perform glottal labiomancy. Eijkman goes so far as to place articulatory movements as accessory to laryngeal. In the speaking voice, as the frequency of the puffs increase, the glottal action becomes less complex. For example in low register, the glottis opens from below, the opening progressing upward and outward. The lower portion is also the first to close. Such phase differences are indications of complexity in glottal actions. Not only is pitch inversely proportional to complexity but also inversely proportional to glottal opening. In physics, puff rate determines frequency in cycles per second, and in psychophysics, frequency has been related to pitch in mels by Stevens.[26]

If this were an article on the singing voice, the issues would be beclouded by scale note references. In the speaking voice, musical pitch is much less important than physiological register. It may come to pass that Ohm's Law of Acoustics, or the vocabulary of frequencies, will not prove the simplest description for practical purposes. Note the discussion of bars above. Also recall that a high speaking voice is not high because it reaches a particular note on the musical scale. A high voice is high because of inappropriate choice of register for the occasion. In the clinic, it is almost trivial to indicate the particular number of cycles per second. Such information is at best a statistical mean, without having included in addition the range, frequency distribution, age, sex, social status, psychological state, medical progress, time of day, activities preceding time studied, site such as to whether the subject were on a stage, in a factory, up-wind, etc., whether he is hurtling through space as a part of a large mass or as an isolated mass, contents inspired, and so on ad infinitum. A high voice for Smith$_1$ may be a low voice for Smith$_2$ or Jones, when frequency is the index, and whether it is high or low is not clear without a case history background. A large amount of detail can be avoided by confining the description to registers, wherein the referends are not acoustic frequencies but physiological modes of glottal behavior. Aside from register, an abnormal voice in the clinic is described physiologically by reference to its hyperfunction.

The four registers of the speaking voice, according to Tarneaud are first the complex one described above. Possibly the most commonly employed register in speaking is that without phase complexities in abduction and adduction. A high speaking voice is sometimes produced when the membranous glottis is active and the cartilagenous processes are open. The highest voice of all is probably an edge tone produced in a small aperture in the anterior glottis. Perhaps it is best to digress here to explain to the classroom teacher that all of these registers are heard in the speaking voice in normal life however infrequently some may be heard in a school's restrictions.

In the vertical plane, the higher the register the higher the relative elevation of the larynx.

The speaking voice is not limited to narrow ranges in melody. To use musical terminology, even in very formal speaking for a short time there was found a 2.5 octave span. Over a period of days the speaking voice will have a greater range than the singing voice. This is particularly noticeable in children. Children have very narrow singing ranges but demonstrate wider voice ranges at play. A young child may have a singing range of half an octave in contrast to a speaking range of 3½ octaves. Three or more registers are used in speaking whereas some singers train themselves to use only one.

Today, it is held that denotative meaning is related to duration intonation and that the affective states in the language situation are conveyed by the melody patterns of the voice. Probably degree of emotion is characterized by definiteness of pattern.

It used to be believed that the greater the excursions of the vocal cords the greater the amplitude of sound. Today, it is held that intensity is a function of the time the glottal chink is closed, the longer the duration of occlusion the greater the intensity at the same puff rate. Traditionally, breath pressure and loudness have been related, and in such terms, a third increase in air consumption yields a hundredfold increase in energy content. Qualitatively, the more explosive the puff, the richer the tone produced, which again suggests that much of what we think of as the timbre of the speaking voice is produced at the glottis.

Subglottal Regions. Physical laboratory apparatus indicates that a system of the form of the trachea and bronchi will influence vibrating rubber wedges when the tubes are coupled to the wedges.[27] But a flesh trachea and bronchi may perhaps show no influence on the glottis in life.

Glottal energy passes down as well as up from the larynx whether voice is inspiratory or expiratory. Since there is no ear to observe the tracheal voice, that part of the energy is wasted. The sensations of vibration in the chest are not of sufficient intensity in the ambient atmospheric ocean to modify the speaking voice. Such parasitic vibrations sap some of the glottal energy uselessly.

Plicae Ventricularis. There is a type of substitution for glottal performance which seems to be constrictive in origin but manifested as a differentiated vicarious voice. Voice originating at a ventricular level has been widely recognized.[28] Supposedly, ventricular phonation can occur simultaneously with glottal phonation.[29]

Laryngeal Sphincter. The thyreoarytaenoideus superior furthermore operates in an entirely different dysintegration in coaction with other eminences at the base of the laryngeal vestibule. The anterior partner is the epiglottidean tubercle, the posterior partner, the cuneiform and corniculate tubercles. In this organization, the thyreoarytaenoideus superiori appear as the lateral tubercles. Thus the laryngeal sphincter is a tuberculoid ring of seven prominences which constrict as a unit together with some reflective action in the aryepiglottidean folds. When it constricts glottal efficiency, it may be the mechanism of twang which is so common in American voices.[30] There are many ways in which defective voice resembles overlaid language, and the action of the laryngeal sphincter in phonetics has been described by Eijkman.

The Oropharynx. Early in the century Scripture differentiated between protoplasmic cavities and the Helmholtz resonators of the physical laboratory. Cotton showed that a flesh tube tuned to a fundamental transmits it with only half the energy transmitted by a metallic tube. Furthermore, flesh tubes will transmit other selected bars equally well. Today we believe that a single cavity can transmit more than one bar. Formerly it was believed that there was a need to invent tandem resonators to explain two frequency regions. This progress is analogous to that in acoustic air filters where it has also been shown that a single system will filter more than one frequency. Where in the last century, it was believed that zero transmission in the Hershel-Quincke tube occurred when the phase differences in the branches

$$\alpha_2 - \alpha_3 = (2n + 1)\Pi$$

where n is a positive integer, Stewart added

$$\alpha_2 + \alpha_3 = 2\Pi n$$

Then when the branch areas $S_2 = S_3$, he reported power transmission $P = O$, as

$$\sin \tfrac{1}{2} \, (\alpha_3 + \alpha_2) \, \cos \tfrac{1}{2} \, (\alpha_3 - \alpha_2) = 0$$

and with the help of Uhler,[31] recently gave for the general case, $P = O$, when

$$S_2 \sin \alpha_3 + S_3 \sin \alpha_2 = 0$$

Cotton showed that restricting wall vibrations resulted in a drop of conduction of the voice bar. Thinner walls react at higher bars than thicker walls and with greater amplitude of movement. Tense walls do not damp sound any more than relaxed walls. More and more clinicians are today discarding relaxation measures.

Probably one should no longer discuss the pharngeal cavity but instead the "pharynx" meaning its bore and vibrating walls together. Thus a hyperfunction might mean a restriction in wall vibration. Schmitz-Svevo has worked with pharyngeal dryness by overcoming hyperfunctions.

In most animals the larynx lies so closely behind the mouth[32] that the pharynx is too short for reactance onto glottal aerodynamics. One patient has been observed where the buccal cavity and laryngeal vestibule were extremely proximal. There was increased loudness of voice with no limitation in speech. The voice quality recalled Trendelenburg's discussion of the excised larynx.

The Nasopharynx. To close the nasopharyngeal aperture requires the action of two overlapping slings of muscles so arranged that a comparatively small variation in muscle fibre length makes a great difference in the calibre of the passage. These are the constrictor pharyngis forming Passavant's ridge and the levator palati, both innervated by the pharyngeal plexus. Phonetic requirements of rapid opening are supplied by the tensor veli palatini innervated by the fifth cranial nerve. This muscle winds around the pterigoid hamulus being retained in position by the origin of the pterygoideus internis.[33]

In the nineteenth century, Brücke finally brought to bear the point that the velum acted against Passavant's ridge and sealed off the nasopharynx to give a normal voice quality in contrast to nasal quality. Cotton found complete closure resulted in the maximum transmission of glottal energy. Considerations of divided oro-nasal air streams are passé and today, as demonstrated by Eijkman, we hold that it is acoustic energy alone that decides between oral and nasal voice. Thus an oral voice occurs even with a mucous diaphragm at the pillars of the fauces completely obstructing air flow.[34]

Eijkman further draws attention to the opening at the posterior part of the buccal cavity.[35] The present view is that nasality can be produced by restricting the mouth opening by 1. raising the back of the tongue toward the velum, 2. approximation of tongue and velum by retraction, 3. lowering the velum towards the tongue, and 4. approximating the pillars of the fauces.

In regard to twang, the American cowboy voice, there seems to have been a swing away and then back to the view of Grützner in Herman's Handbook of 1877. Grützner stressed raising the larynx, depressing the velum, and raising the back of the tongue. This combines a buccal oropharyngeal hyperfunction producing nasality with a laryngeal hyperfunction producing twang. D. Weiss has mentioned the characteristic tension in the velum and pillars. Cotton suggests that whang may sometimes be an attempt at self-correction of rhinophonia since a louder voice results when whang is substituted for nasality.

In both whang and nasality, the oral and nasal acoustic components are of the same order of magnitude. However, there is no co-vibration in the nasal cavities when the nasopharynx is closed that contributes to the speaking voice. Neither the teeth nor the hard palate act as sounding boards. Any surface vibrations of the bones of the face or head, although not contributing to the speaking voice, are wasteful of glottal energy.

Labial Aperture. The labial aperture makes the coupling with the external air. It is elucidating to note in a crowd how much louder and more intelligible is a child's speaking voice than an adult's, and with comparable expenditure of energy. It is easier to learn a secondary language from a child than a professor simply because more often it is the child who can be clearly understood. Apparently, as we grow up, we gradually close the labial aperture more and more and as a result our voices become less and less available for communication. Very profound vocal limitations can be observed in patients obsessed with the need to hide dental blemishes or even in ordinary people who feel a need for maintaining prosthetic dentition. In these cases, it becomes obvious to what extent bad voices destroy speech. Occasionally one can observe careful pronunciation combined with small labial openings and reduced articulatory excursions. One regularly fails to understand such speech without labiomancy and occasionally fails to realize any vocalization has occurred at all. Speech teachers make the mistake of classifying all such symptoms as dyslalia and endlessly apply circuitous exercises, whereas simple masticatory dysphonia therapy is indicated. Froeschels is one of the few to consider hyperfunction at the lips as a part of voice disorders.

Consider an analogy. Using a megaphone increases one's effective mouth opening for acoustic coupling with the external air. Using a megaphone increases the distance to which a voice reaches and speech is understood. Yet the amplitude at the mouth of the megaphone horn may be less than at the mouth of the speaker unassisted by a horn. The megaphone transmits to the atmosphere a much larger amount of sound energy with no more energy created by the speaker. The occlusions at the glottis are of no greater duration, there is no more breath consumed, yet there is more effective coupling of the glottis to the outside air when the mouth (lips and jaws) open wider.

GENERAL MEASURES

The conclusions which can be drawn from the preceding description of the physiology of the voice indicate the principles for therapy for dysphonia and twentieth century education of the speaking voice. The theory might be summarized as 1. that much of the quality of the speaking voice is produced by the aerodynamics at the glottis, 2. that a more efficient acoustic generator results and clearer speech results when there is a minimum of interference with the mechanical action of the glottal musculature, 3. that most glottal energy created is wasted, but that there is a limit to that waste beyond which is the region of the dysphonias, 4. that the supraglottal areas can be so integrated as to result in the maximum coupling and transmission of glottal energy to the ambient atmospheric ocean.

Some schools of singing provide training in voice which is purposely unintelligible but no speaking voice which masks speech is effective.

Insight into what to do to procure vocal efficiency has to be provided for the subject by the clinician or teacher. A subject can not be advised to contract or expand a vocal muscle such as the oblique arytenoids since the mechanism of the speaking voice is in part involuntary. Froeschels has given a more complete description of the psychology involved and the degree to which the vocal mechanism is involuntary.[36] The teacher must capitalize on the view that the voice is related to broad physiological synergies. The clinician can employ pandiculation, regurgitation, mastication, acts that are easily possible for the subject to perform. The subject should never actually perform pandiculation, regurgitation or mastication but, as an actor mimics, he should perform imaginary, intense exercises similar to these physiological synergies.

The subject can be taught to provide an avenue for atmospheric coupling with the glottis. The subject can be taught to relieve the hypertensions which restrict this avenue by opening up the avenue as a whole. This can be accomplished by static or dynamic measures. With some subjects it is advisable to have them produce vocalization while maintaining a stance which is vocally effective. But wherever feasible it is advisable to employ dynamic measures, to produce vocalization in an active, and therefore more readily usable, vocal mechanism.

Incipient Pandiculation. I have proposed for clinic use what I call incipient pandiculation. I start with a yawning exercise and then train the subject to just start to yawn and go no further. He then studies his vocal mechanism topographically in a mirror. He notes his mouth opening, the position of the Adam's apple, the chest expansion, etc. He tries to feel the condition of the interior by giving attention to the breath sensations. Then through breathing, whispering, voicing and other exercises, the subject is gradually taught to use this voice for speech.

Bronchoscopic Position. This is similar to regurgitation synergies. In more severe cases, I use a full prone laryngoscopic (bronchoscopic or esophagoscopic) position. Ordinarily I use a simulated position in a chair for adults or during play activity in children. In the prone position, the scapulae rest on the edge of the table and the neck and head are held in the position described by Jackson.[37] In the simulated position, in the chair or standing, I try to press forward the neck while pulling back the forehead to approach as nearly as possible the interior relationships achieved in the prone position. The session starts with breathing and then phonation. The subject is instructed to note the details of the sound of the voice he is producing. When he has a clear auditory image, he is released and instructed to mimic that voice. In practice, it is possible to over-

come the interferences and hyperfunctions while in this un-
comfortable position.

Dynamics for Group Education. The problem of what to do
with school children has been solved by Heltman.[38] He gives
each teacher the child meets through his school life a theory
and clinic course on how to improve speech and voice. He ob-
tains striking results.

Here we are concerned with what method Heltman should
apply for the speaking voice. I would recommend a masticatory
method developed in the ambulatory clinic by Froeschels and
called the chewing method. The method is practical for individual therapy and being dynamic will lend itself to any group
of adults or school children. (See Chapter XV).

The contribution of the twentieth century to education of
the speaking voice as far as methodology is concerned that
needs to be pointed out is that there has been a gradual discarding of relaxation procedures. No one can conceive of the
user of the speaking voice as being a relaxed person. Yet there
have been speech teachers who offered a general drowsiness as
a voice improvement panacea. An athlete running a race may
have hyperfunctions which cut his speed and that his coach
attempts to relieve. The coach can not advise drowsiness since
there is no such thing as a drowsy sprinter. Likewise with the
speaking voice, we want to produce wide awake, active speakers, with every muscle in co-contraction with definite polarity
towards the speaking situation. We want the speaker to obviously devote considerable attention to speaking. So in conclusion, let me point out that no one of the above general therapy
measures involves relaxation or is directed to procure relaxation
but instead they are directed at a more modern education for
the speaking voice.

REFERENCES

1. *Dudley, H.:* A Synthetic Speaker. Bell System Monographs, B-1148, B-1169, B-1171.
2. *Potter, R. K.:* Visible Patterns of Sound. Bell Telephone Monographs, B-1368.
3. *Lord Rayleigh (John William Strutt):* The Theory of Sound. First Edition 1877, Rev. 1894. New York: Dover Publications, 1945.
4. *Voelker, C. H.:* An Investigation of Vibrato. Speech Monographs, 2: 105-151, 1935.
5. *Seashore, C. E.:* Psychology of Music. New York: McGraw-Hill Book Co., 1938. The Vibrato. University of Iowa Studies in the Psychology of Music, Vol. 1, 1932, Vol. III, 1936, Vol. IV, 1937.
6. *Stanley, D.:* The Science of Voice. New York: Carl Fischer, Inc., 1939.
7. *Tarneaud, J.:* La Stroboscopie du Larynx. Paris: Norbert Maloine, 1937. Le Nodule de la Corde Vocale. Paris: Norbert Maloine, 1935. Einseitige Stimmlippenroetung auf vasomotorischer Grundlage. Monatsschrift für Ohrenheilkunde und Laryngo-Rhinologie, 1934. La Corde Vocal en Attitude de Phonation. Revue de Laryngologie, Otologie, Rhinologie, 1937. L'ipercinesia laringea nella fonazione. Il Valsalva, 1937. La vibracion de una Sola cuerda en la Fonacion. Pasture, 1934. L'etude du larynx et de la voix par la stroboscopie. La Clinique, 1933. Etude des conditions expérimentales et cliniques permettant d'établir et de classer les dyskinésies de la parole et du chant. Bull. Acad. méd., 1932. La mécanique des cordes vocales dans la phonation. (Avec Husson) Revue de Laryngologie, 1932. La laryngostroboscopie. La Vie méd., 1932.
8. *Cotton, J. C.:* Etude quantitative de la resonance thoracique. Rev. franc. de phon., 6: 165-167, 1938. A Study of Certain Phoniatric Resonance Phenomena. American Documentation Institution Science Service Microfilm, Washington, D.C. Abstract in Journal of Speech Disorders, 5: 289-293, 1940. Resonance in Soft Walled Cylinders. Journal of the Acoustical Society of America, 5: 208-211, 1934. Tongue Movements and Vowel Quality. Speech Monographs, pp. 38-43, 1937.
9. *Froeschels, Emil:* Versuch einer akustischen Lokalisation stimmlicher Hyperfunktionen. Mitteilungen über Sprach- und Stimm-Heilkunde, Vol. 1, No. 8-9, Wien, 1935. Eine Belastungsprobe der menschichen Stimme. Practica Oto-Rhino-Laryngologia, Vol. 1, No. 1, Basel, pp. 56-60. Laws of the Occurrence and Development of Hyperfunctional Voice Failure. Speech, Journal of the British Society of Speech Therapists Trans. by Miss J. Van Thal, Vol. 3, No. 1, pp. 13-17, London, 1937. Law of the Appearance and the

Development of Voice-Hyperfunctions. Journal of Speech Disorders, 5: 1-4, 1940. Hygiene of Voice. Archives of Otolaryngology, 38: 122-130, 1943.

10. *Canuyt, G.:* Les Maladies du Pharynx. Paris: Masson et Cie, 1936.

11. *Jackson, C. and C. L. Jackson:* Myasthenia Laryngis, Observations on the Larynx as an Air Column Instrument. Archives of Otolaryngology, 33: 45-55, 1941.

12. *Voelker, C. H.:* A Preliminary Investigation for a Normative Study of Fluency. The American Journal of Orthopsychiatry, 14:285-294, 1944.

13. *Tarrasch, H.:* Muscle Spasticity in Functional Aphonia and Dysphonia. Speech Monographs, 12: 37-46, 1945. Clinical Aspects of Functional Hoarseness. Archives of Otolaryngology, 36: 53-70, 1942.

14. *Schmitz-Svevo, F. S.:* Relaxation Therapy for the Embarrassment of Breathing in Asthmatics. The New York Physician, Vol. 20, No. 3, 1943.

15. *Muckey, F. S.:* The Natural Method of Voice Production in Speech and Song. New York: Chas. Scribner's Sons, 1915.

16. *Curry, R.:* The Mechanism of the Human Voice. London: J. & A. Churchill Ltd., 1940.

17. *Fletcher, H.:* Speech and Hearing. New York: Van Nostrand, 1929.

18. *Crandall, I. B.:* Vibrating Systems and Sound. New York: Van Nostrand, 1925.

19. *Paget, R.:* Human Speech. Boston: Harcourt, 1930.

20. *Kopp, G. A. and H. C. Green:* Basic Phonetic Principles of Visible Speech. Journal of the Acoustical Society of America, 18: 74-90, 1946.

21. *Farnsworth, D. W.:* High Speed Motion Pictures of the Human Vocal Cords. Bell Laboratories Record, 18: 203-209, 1940.

22. *Husson, R. and J. Tarneaud:* Les phénomenès réactionels de la voix. Rev. franc. de phon., 4: 62, 1933.

23. *Tiffin, J.:* An Approach to the Analysis of the Vibration of the Vocal Cords (with J. Saetveit and J. Snidecor). The Quarterly Journal of Speech, 24: 1-11, 1938.

24. *Stewart, G. W. and R. B. Lindsay:* Acoustics. New York: Van Nostrand, 1930.

25. *Mason, W. P.:* The Approximate Networks of Acoustic Filters. Bell Telephone Monographs B-493, 1930. Regular Combination of Acoustic Elements. Bell Telephone Monographs, B-256, 1927. Propagation Characteristics of Sound Tubes and Acoustic Filters. Bell Telephone Monographs, B-295, 1926.

26. *Stevens, S. S. and H. Davis:* Hearing. New York: Wiley, 1938.

27. *Eijkman, L. P. H.:* The Internal Aspect of the Larynx in Speech.

Archives Néerlandaises de Phonétique Expérimentale, 8-9: 122-129, 1933. The Influence of the Subglottal Passage and the Nasal Cavity on Non-Nasal Speech Sounds. Archives Néerlandaises de Phonétique Expérimentals, 11: 29-38, 1935.

28. *Voelker, C. H.:* Phoniatry in Dysphonia Ventricularis. Annals of Otology, Rhinology and Laryngology, 44: 471, 1935.

29. *Jones, S.:* Observations on a Case of Double Voice. Proceedings of the Second International Congress of Phonetic Sciences, pp. 232-235, 1935, London.

30. *Russell, G. O.:* Speech and Voice. New York: Macmillan, 1931.

31. *Stewart, G. W.:* The Theory of the Herschel-Quincke Tube. Journal of the Acoustical Society of America, 17: 107-108, 1945.

32. *Negus, V. E.:* The Mechanism of the Larynx. St. Louis: C. V. Mosby, 1931.

33. *Brown, D.:* The Closure of the Nasopharynx. Speech, Journal of the British Society of Speech Therapists, 2: 15-20, 1936.

34. *Perrett, W.:* Some Light on the Soft Palate. Volta Review, 23: 242, 1921.

35. *Eijkman, L. P. H.:* Gesloten en Open Neusgang. Logopaedie en Phoniatrie, 1934, pp. 1-14.

36. *Froeschels, Emil, and A. Jellinek:* Practice of Speech and Voice Therapy. Boston: Expression Co., 1941.

37. *Jackson, C. and C. L. Jackson:* Diseases and Injuries of the Larynx. New York: Macmillan, 1942.

38. *Heltman, H. J.:* A Practical Program of Speech Correction. The American School Board Journal, June, 1938.

FREDERICA SCHMITZ-SVEVO
Voice and Speech Therapist of the Department of Oto-Rhino-
Laryngology, City Hospital, Welfare Island, New York, N. Y.

Chapter XXI

EDUCATION AND RE-EDUCATION OF THE SINGING VOICE

TO some degree it is obviously possible to educate any voice to singing. However, we are here concerned only with voice training of the prospective professional artist.

In recent years, some attention has justly been given to the question of who might be best fitted for the task of training the singing voice. D. Weiss[1] suggests that the voice production of the vocal genius and the flawlessly trained singer rather than the so-called natural voice should be considered as physiologically exemplary. According to him, then, those rare exceptional cases should provide the most competent teachers. In opposition to this, it is to be argued that those great artists do only very rarely devote themselves to the teaching profession; and even if and when they do, they are by no means always able to teach their own technique to the student. One need only recall the confusion caused in vocalist circles by the writings of Lili Lehmann, Caruso and others, on the art of singing; and this despite the fact that some of them, and particularly Lili Lehmann's book, contained a goodly amount of sound ideas well worth noting. — A good teacher must be born to his profession—just like the artist. The teacher owes it to the student

291

to provide him with a system which will enable him to use his
voice with ease as the organ of his artistic personality. The
teacher must be capable of uniting the important factors into
one working principle, and to avoid confusion. That corresponds with what we consider our artistic ideal.

In his book on the training and care of the voice, Gutzman[2]
says "If we wish to learn the proper development and care of
the voice, it is indispensable also to learn to know about those
organs and their functions which actually make possible the
emission of the voice and control its sound: the respiratory organ and the vocal organ." To this may be added that Phonetics,
the science of the voice, of articulation, enunciation, etc., is of
basic importance in the instruction in singing. These are the
essential requirements for a voice pedagogue on which we must
insist just as much as on his musical training and his reliably
critical ear. — But, in our time and age it is also no longer possible to leave the pupil in ignorance of the Why and Wherefore
of what he is being taught. That would be wrong, alone from
the psychological point of view. Knowledge gives assurance
and independence, and these are essential to the singer, both
technically and artistically.

For decades, most of the methods which were being taught
in the different countries relied mainly on imitation and on
certain rules of articulation. According to Cornelia van Zanten[3],
the older methods of vocal instruction may be summed up approximately as follows:

Italian methods: Predominance of vowel singing; as a result
of the temperamental language quick change of the tongue
position in passing from consonant to vowel; an almost excessive stretching of the mouth which causes the tone to vibrate
also in the nasal passages as a secondary sphere of resonance.
Stress on tonal beauty, sometimes to the detriment of textual
significance and musical expression.

French methods: Likewise predominance of vowel technique, but with the nose used as direct sphere of resonance. The required nasality, called for by the French language, frequently causes pathologic slackening of the palate.

German methods: Predominance of consonant and semi-vowel technique by virtue of emphasis on the consonants, an exaggeratedly high placing of the tongue, and not sufficiently fast change of the tongue position in the transfer from consonant to vowel formation. Great interest in the artistic and dynamic delivery, sometimes to the detriment of tonal beauty. Thorough theoretical training in musical and dramatic expression.

And then she finds a prophetic word: The methodical system of the future can only be that which is able to retain all the advantages of the older schools and produce voice above the throat with the least exertion of physical force, by utilization of the sung language.

Of the newer methods, two may be mentioned here, based on radically deviating principles. One is George Arnim's "Stauprinzip." This method aroused violent discussions and was widely opposed—and justly so as was subsequently amply proved. The method was based on the forced holding and emitting of the breath. "Breathing technique," says Arnim,[4] "consists in holding the breath. Against the driving force which presses the accumulated air forward with the aim of bursting the tightly closed vocal cords, another force must be employed which does not merely neutralize the former but pushes it backward." Under this "other force" we are to understand a force which diverts the air pressure to the chest. Thus, we find in Arnim's system the requirement that the singer manipulate consciously with organic sensations. And, in fact, similar demands are made by many pedagogues.

In opposition to this, is David C. Taylor who in his "Self-help for Singers"[5] states: "It is impossible to help the voice in its adjustments. Any attempt of this kind can have only the opposite effect—to cause throat stiffness, and so to interfere with the normal instinctive operations of the voice. With many students merely thinking of the vocal organs while practising is enough to cause an involuntary tension of the throat. . . . To attain the correct use of the voice, the best and quickest way is this:—To practise singing correct musical tones, guiding the voice solely by the ear and paying no attention to the operations of the vocal organs." Accordingly, Taylor discards all breathing exercises.

The fact that such diametrically opposed opinions are being held and taught simultaneously proves that there is a need for a system to be introduced which properly coordinates physiological, psychological, hygienic and artistic values.

There are so many different methods used by singing teachers that it is difficult to classify them, particularly in view of the fact that almost every system uses parts of another. But if we disregard this overlapping, a certain grouping is possible, and one may divide the methods into 1) those based especially upon breath training, 2) those primarily interested in enlarging the range and in teaching the several degrees of loudness (pianissimo, piano, mezzoforte, forte, fortissimo), and 3) those starting with register formation (head register, chest register, mixed register).

1) The "breath methods" may be subdivided into those that prefer abdominal breathing, flank breathing (using especially the intercostal muscles of the lower ribs and the diaphragm at the same time), and finally those that train the abdominal and the thoracic breathing as a unity. Exclusively thoracic breathing is hardly ever recommended. Some teachers start with voiceless breathing while others have the breathing exercises made with voice production. All these methods aim at strengthening and regulating the function which is primarily responsible for the production of voice, the human voice mechanism being a kind of wind instrument.

2) The methods aimed at enlarging the range and regulating the loudness naturally involve the breathing technique although they direct the pupil's attention chiefly to the acoustic result. These methods, as well as some of group 3), frequently also take advantage of the fact that some consonants preceding vowels somehow transfer the impulse of the articulatory organs upon the breathing mechanism, and most probably upon the muscles that stretch the vocal cords and bring them together. F.i., in singing the syllable "Tah" the elastic tension of the tongue will be reflected upon the other muscles employed in singing because the whole singing mechanism is a functional unity although consisting of separate anatomic parts. — Some teachers prefer to use single vowels in the early stages of instruction. The vowel "Ah," produced of course with wide open mouth, may also help to open the throat, while "Oo" may help to throw the sound waves more strongly toward the hard palate, thus enlarging the nose resonance. On the other hand, "Oo" is spoken with a dropped larynx and—in accordance with the law of functional unity—may therefore help to bring other muscles into a less contracted state.

3) There are several ways to enlarge head resonance; as already mentioned, the use of certain vowels, or the device of directing the voice towards the forehead, the nose, the upper teeth. Breath resonance, on the other hand, these methods teach, may be strengthened by throwing the sound waves back into the thorax using tactile control (putting hands on chest wall). Also certain postures of the body are said to influence resonance formation.

This attempt at classifying the various methods of voice training is certainly not complete but throws at least some light on the variety of the methods employed. It is worth mentioning that in the application of any and all of these methods it is necessary to take into consideration the specific psychological type (acoustic, visual, motor-kinesthetic) of each pupil. This does not hold, however, for the chewing method which I use to the exclusion of any other, precisely because it relies on a congenital function which need not be taught; consequently, there is no reason to appeal to the congenital psychological type of the pupil for help.

Despite all the fine talk of a method of the future, singing instructions today are sometimes still of the sort which sooner or later may harm the vocal organ. They cause hyperfunctions, that is over-exertion of muscles, some of which have no connection with voice production, over-articulation, using false points of support in the respiratory apparatus and in the Ansatzrohr; these may lead to serious impairment of the voice, above all to phonasthenia. Phonasthenia consists primarily—and sometimes for a long period—of the signs of over-exertion of the pharyngeal and laryngeal muscles, and later of signs of functional weakness especially of the closers of the glottis. For the latter type, but only for that, the term "myastenia laryngis" (Chevalier Jackson[6]) can be used. — Of prime importance to the voice is not how much but how it is being employed. A well trained singer, when in good health and not physically tired, will not feel any specific disturbance of the voice. Incorrect evaluation of the voice range is another factor which tends to cause over-exertion of the vocal apparatus, and therewith damage to it.

As a result of my experiences gained over a period of years of clinical and private contact with defective voices as well as with vocal students, both beginners and advanced, I am convinced that it is the "Chewing Method" (Froeschels[7]) (See Chapter XV) which is the answer to the requirements of education and re-education of the singing voice.

When describing this method of breath-chewing as training system for the singing voice, I must go back to its first therapeutic use as a corrective for functional voice defects. — Up till then, various forms of educational therapy were being applied. Then, about 15 years ago, the first experiments were made with the chewing method. The results were amazing. As a matter of fact, a complete singing method could be deduced from the very therapeutic process. Often, after a singer had been cured of his voice trouble, it proved difficult to make him return to his old teacher; usually the student resisted being discharged from treatment because he felt that he had learned a new method but was not yet capable of continuing in it without further aid. Yet, the teachers, on their part, refused to give up their complicated methods and concepts.

The student must be made aware of the identity of the motions in speaking and chewing: he must be shown that it is possible to chew and speak at the same time while no other organ of the human body is capable of carrying out two functions simultaneously; that in the brain is located a common center for the chewing and speaking motions; that there is only one short step from the chewing motions to articulated language. It must be made clear to him that the singing voice can be developed from the speaking voice and that singing is but an intensified (heightened) form of speaking. The student should be taught to perform vigorous eating motions with sonorous (sounded) exhalation. The chewing method, while excluding any hyperfunction, brings the entire vocal apparatus to just the right degree of tension, or in other words, into the best possible condition for perfect functioning. The student begins to feel that the melodic tone production results from the harmonious cooperation of all parts of the singing apparatus, from the diaphragm to the Ansatzrohr. The imaginary action of chewing serves as an aid to avoid the waste of breath in singing, precisely because the student thinks that he is taking in something.

For the beginner, this is the safest and simplest manner of voice training. Chest-sound and head-sound functions go on in the natural way thereby causing the isolated registers to disappear completely and giving way to the ideal mixed registers.

The voice expands equally up and down, to its maximum range.

The voice category can be ascertained beyond doubt. For it is not alone the length of the vocal cords which determine the category of a voice but also the timbre. The same tones sound very different when sung by an alto or by a soprano. The same goes for the baritone and the tenor voice. And here the chewing method is most clarifying by showing the natural timber of the voice. — And when we finally consider the psychological value of this method, we find that with it we are well on the way to remedy also that old and serious evil: the student's fear of the difficulty of his task. For the chewing method is not a difficult task at all but rather a natural function commensurate with the talented singer's capabilities. The training of the vocal organ consists essentially in the clearing of the way for the rising tone by means of uninhibited use of the resonating cavities. The chewing method permits full achievement of this requisite.

A few cases of re-education, education and therapy of the singing voice follow:

A 30 year old singer who after studying for 10 years was in doubt whether he had a baritone or a tenor voice, complained of pains in the chest, extreme tension in the larynx during phonation, was hardly able to sing through even a short song, and in general reported a whole series of familiar troubles: He suffered repeatedly from laryngitis and was often unable for weeks to carry on his profession. His speaking voice was too high, the singing voice hyper-functional throughout. — I explained to him that he would have to submit to complete re-education; he agreed, under the condition that he would be able to continue with his professional singing throughout the period of his re-training. I cite this case especially because of the fact that actually re-education of the singing voice was carried on without even a short interruption of professional activity. — I pointed out to the student the great difficulties of working under such conditions. But his strong will power and exceptionally cooperative attitude were of great help to me in this experiment. The chewing method soon permitted to determine clearly that the man was really a tenor. His speaking voice has come down to his normal pitch; the singing voice has grown to a range of 2½ octaves. All pains, uneasiness and nervousness have disappeared now that after years of trials and errors he has found a reliable and simple method.

A young singer of 23, beginner, was of the opinion that he was a tenor because he could easily reach b-flat 1. After the chewing method had been explained and after only a few exercises he was able to find out that he was really a baritone. Speaking and singing voice now are normal and he is getting on well with his studies.

A twenty year old singer had been advised by her teacher to consult a doctor with regard to serious pains following singing and to a phonasthenic speaking voice. The doctor sent her to me. Her very conscientious teacher, who came with her, feared that she was suffering from a serious malady of the vocal or the respiratory organ, since she was also very short of breath. There were swelling and redness of the upper cords but no other pathological symptoms. The condition had already persisted for several months so that the girl could neither carry out her profession nor continue with her singing lessons.—I explained the chewing method to both of them, and the teacher advised his pupil to try the method. She was very intelligent and talented, and she kept her teacher informed. After only a few lessons, her troubles disappeared and her speaking voice was perfectly clear. Soon she was able to sing again in public at various occasions, and to take up her lessons with her teacher who remained interested in the chewing method. The girl even reports that now her speaking voice becomes better, the more she sings.

A singer of many years standing came to me fully convinced

that she was losing her voice. It was soon obvious to me that her condition was caused by hyperfunction and not by any organic disorder. After four weeks of using the chewing method she was on the road to recovery, and at the end of one year she gave an outstanding recital. Being also a well-established singing teacher, she has adopted the chewing method in her private instruction as well as in her classes in one of the foremost colleges. She claims that her results with this method, as compared to those she formerly used, are not only achieved in a shorter time, but exceeded her former achievements remarkably.

Another case treated with the chewing method by a therapist of our school, with whose permission the case history is published, is that of a singer of world renown who at the age of 60 not only lost his voice but showed a blood extravasate of the size of a small pea on one vocal cord. His singing career had already been interrupted for a whole year during which time he was treated locally by several laryngologists, but without success. — The voice examination showed his range reduced to about half his former range. The loudness was considerably diminished, and his pianissimo for which he had been especially famed, was non-existent. Within a few days of using the chewing method, the range started to grow again until at the end of two weeks it was fully restored. Simultaneously, the loudness began and continued to increase, and the pianissimo reappeared in its full beauty. The blood extravasate was gradually being absorbed. Three weeks after starting the treatment, he gave a very successful concert in a large music hall.

REFERENCES

1. *Weiss D.:* Naturwissenschaftliches zum Regitser Problem. Mitteilungen über Sprach- und Stimmheilkunde.
2. *Gutzmann, H.:* Stimmbildung und Stimmpflege Verlag. J. F. Bergmann Wiesbaden 1920.

3. *Van Zanten, Cornelia:* Belcanto des Wortes. Chr. Friedrich Vierweg. Berlin.
4. *Armin, George:* Das Stauprinzip Strassburg i. Elsass 1909.
5. *Taylor, David:* Self Help for Singers. Berlin, Leipzig 1912.
6. *Jackson, C.:* Myasthenia Laryngis. Arch. of Otolaryngology. 32: 434-463.
7. *Froeschels, E.:* Hygiene of the Voice. Archives of Otolaryngology. Aug. 1943. Vol. 38, pp. 122-130.

CHARLES R. STROTHER, PH.D.
Associate Professor of Speech and Psychology, University of Iowa.

Chapter XXII

VOICE TRAINING AFTER LARYNGECTOMY

ESOPHAGEAL SPEECH

COMPLETE extirpation of the larynx, necessitated by carcinoma or other laryngeal disease, produces a total loss of voice. Post-operatively, the development of some type of speech is a major factor in the rehabilitation of the patient. Fortunately, the prognosis for development of a serviceable voice after laryngectomy is good if the patient is willing and able to make the necessary effort and if adequate instruction is available. The results obtained are dependent on a number of factors, including the surgical technique used, the post-operative condition of the patient, adequate management of the psychological factors involved, the method of speech instruction and the type and quality of the artificial larynx, if such a device is employed.

Total laryngectomy involves removal of the larynx from below the cricoid cartilage up to the hyoid bone. The tracheal stump is sutured to the skin of the neck and respiration must subsequently occur through this fistula rather than through the nose or mouth. The larynx is dissected out and removed and the opening from the pharynx into the larynx is closed. The ends of the inferior constrictor of the pharynx, which have

302

been dissected away from their laryngeal attachments, are over-lapped and sutured together. The patient is, of course, no longer able to produce voice in the normal way. The entire vibrating mechanism has been removed and air no longer passes through the throat on respiration but is inhaled and ex-pired through the tracheal opening at the base of the neck. If the patient is to speak again, some entirely new method of pro-ducing tone must be developed.

Two methods are available: the use of an artificial larynx or the development of a pseudo-glottis which will make possible the production of tone by structures in the patient's own throat. The second method is usually preferred. The resulting tone is much more natural than that produced by an artificial larynx. The quality is less harsh and metallic and, with train-ing, voiced and unvoiced sounds can be produced and com-bined more naturally. Then, too, an artificial larynx is con-spicuous, requires care, and leaves the patient without speech when it is in disrepair or otherwise not immediately available. It is, however, relatively easy to learn to speak with an arti-ficial larynx. Many patients who are unable to acquire esoph-ageal speech find artificial larynges quite satisfactory and are enabled by them to carry on an active business and social life.

There are two types of artificial larynx available: a "buzzer" type which is electrically driven by current supplied by bat-teries, and a "reed" type which is air-driven. In the buzzer type, the vibrating mechanism consists of a diaphragm encased in a shell. This is placed against the throat and, when the cur-rent is turned on, produces a noise which may then be articu-lated by the usual movements of the mouth. The air-driven type, of which there are several designs, consists essentially of a tube, one end of which is fitted over the tracheal opening. One section of the tube contains a reed which is set into vibra-tion by the air stream passing into the tube from the tracheal opening. These vibrations are then conveyed through a flexible rubber tube into the mouth. It is necessary for the patient to hold the instrument in one hand while speaking.

Since the artificial larynx is generally less satisfactory than esophageal speech, it should be resorted to only when the patient is unable to acquire a sufficiently good esophageal voice. Care should be exercised in the selection of the model to be used. Factors which should be considered are cost, likelihood of mechanical difficulty, ease of cleaning and replacement of parts, the quality of the tone produced, the possibility of pitch variation, comfort, degree of interference with articulation and, in the air-driven models, the strength of the air blast required to operate the reed. After the artificial larynx has been selected, the principal problem is to learn how to articulate clearly with it. In the air-driven type, a flexible rubber tube must be inserted into the side of the mouth, past the teeth, with the end lying alongside the tongue fairly far back in the mouth. With some practice, the patient learns to make the necessary articulatory movements of the tongue with a minimum of interference from the tube. It is sometimes possible to vary the pitch of the tone either by controlling the strength of the air blast or, in some models, by manipulation of the reed. While the tone is inevitably monotonous and metallic, the speech is quite intelligible and is loud enough to be heard easily in a group or over the telephone.

When a pseudo-voice can be developed, as it usually can, it is to be preferred to an artificial larynx. There are several different ways of producing a pseudo-voice. In some cases, attempts have been made to provide a fistula from the trachea into the pharynx, so that air pressure from the lungs can be used to drive a pseudo-glottis. There is one case on record in which the patient produced such a fistula himself with a hot wire and obtained satisfactory voice. The presence of a fistula, unfortunately, creates a serious risk of ingestion of liquids, food or other foreign matter into the trachea through the opening from the pharynx. The consensus among surgeons is that this procedure is rarely feasible at the present time.

A second type of pseudo-voice is called the "buccal whisper." This is a whisper which many patients develop spontaneously. The whispered speech is produced by buccal or bucco-lingual compression of air held in the mouth. While intelligible speech can be produced in this manner, the sound is not loud enough to be useful except in a quiet place and over a short distance. Development of the buccal whisper is to be discouraged since it frequently makes learning of esophageal speech more difficult.

A third, and the most commonly used, type of pseudo-voice is the esophageal voice. This is produced by a pseudo-glottis located in the pharynx or at the esophageal opening and activated by air pressure from an esophageal reservoir or from the stomach. The resulting tone, while somewhat husky, is quite natural in quality. When the patient has learned to take in air inconspicuously, has developed sufficient loudness and mastered the art of phrasing, his speech will be adequate for all ordinary circumstances and sufficiently natural so that few people will suspect that he is not using his normal voice.

The primary consideration in the development of esophageal speech is the attitude of the patient. Psychologically, a laryngectomy is a very traumatic experience. On recovering consciousness after the operation, he discovers that he is completely unable to talk. He cannot dislodge objects from his throat by coughing. He cannot sneeze or blow his nose. The disruption of these important conservative functions produces an initial anxiety not unlike that observed in patients suffering respiratory distress. In addition to this physiologic threat, the loss of voice also constitutes a severe psychological threat. The patient finds himself unable to communicate readily with others, incapacitated for his work and unable to participate in most types of social activity. This inability to express themselves plus the physical limitations imposed by the operation and fear of a recurrence of the disease which has necessitated the laryngectomy leads many patients to become discouraged and to accept unnecessarily the status of a chronic invalid.

Proper psychological management of the patient will minimize or prevent development of these reactions, thus greatly facilitating convalescence and motivating the patient's efforts toward rehabilitation. When the diagnosis has been established, the patient must be carefully and tactfully informed of his condition. The necessity for surgery must be discussed and the general nature of the operation should be described. He should be given as favorable a statement of the prognosis as his condition warrants. A detailed description of the way in which the operation will affect established functions, including smelling, breathing, coughing, sneezing, speaking, lifting and defecating, will prepare the patient for these changes and minimize his anxiety. He should be reassured about the prospects of recovering speech. Every patient can learn to use an artificial larynx and the majority can develop adequate esophageal speech. Conversation with a laryngectomized patient who has succeeded in developing good speech or recordings or sound films of good esophageal voices will give added reassurance.

Where possible, the actual speech training should be begun pre-operatively. With the aid of charts or sketches, the normal respiratory tract is described, and the function of the glottis explained. The patient is then shown how these structures will be altered by the operation, i.e., that the larynx is to be removed, the passageway from the trachea into the pharynx closed and that respiration will subsequently occur through the tracheal opening at the base of the neck. The location and normal functions of the esophagus are then described and the patient is told that he is to learn to speak by swallowing air into the esophagus. He is reminded that he is already able to produce sound in that way by belching and that by learning to prolong and improve this tone he will be able to talk again. If he needs re-assurance at this point about the quality of the tone, it is well to have a good sample for him to hear.

Following some such explanation, the first step in the actual training may be begun. This involves teaching the patient how to swallow air. It is important that the therapist be able to demonstrate this himself. There are two procedures which may be used. The easier is to fill the mouth with air and force it into the esophagus by a swallowing movement. Air may also be drawn into the esophagus by closing the glottis firmly and ex-panding the thorax. If this second procedure is used post-op-eratively, it will often be necessary for the patient to place a finger lightly over the tracheal opening. Too much pressure on the tracheal fistula will, of course, compress the esophagus and prevent the intake of air. Learning to swallow air is probably the most difficult part of the training process. Practice periods must be very short in order to avoid fatigue or soreness of the throat muscles. If difficulty seems to lie in opening the esoph-agus to admit the air bubble, swallowing while in a reclining position or procedures designed to relax the throat before swal-lowing if attempted may help. With persistent effort, the pa-tient will be able to take air into the esophagus, although it may take him several days to learn to do so.

As soon as he can take in a bubble of air, it is well to go ahead to the next step even though the amount inspired may be small and the intake noisy. These faults can be dealt with later. The second step involves learning to expel the air and to use it for phonation. The patient is instructed to force the bubble from the esophagus by a slight expiratory contraction of the thoracic musculature. He is encouraged to produce a belch-ing noise as the bubble leaves the esophagus. This is accom-plished by a slight contraction of the crico-pharyngeus muscle, which brings the lips of the esophagus together to form a pseudo-glottis. At first, the patient may find that air, once it is taken in, tends to pass on down the esophagus into the stomach. Indeed, some speech therapists advise the use of the stomach air in esophageal speech. Better results are usually obtained by development of an air reservoir high up in the esophagus but if the air does pass into the stomach in the initial stages of training, the patient is told to keep on swallowing air until he is able to expel it from the stomach and produce tone. When a tone can be produced, the patient is then taught to phonate single vowels.

At this point, a number of problems may develop. The intake of air may be accompanied by unpleasant noise. The patient may have difficulty in bringing up the air bubble because it has passed into the stomach or lies too low in the esophagus. The bubble may be too small to sustain more than a very brief phonation or the sound may be very weak. Expiration may be accompanied by a distracting and noisy blast from the tracheal opening. Undesirable movements of the head may occur on inspiration. Each of these difficulties requires attention if optimally effective speech is to be developed.

Movements of the head on inspiration occur in an effort to stretch open the mouth of the esophagus. This tendency should be detected early and prohibited. Otherwise it tends to become a habit, which is undesirable because it makes the act of inspiration unnecessarily conspicuous. Inspiratory noises are due to excessive tension at the mouth of the esophagus and probably to other factors which have not been clearly defined. Theoretically, there is some reason to believe that shortening of the crico-pharyngeus during surgery may be responsible for some of the difficulty in forcing air into the esophagus. At any rate, remedial efforts must be directed toward relaxing the esophageal opening on inspiration. In some cases it appears to be impossible to eliminate inspiratory noise completely but it can usually be reduced to a level at which it is not too distracting. A tendency for the air to pass too far down the esophagus may usually be counteracted by having the patient attempt to expel the air bubble as soon as it has passed into the esophagus. Where the amount of air taken in is too small, swallowing two or three times before each phonation will enable the patient gradually to develop an adequate reservoir of air.

The principal difficulties encountered on the expiratory phase are weakness of the tone and the presence of a noisy expiratory blast from the tracheal opening. Weakness of the tone is usually caused by hypotonicity or incomplete adduction of the muscles which form the pseudo-glottis. This condition ordinarily improves with continued phonation but if necessary special exercises may be used. Unless the tone is too weak to work with, it is well to leave the development of loudness until fairly late in the training process. The exercises required involve considerable voluntary tension of the pharyngeal constrictors and unless used carefully are likely to produce soreness and irritation which will necessitate a period of vocal rest and interrupt progress. The presence of a distracting expiratory blast from the tracheal opening on phonation is caused by the use of too forceful a contraction of the expiratory musculature of the thorax. The patient must learn to expel air from the esophagus with less force. If a tracheal cannula is being worn, noise may be produced by air turbulences set up at the lower or upper openings of the cannula. If the cannula is to be dispensed with shortly, no attention need be paid to this but if the patient is likely to have to wear it indefinitely, the aid of a technician should be enlisted to modify the tube openings so as to eliminate the difficulty.

When the patient is able to swallow air fairly easily, to retain a good-sized bubble in the upper end of the esophagus, to expel it at will and produce an audible tone, training on sounds should be begun. The easiest sounds with which to start are the pure vowels: *a* as in *arm*, *i* as in *it*, *ee* as in *meet*, *a* as in *at*, etc. Next the diphthongs *ou* as in *no*, *ai* as in *my*, *oi* as in *boy*, *au* as in *out,* which require slightly longer duration of tone and involve tongue and jaw movement, are taught. These may be followed by certain short words and phrases, such as *oh no, oh yeah,* and *I know.* The patient is then taught to produce the unvoiced consonants *p, t, k, s, sh, f,* etc., using buccal air only —not esophageal tone. The vowels are next combined with unvoiced consonants in words such as *eat, each, at, us, tea, key, teach, keep.* Drill periods still need to be kept short—from five to ten minutes in length—but the patient should be able to practice six or seven periods a day without feeling fatigued or developing soreness of the throat.

From words, the patient progresses to short sentences, with a separate intake of air for each word—as, *I / bought / a / peach; I / ate / some / meat; Keep / at / it.* As his ability to prolong the tone increases, one intake is used for the pronunciation of shorter and gradually longer phrases and practice is given in oral reading and in conversation. At this stage, the principal problems are learning to take in the air more quickly, to sustain the tone throughout the phrase, to obtain increased loudness, and to break sentences up into phrases that are sufficiently short. The most efficient intake of air is accomplished by combining a partial swallowing movement with an inspiratory movement of the thorax. With practice, air can be taken in in this manner quite inconspicuously and within the period of a natural pause. Duration of the tone is a function of the amount of air taken in and the rate at which the air is released. Control over the release can be established by exercises in which the patient attempts to release a very small amount of air, then stop the escape, emit a bit more, etc. Another useful exercise for this purpose is to time the duration of the tone and drill on increasing the period of phonation. Exercises used for increasing loudness are similar to those used with normal voices, e.g., the production of tones of increasing loudness, starting with the softest tone which the patient can produce.

Proper phrasing is a very important aspect of good esophageal speech. The length of the phrase is determined by the length of time that tone can be sustained on a single intake of air. The most common error is to attempt too long a phrase, so that the tone becomes weak and forced at the end of the phrase. Better results are obtained if the phrase is kept fairly short. This requires a good deal of practice in breaking up sentences into short, logical units. The use / of reading material / broken up / into phrases / as in this / sentence / will be found / quite helpful. Short phrases can be combined into longer ones as capacity improves but the phrases should always be kept well within the limit of the patient's air supply.

The time required to develop esophageal speech varies greatly from patient to patient. On the average, a week is required for the initial training in swallowing the air and bringing it up again, with two short training sessions and several three to five minute practice periods a day. A second week is usually required for drill on sounds and sound combinations. By the end of this time the patient should be able to produce a number of intelligible words. By the third week, work on sentences and phrasing is under way and the patient can begin to use speech for communication. Some patients progress much more rapidly than this but in other cases difficulties arising at various stages may retard the process. Ultimately, unless difficulties arise, the patient is able to carry on all the conversation required to run a retail business and can talk so normally that casual observers are unaware that there is anything unusual about his speech.

BIBLIOGRAPHY

1. *Brighton, G. R., and Boone, W. H.:* Roentgenographic demonstration of method of speech in cases of complete laryngectomy. Amer. J. Roentgenology, 1937, 38, 571-583.
2. *Guttman, M. R.:* Tracheohypopharyngeal fistulization: a new procedure for speech production in the laryngectomized patient. Trans.

Amer. Laryngological, Rhinological, and Otological Society, Inc., 1935, 41, 219-226.

3. *Hanson, W. L.:* A new artificial larynx with a historical review. Illinois med. J., 1940, 78, 483-486.

4. *Jackson, C. L.:* The voice after direct laryngoscopic operations, laryngofissure, and laryngectomy. Arch. Otolaryng., 1940, 31, 23-26.

5. *Kallen, L. A.:* Vicarious vocal mechanisms; the anatomy, physiology, and development of speech in laryngectomized persons. Arch. Otolaryng., 1934, 20, 460-503.

6. *Levin, N. M.:* Teaching the laryngectomized patient to talk. Arch. Otolaryng., 1940, 32, 299-314.

7. *Lindsay, J, R., Morgan, R. H., and Wepman, J. M.:* The cricopharyngeus muscle in esophageal speech. Laryngoscope, 1944, 54, 55-65.

8. *McCall, J. W.:* Preliminary voice training for laryngectomy. Arch. Otolaryng., 1943, 38, 10-16.

9. *Morrison, W.:* The production of voice and speech following total laryngectomy. Arch. Otolaryng., 1931, 14, 413-431.

10. *Morrison, W.:* Physical rehabilitation of the laryngectomized patient. Arch. Otolaryng., 1941, 34, 1101-1112.

11. *Schall, L. A.:* Psychology of laryngectomized patients. Arch. Otolaryng., 1938, 28, 581-584.

12. *Stetson, R. H.:* Esophageal speech; methods of instruction after laryngectomy. Arch. Néerlandaises de Phonétique Experimentale, 1937, 13, 95-110.

INDEX

313